# AS-Level

# Chemistry

# for OCR A

The Complete Course for OCR A

# Contents

## Introduction

How to use this book     i

## How Science Works

The Scientific Process     1

## Unit 1

### Module 1: Atoms and Reactions

| | |
|---|---|
| 1. The Atom | 5 |
| 2. Atomic Models | 8 |
| 3. Relative Mass | 11 |
| 4. The Mole | 15 |
| 5. Concentration Calculations | 17 |
| 6. Formulas | 20 |
| 7. Calculating Formulas | 22 |
| 8. Balancing Equations | 26 |
| 9. Equations and Calculations | 28 |
| 10. Acids, Bases and Salts | 31 |
| 11. Anhydrous and Hydrated Salts | 34 |
| 12. Titrations | 36 |
| 13. Oxidation States | 40 |
| 14. Redox Reactions | 44 |
| **Exam-style Questions** | **47** |

### Module 2: Electrons, Bonding and Structure

| | |
|---|---|
| 1. Electronic Structure | 50 |
| 2. Ionisation Energies | 54 |
| 3. Ionic Bonding | 57 |
| 4. Covalent Bonding | 61 |
| 5. Shapes of Molecules | 65 |
| 6. Polarisation | 69 |
| 7. Intermolecular Forces | 70 |
| 8. Metallic Bonding | 74 |
| **Exam-style Questions** | **76** |

### Module 3: The Periodic Table

| | |
|---|---|
| 1. The Periodic Table | 79 |
| 2. Periodic Trends | 83 |
| 3. Group 2 — The Alkaline Earth Metals | 88 |
| 4. Group 7 — The Halogens | 92 |
| 5. Disproportionation and Water Treatment | 96 |
| **Exam-style Questions** | **100** |

## Unit 2

### Module 1: Basic Concepts and Hydrocarbons

| | |
|---|---|
| 1. Organic Chemistry | 103 |
| 2. Formulas | 104 |
| 3. Structural Isomers | 108 |
| 4. Stereoisomers | 111 |
| 5. Chemical Yield | 113 |
| 6. Atom Economy | 115 |
| 7. Alkanes and Nomenclature | 118 |
| 8. Properties of Alkanes | 121 |
| 9. Petroleum | 124 |
| 10. Fossil Fuels | 128 |
| 11. Bond Fission | 130 |
| 12. Substitution Reactions | 131 |
| 13. Alkenes and Their Properties | 133 |
| 14. Polymers | 137 |
| 15. Disposing of Polymers | 139 |
| 16. Reactions of Alkenes | 142 |
| **Exam-style Questions** | **147** |

## Module 2: Alcohols, Halogenoalkanes and Analysis

| | |
|---|---|
| 1. Alcohols and their Uses | 151 |
| 2. Reactions of Alcohols | 154 |
| 3. Oxidising Alcohols | 156 |
| 4. Esterification and Esters | 160 |
| 5. Halogenoalkanes | 161 |
| 6. More Halogenoalkanes | 163 |
| 7. Infrared Spectroscopy | 167 |
| 8. Mass Spectrometry | 170 |
| **Exam-style Questions** | **175** |

## Module 3: Energy

| | |
|---|---|
| 1. Enthalpy Changes | 178 |
| 2. Bond Enthalpies | 180 |
| 3. Measuring Enthalpy Changes | 183 |
| 4. Hess's Law | 186 |
| 5. Reaction Rates | 191 |
| 6. Catalysts | 194 |
| 7. Reversible Reactions | 197 |
| **Exam-style Questions** | **202** |

## Module 4: Resources

| | |
|---|---|
| 1. Green Chemistry | 205 |
| 2. Global Warming | 208 |
| 3. The Ozone Layer | 211 |
| 4. Air Pollution | 214 |
| **Exam-style Questions** | **218** |

## Practical Skills in Chemistry

HOW SCIENCE WORKS

| | |
|---|---|
| 1. Variables and Data | 221 |
| 2. Graphs and Charts | 223 |
| 3. Conclusions and Evaluations | 224 |

## Exam Help

EXAM HELP

| | |
|---|---|
| 1. Exam Structure and Technique | 226 |
| 2. Formulas and Equations | 231 |
| 3. Units | 232 |
| 4. The Periodic Table — Facts and Trends | 234 |

## Reference

| | |
|---|---|
| Answers | 235 |
| Glossary | 264 |
| Acknowledgements | 270 |
| Index | 271 |
| Periodic Table | 274 |

# How to use this book

## Learning Objectives

- These tell you exactly what you need to learn, or be able to do, for the exam.
- There's a specification reference at the bottom that links to the OCR specification.

## Exam Tips

There are tips throughout the book to help with all sorts of things to do with answering exam questions.

## Tips

These are here to help you understand the theory.

---

**Learning Objective:**
- Know that structural isomers are compounds with the same molecular formula but different structural formulas.
  **Specification Reference 2.1.1**

## 3. Structural Isomers

*You can put the same atoms together in different ways to make completely different molecules. Two molecules that have the same molecular formula but are put together in a different way are isomers of each other.*

### What are structural isomers?

In structural isomers, the molecular formula is the same, but the structural formula is different. There are three different types of structural isomer:

**1. Chain isomers**

The carbon skeleton can be arranged differently — for example, as a straight chain, or branched in different ways. Molecules that have different arrangements of the carbon skeleton are called **chain isomers**.

─ Examples ─

There are different chain isomers of $C_4H_{10}$. The diagrams below show the straight chain isomer butane and a branched chain isomer methylpropane.

*Here the longest carbon chain is 4 carbon atoms.*
*Here the longest carbon chain is 3 carbon atoms.*

butane        methylpropane

There are different chain isomers of $C_4H_8O_2$. The diagrams below show the straight chain isomer butanoic acid and a branched chain isomer methylpropanoic acid.

*Here the longest carbon chain is 4 carbon atoms.*
*Here the longest carbon chain is 3 carbon atoms.*

butanoic acid        methylpropanoic acid

Chain isomers have similar chemical properties — but their physical properties, like boiling point, will be different because of the change in shape of the molecule.

**2. Positional isomers**

The skeleton and the functional group could be the same, only with the group attached to a different carbon atom. These are called **positional isomers**.

─ Example ─

There are two positional isomers of $C_4H_9Cl$. The chlorine atom is attached to different carbon atoms in each isomer.

*The Cl is attached to the first carbon atom.*

1-chlorobutane

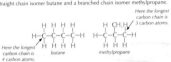

**Figure 1:** Molecular models showing two chain isomers of $C_4H_{10}$ — butane (left) and methylpropane (right).

**Exam Tip**
You don't always have to draw all of the bonds when you're drawing a molecule — writing $CH_3$ next to a bond is just as good as drawing out the carbon atom, three bonds and three hydrogen atoms. But if you're asked for a displayed formula you <u>must</u> draw out all of the bonds to get the marks.

**Tip:** If the chlorine atom was attached to the carbon atom on the left, it would still be the <u>same molecule</u> — just drawn the other way round. It would still be 1-chlorobutane.

---

## Exam Help

There's a section at the back of the book stuffed full of things to help with your exams.

## How Science Works

- For AS Chemistry you need to know about How Science Works. There's a section on it at the front of the book.
- How Science Works is also covered throughout the book wherever you see this symbol.

## Examples

These are here to help you understand the theory.

---

**Learning Objectives:**
- Know that a hydrocarbon is a compound that contains hydrogen and carbon only.
- Know that alkanes and cycloalkanes are saturated hydrocarbons.
- Be able to apply IUPAC rules for naming alkanes.
- Know the names of the first ten members of the alkanes homologous series.
  **Specification Reference 2.1.1, 2.1.2**

## 7. Alkanes and Nomenclature

*Alkanes are molecules with hydrogen atoms, carbon atoms and single bonds. Nomenclature is just a fancy word for naming organic compounds.*

### Structure of alkanes

Alkanes have the general formula $C_nH_{2n+2}$. They've only got carbon and hydrogen atoms, so they're **hydrocarbons**. Every carbon atom in an alkane has four single bonds with other atoms. It's impossible for carbon to make more than four bonds, so alkanes are **saturated**. Here are a few examples of alkanes —

methane        ethane        propane

You get **cycloalkanes** too. They have a ring of carbon atoms with two hydrogens attached to each carbon. Cycloalkanes have two fewer hydrogens than other alkanes (assuming they have only one ring) so cycloalkanes have a different general formula from that of normal alkanes ($C_nH_{2n}$), but they are still saturated.

cyclohexane, $C_6H_{12}$

### Naming alkanes

The IUPAC system for naming organic compounds is the agreed international language of chemistry. Years ago, organic compounds were given whatever names people fancied, such as acetic acid and ethylene. But these names caused confusion between different countries.

The IUPAC system means scientific ideas can be communicated across the globe more effectively. So it's easier for scientists to get on with testing each other's work, and either confirm or dispute new theories.

You need to be able to name straight-chain and branched alkanes using the IUPAC system for naming organic compounds.

**Straight-chain alkanes**

There are two parts to the name of a straight-chain alkane. The first part (the stem) states how many carbon atoms there are in the molecule. The second part is always "-ane". It's the "-ane" bit that lets people know it's an alkane.

─ Example ─

This molecule is pentane:

The stem is pent-, which tells you that the molecule has 5 carbons in it, and the -ane bit at the end tells you it's an alkane.

You need to know the names of the first ten alkanes — see Figure 2.

**Figure 1:** Molecular models of cyclohexane and hexane.

**Tip:** There's more on the IUPAC rules for naming different organic compounds throughout Unit 2 Module 1 and Unit 2 Module 2 in this book.

**Tip:** The alkanes are an example of a homologous series. See page 105 for more on this.

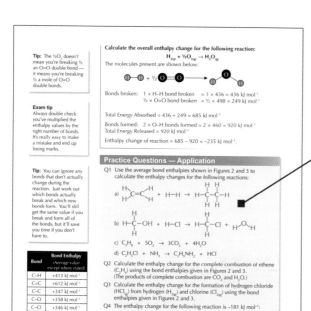

Calculate the overall enthalpy change for the following reaction:

$$H_{2(g)} + \tfrac{1}{2}O_{2(g)} \rightarrow H_2O_{(g)}$$

The molecules present are shown below:

Bonds broken:  $1 \times$ H–H bond broken  $= 1 \times 436 = 436$ kJ mol⁻¹
$\tfrac{1}{2} \times$ O=O bond broken  $= \tfrac{1}{2} \times 498 = 249$ kJ mol⁻¹

Total Energy Absorbed $= 436 + 249 = 685$ kJ mol⁻¹
Bonds formed:  $2 \times$ O–H bonds formed $= 2 \times 460 = 920$ kJ mol⁻¹
Total Energy Released $= 920$ kJ mol⁻¹
Enthalpy change of reaction $= 685 - 920 = -235$ kJ mol⁻¹.

### Practice Questions — Application

Q1 Use the average bond enthalpies shown in Figures 2 and 3 to calculate the enthalpy changes for the following reactions:

a)

b)

c) $C_3H_8 + 5O_2 \rightarrow 3CO_2 + 4H_2O$

d) $C_2H_5Cl + NH_3 \rightarrow C_2H_5NH_2 + HCl$

Q2 Calculate the enthalpy change for the complete combustion of ethene ($C_2H_4$) using the bond enthalpies given in Figures 2 and 3. (The products of complete combustion are $CO_2$ and $H_2O$.)

Q3 Calculate the enthalpy change for the formation of hydrogen chloride ($HCl_{(g)}$) from hydrogen ($H_{2(g)}$) and chlorine ($Cl_{2(g)}$) using the bond enthalpies given in Figures 2 and 3.

Q4 The enthalpy change for the following reaction is $-181$ kJ mol⁻¹:

$$2NO_{(g)} \rightarrow N_{2(g)} + O_{2(g)}$$

Use this value for $\Delta H_r$, along with the data in Figure 2, to estimate a value for the average bond enthalpy for the bond between nitrogen and oxygen in NO.

### Practice Questions — Fact Recall

Q1 Is bond breaking exothermic or endothermic?
Q2 In an exothermic reaction, which is larger — the energy required to make bonds or the energy required to break bonds?
Q3 What is average bond enthalpy?
Q4 Give the formula for calculating the enthalpy change of a reaction.

| Bond | Bond Enthalpy (Average value except where stated) |
|---|---|
| C–H | +413 kJ mol⁻¹ |
| C=C | +612 kJ mol⁻¹ |
| C–C | +347 kJ mol⁻¹ |
| C–O | +358 kJ mol⁻¹ |
| C–Cl | +346 kJ mol⁻¹ |
| C=O (in CO₂) | +805 kJ mol⁻¹ |
| C–N | +286 kJ mol⁻¹ |
| H–Cl | +432 kJ mol⁻¹ |
| Cl–Cl | +243.4 kJ mol⁻¹ |

***Figure 3:*** *Table of bond enthalpies.*

## Practice Questions — Application

- Annoyingly, the examiners expect you to be able to apply your knowledge to new situations — these questions are here to give you plenty of practice at doing this.
- All the answers are in the back of the book (including any calculation workings).

## Practice Questions — Fact Recall

- There are a lot of facts to learn for AS Chemistry — these questions are here to test that you know them.
- All the answers are in the back of the book.

## Glossary

There's a glossary at the back of the book full of all the definitions you need to know for the exam, plus loads of other useful words.

## Exam-style Questions

- Practising exam-style questions is really important — you'll find some at the end of each section.
- They're the same style as the ones you'll get in the real exams — some will test your knowledge and understanding and some will test that you can apply your knowledge.
- All the answers are in the back of the book, along with a mark scheme to show you how you get the marks.

## Practical Skills in Chemistry

- For AS Chemistry you'll have to complete Unit F323 — Practical Skills in Chemistry 1.
- There's a section at the back of the book with loads of stuff to help you plan, analyse and evaluate experiments.

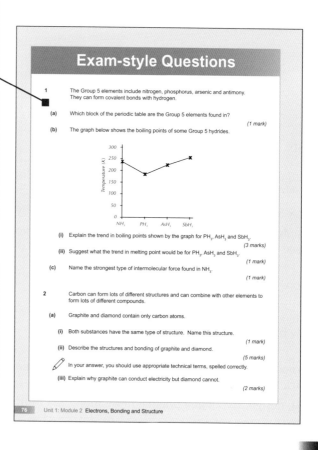

### Exam-style Questions

1  The Group 5 elements include nitrogen, phosphorus, arsenic and antimony. They can form covalent bonds with hydrogen.

(a)  Which block of the periodic table are the Group 5 elements found in?
*(1 mark)*

(b)  The graph below shows the boiling points of some Group 5 hydrides.

(i)  Explain the trend in boiling points shown by the graph for $PH_3$, $AsH_3$ and $SbH_3$.
*(3 marks)*

(ii)  Suggest what the trend in melting point would be for $PH_3$, $AsH_3$ and $SbH_3$.
*(1 mark)*

(c)  Name the strongest type of intermolecular force found in $NH_3$.
*(1 mark)*

2  Carbon can form lots of different structures and can combine with other elements to form lots of different compounds.

(a)  Graphite and diamond contain only carbon atoms.

(i)  Both substances have the same type of structure. Name this structure.
*(1 mark)*

(ii)  Describe the structures and bonding of graphite and diamond.
*(5 marks)*

In your answer, you should use appropriate technical terms, spelled correctly.

(iii)  Explain why graphite can conduct electricity but diamond cannot.
*(2 marks)*

Published by CGP

Editors:
Katie Braid, Mary Falkner, Helen Ronan, Megan Tyler, Karen Wells.

Contributors:
Antonio Angelosanto, Vicky Cunningham, Ian Davis, John Duffy, Max Fishel, Emma Grimwood, Richard Harwood, Lucy Muncaster, Derek Swain, Paul Warren, Chris Workman.

ISBN: 978 1 84762 793 3

With thanks to Katherine Craig, Chris Elliss, Glenn Rogers and Jamie Sinclair for the proofreading.
With thanks to Anna Lupton for the copyright research.

OCR Specification reference points are reproduced by permission of OCR.

Graph to show trend in atmospheric $CO_2$ concentration and global temperature on page 209 based on data by EPICA Community Members 2004 and Siegenthaler et al 2005.

Groovy website: www.cgpbooks.co.uk

Printed by Elanders Ltd, Newcastle upon Tyne.
Jolly bits of clipart from CorelDRAW®

# The Scientific Process

*Science tries to explain how and why things happen. It's all about seeking and gaining knowledge about the world around us. Scientists do this by asking questions and suggesting answers and then testing them, to see if they're correct — this is the scientific process.*

## Developing and testing theories

A **theory** is a possible explanation for something. Theories usually come about when scientists observe something and wonder why or how it happens. (Scientists also sometimes form a **model** too — a simplified picture or representation of a real physical situation.) Scientific theories and models are developed and tested in the following way:

**Tip:** A theory is only scientific if it can be tested.

- Ask a question — make an observation and ask why or how whatever you've observed happens.

- Suggest an answer, or part of an answer, by forming a theory or a model (a possible explanation of the observations or a description of what you think is happening actually happening).

- Make a prediction or **hypothesis** — a specific testable statement, based on the theory, about what will happen in a test situation.

- Carry out tests — to provide evidence that will support the prediction or refute it.

### Examples

**Question: Why does sodium chloride dissolve in water?**

**Theory:** Sodium chloride is made up of charged particles which are pulled apart by the polar water molecules (see page 60).

**Hypothesis:** Sodium chloride will dissolve in polar solvents but not in non-polar solvents.

**Test:** Add sodium chloride to polar solvents such as water and to non-polar solvents such as toluene. If it dissolves in the polar solvents but not in the non-polar solvents then the evidence would support the hypothesis.

**Question: Why does changing the temperature affect the yield of a reversible reaction?**

**Theory:** The equilibrium moves to counteract the change, favouring either the forward or reverse reaction, which increases the yield of this reaction and reduces the yield of the other.

**Hypothesis:** Increasing the temperature of an exothermic reversible reaction at equilibrium will decrease the yield, but for an endothermic reaction it will increase the yield.

**Test:** Measure the yield from exothermic and endothermic reversible reactions carried out at different temperatures. If the yield from the exothermic reactions decreases with increasing temperature, but the yield from the endothermic reactions increases with increasing temperature, then this evidence supports the hypothesis.

***Figure 1:*** *Sodium chloride dissolving in water.*

**Tip:** The results of one test can't prove that a theory is true — they can only suggest that it's true. They can however disprove a theory — show that it's wrong.

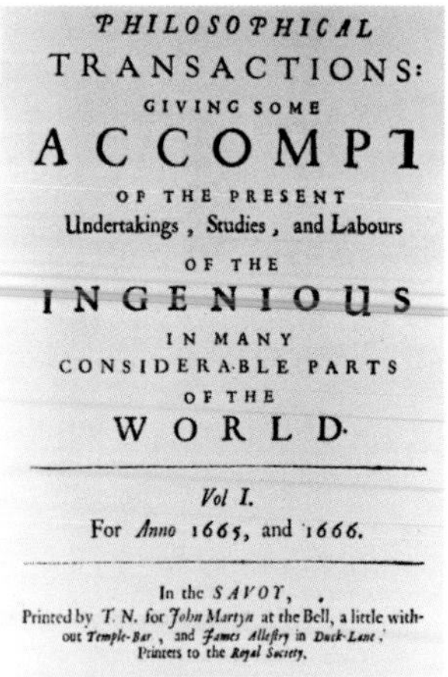

PHILOSOPHICAL
TRANSACTIONS:
GIVING SOME
ACCOMPT
OF THE PRESENT
Undertakings, Studies, and Labours
OF THE
INGENIOUS
IN MANY
CONSIDERABLE PARTS
OF THE
WORLD.

Vol I.
For *Anno* 1665, and 1666.

In the *SAVOY*,
Printed by *T. N.* for *John Martyn* at the Bell, a little without *Temple-Bar*, and *James Allestry* in *Duck-Lane*;
Printers to the *Royal Society*.

*Figure 2: The first scientific journal, 'Philosophical Transactions of the Royal Society', published in 1665.*

**Tip:** Scientific research is often funded by companies who have a vested interest in its outcomes. Scientists are ethically obliged to make sure that this does not bias their results.

**Tip:** Once an experimental method is found to give good evidence it becomes a protocol — an accepted method to test that particular thing that all scientists can use.

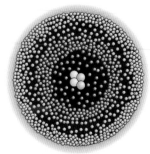

*Figure 3: The quantum model of an atom — one of the current theories of atomic structure.*

# Communicating results

The results of testing a scientific theory are published — scientists need to let others know about their work. Scientists publish their results in scientific journals. These are just like normal magazines, only they contain scientific reports (called papers) instead of the latest celebrity gossip.

Scientists use standard terminology when writing their reports. This way they know that other scientists will understand them. For instance, there are internationally agreed rules for naming organic compounds, so that scientists across the world will know exactly what substance is being referred to (see page 118).

Scientific reports are similar to the lab write-ups you do in school. And just as a lab write-up is reviewed (marked) by your teacher, reports in scientific journals undergo **peer review** before they're published. The report is sent out to peers — other scientists who are experts in the same area. They go through it bit by bit, examining the methods and data, and checking it's all clear and logical. Thorough evaluation allows decisions to be made about what makes a good methodology or experimental technique. Individual scientists may have their own ethical codes (based on their humanistic, moral and religious beliefs), but having their work scrutinised by other scientists helps to reduce the effect of personal bias on the conclusions drawn from the results.

When the report is approved, it's published. This makes sure that work published in scientific journals is of a good standard. But peer review can't guarantee the science is correct — other scientists still need to reproduce it. Sometimes mistakes are made and bad work is published. Peer review isn't perfect but it's probably the best way for scientists to self-regulate their work and to publish quality reports.

# Validating theories

Other scientists read the published theories and results, and try to test the theory themselves. This involves repeating the exact same experiments, using the theory to make new predictions, and then testing them with new experiments. This is known as **validation**. If all the experiments in the world provide evidence to back it up, the theory is thought of as scientific 'fact' (for now). If new evidence comes to light that conflicts with the current evidence the theory is questioned all over again. More rounds of testing will be carried out to try to find out where the theory falls down. This is how the scientific process works — evidence supports a theory, loads of other scientists read it and test it for themselves, eventually all the scientists in the world agree with it and then bingo, you get to learn it.

## Example

**The structure of the atom**

It took years and years for the current model of the atom to be developed and accepted — this is often the case with the scientific process.

Dalton's theory in the early 1800s, that atoms were solid spheres, was disputed by the results of Thomson's experiments at the end of that century. As a result, Thomson developed the 'plum pudding' model of the atom, which was proven wrong by Rutherford's alpha scattering experiments in 1909. Rutherford's 'nuclear model' has since been developed and modified further to create the currently accepted model of the atom we use today — but scientists are still searching for more accurate models (see pages 8-10).

# How do theories evolve?

Our currently accepted theories have survived this 'trial by evidence'. They've been tested over and over again and each time the results have backed them up. But they never become totally indisputable fact. Scientific breakthroughs or advances could provide new ways to question and test the theory, which could lead to changes and challenges to it. Then the testing starts all over again. This is the tentative nature of scientific knowledge — it's always changing and evolving.

**Tip:** Sometimes data from one experiment can be the starting point for developing a new theory.

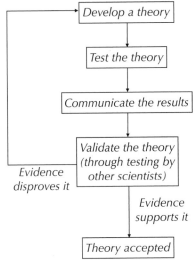

**Figure 4:** *Flow diagram summarising the scientific process.*

---
### Example
**CFCs and the ozone layer**

When CFCs were first used in fridges in the 1930s, scientists thought they were problem-free — well, why not? There was no evidence to say otherwise. It was decades before anyone found out that CFCs were actually making a whopping great hole in the ozone layer (see page 212).

A couple of scientists developed a theory that CFCs were destroying ozone in the stratosphere, and this was tested, shared and validated by other scientists worldwide. The rigour of the scientific process meant that there was strong enough evidence against CFCs that governments could impose bans and restrictions in order to protect the ozone layer.

**Figure 5:** *Dumped fridges containing CFCs.*

## Collecting evidence

### 1. Evidence from lab experiments

Results from controlled experiments in laboratories are great. A lab is the easiest place to control **variables** so that they're all kept constant (except for the one you're investigating). This means you can draw meaningful conclusions.

**Tip:** There's more about variables and drawing conclusions from lab experiments on pages 221 and 224 in the Practical Skills in Chemistry section.

---
### Example
**Reaction rates**

If you're investigating how temperature affects the rate of a reaction you need to keep everything but the temperature constant. This means controlling things like the pH of the solution, the concentration of the solution, etc. Otherwise there's no way of knowing if it's the change in temperature that's affecting the rate, or some other changing variable.

## 2. Investigations outside the lab

There are things you can't study in a lab. And outside the lab controlling the variables is tricky, if not impossible.

*Figure 6:* Tap water can be chlorinated, but it's hard to design a fair and ethical test to measure its true effects.

**Examples**

**Are increasing $CO_2$ emissions causing climate change?**

There are other variables which may have an effect, such as changes in solar activity. You can't easily rule out every possibility. Also, climate change is a very gradual process. Scientists won't be able to tell if their predictions are correct for donkey's years.

**Does drinking chlorinated tap water increase the risk of developing certain cancers?**

There are always differences between groups of people. The best you can do is to have a well-designed study using matched groups — choose two groups of people (those who drink tap water and those who don't) which are as similar as possible (same mix of ages, same mix of diets etc.). But you still can't rule out every possibility. Taking newborn identical twins and treating them identically, except for making one drink gallons of tap water and the other only pure water, might be a fairer test, but it would present huge ethical problems.

## Science and decision-making

**Tip:** Don't get mixed up — it's not the scientists who make the decisions, it's society. Scientists just produce evidence to help society make the decisions.

Lots of scientific work eventually leads to important discoveries that could benefit humankind and improve everyone's quality of life. But there are often risks attached (and almost always financial costs). Society (that's you, me and everyone else) must weigh up the information in order to make decisions — about the way we live, what we eat, what we drive, and so on. Information can also be used by politicians to devise policies and laws. However, there is not always enough information available for society and politicians to be certain about the decisions made. The scientific evidence we do have can also be overshadowed by other influences such as personal bias and beliefs, public opinion, and the media. Decisions are also affected by social, ethical and economic factors.

**Examples**

**Disinfecting water**

Chlorine is added to water in small quantities to disinfect it (see page 97). Some studies link drinking chlorinated water with certain types of cancer. But the risks from drinking water contaminated by nasty bacteria are far, far greater. There are other ways to get rid of bacteria in water, but they're heaps more expensive.

**Fuels for cars**

Scientific advances mean that non-polluting hydrogen-fuelled cars can be made. They're better for the environment, but are really expensive. Also, it'd cost a fortune to adapt the existing filling stations to store hydrogen.

*Figure 7:* A hydrogen powered car being refuelled as part of a study into the use of hydrogen fuels.

**Developing drugs**

Pharmaceutical drugs are really expensive to develop, and drug companies want to make money. So they put most of their efforts into developing drugs that they can sell for a good price. Society has to consider the cost of buying new drugs — the NHS can't afford the most expensive drugs without sacrificing something else.

# 1. The Atom

*Atoms are the basis of all of chemistry. You learned about them at GCSE and they're here again at AS-Level. They're super important.*

## The structure of the atom

All elements are made of **atoms**. Atoms are made up of 3 types of particle — **protons**, **neutrons** and **electrons**. Figure 1 shows how they are arranged in the atom.

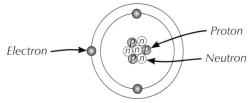

*Figure 1: The atom.*

Electrons have 1– charge. They whizz around the nucleus in orbitals. The orbitals take up most of the volume of the atom. Most of the mass of the atom is concentrated in the **nucleus**. The diameter of the nucleus is rather titchy compared to the whole atom. The nucleus is where you find the protons and neutrons. The mass and charge of these subatomic particles is really small, so relative mass and relative charge are used instead. The mass of an electron is negligible compared to a proton or a neutron — it's about 2000 times smaller. Figure 2 shows the relative masses and charges of protons, neutrons and electrons.

| Subatomic particle | Relative mass | Relative charge |
|---|---|---|
| Proton | 1 | 1+ |
| Neutron | 1 | 0 |
| Electron, $e^-$ | $\frac{1}{2000}$ | 1– |

*Figure 2: Relative masses and charges of subatomic particles.*

## Nuclear symbols

You can figure out the number of protons, neutrons and electrons from the nuclear symbol.

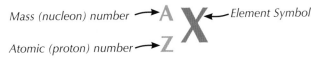

*Figure 3: Nuclear symbol.*

### Mass (nucleon) number
This is the total number of protons and neutrons in the nucleus of an atom.

### Atomic (proton) number
This is the number of protons in the nucleus of an atom — it identifies the element. All atoms of the same element have the same number of protons. Sometimes the atomic number is left out of the nuclear symbol, e.g. $^7Li$. You don't really need it because the element's symbol tells you its value.

**Learning Objectives:**

- Be able to describe the distribution of mass and charge within an atom.
- Be able to describe protons, neutrons and electrons in terms of relative charge and relative mass.
- Be able to describe the contribution of protons and neutrons to the nucleus of an atom, in terms of atomic (proton) number and mass (nucleon) number.
- Be able to deduce the numbers of protons, neutrons and electrons in an atom given its atomic and mass number and in an ion given its atomic number, mass number and ionic charge.
- Be able to explain the term isotopes as atoms of an element with different numbers of neutrons and different masses.

**Specification Reference 1.1.1**

**Tip:** You can find the symbols and atomic numbers for each element using the Periodic Table. The other number in the periodic table isn't the mass number though — it's the relative atomic mass, which is a bit different. (See page 11 for more on relative atomic mass.)

# Atoms and ions

For neutral atoms, which have no overall charge, the number of electrons is the same as the number of protons. The number of neutrons is just mass number minus atomic number, i.e. 'top minus bottom' in the nuclear symbol. Figure 4 shows some examples.

| Nuclear symbol | Atomic number, Z | Mass number, A | Protons | Electrons | Neutrons |
|---|---|---|---|---|---|
| $^{7}_{3}Li$ | 3 | 7 | 3 | 3 | $7 - 3 = 4$ |
| $^{80}_{35}Br$ | 35 | 80 | 35 | 35 | $80 - 35 = 45$ |
| $^{24}_{12}Mg$ | 12 | 24 | 12 | 12 | $24 - 12 = 12$ |

**Figure 4:**  Calculating the number of neutrons in atoms.

**Ions** have different numbers of protons and electrons. Negative ions have more electrons than protons and positive ions have fewer electrons than protons. It kind of makes sense if you think about it.

**Tip:** Ions have the same number of protons and neutrons as atoms do — it's only the number of electrons that changes.

— Examples —

**Br$^-$ is a negative ion**

The negative charge means that there's 1 more electron than there are protons. Br has 35 protons (see table above), so Br$^-$ must have 36 electrons. The overall charge $= +35 - 36 = -1$.

**Mg$^{2+}$ is a positive ion**

The 2+ charge means that there's 2 fewer electrons than there are protons. Mg has 12 protons (see table above), so Mg$^{2+}$ must have 10 electrons. The overall charge $= +12 - 10 = +2$.

**Tip:** Ions are easy to spot — they've always got a $^+$ or a $^-$ next to them. If they've got a $^+$ it means they've lost electrons, if it's a $^-$ then they've gained electrons. If there's a number next to the sign it means more than one electron has been lost or gained. For example, $^{3+}$ means 3 electrons have been lost, $^{2-}$ means that 2 have been gained.

# Isotopes

**Isotopes** of an element are atoms with the same number of protons but different numbers of neutrons.

— Examples —

Chlorine-35 and chlorine-37 are examples of isotopes. They have different mass numbers which means they have different numbers of neutrons. The atomic numbers are the same. Both isotopes have 17 protons and 17 electrons.

**Chlorine-35:**  $^{35}_{17}Cl$

$35 - 17 = 18$ neutrons

**Chlorine-37:**  $^{37}_{17}Cl$

$37 - 17 = 20$ neutrons

Here's another example — naturally occurring magnesium consists of 3 isotopes.

| $^{24}Mg$ (79%) | $^{25}Mg$ (10%) | $^{26}Mg$ (11%) |
|---|---|---|
| 12 protons | 12 protons | 12 protons |
| 12 neutrons | 13 neutrons | 14 neutrons |
| 12 electrons | 12 electrons | 12 electrons |

**Figure 5:**  Subatomic particles in Mg isotopes.

**Tip:** You can show isotopes in different ways. For example, the isotope of magnesium with 12 neutrons can be shown as:

**Magnesium-24,**

$^{24}Mg$  or  $^{24}_{12}Mg$

It's the number and arrangement of electrons that decides the chemical properties of an element. Isotopes have the same configuration of electrons, so they've got the same chemical properties. Isotopes of an element do have slightly different physical properties though, such as different densities, rates of diffusion, etc. This is because physical properties tend to depend more on the mass of the atom.

## Practice Questions — Application

Q1 Aluminium has the nuclear symbol: $^{27}_{13}\text{Al}$

   a) How many protons does an atom of aluminium have?
   b) How many electrons does an atom of aluminium have?
   c) How many neutrons does an atom of aluminium have?

Q2 A potassium atom has 19 electrons and 20 neutrons.
   a) How many protons does a potassium ion have?
   b) What is the mass number of a potassium atom?
   c) Write the nuclear symbol for potassium.
   d) Potassium ions have a charge of 1+. How many electrons does a potassium ion have?

Q3 Calcium has the nuclear symbol: $^{40}_{20}\text{Ca}$
   It forms $Ca^{2+}$ ions.
   a) How many electrons does a $Ca^{2+}$ ion have?
   b) How many neutrons does a $Ca^{2+}$ ion have?

Q4 Element A has 41 protons and 52 neutrons.
   a) Write the nuclear symbol for element A.
   b) Write the nuclear symbol of a different isotope of element A.

Q5 This question relates to the atoms or ions A to D:

   A $^{16}_{8}\text{O}^{2-}$   B $^{17}_{7}\text{N}$   C $^{20}_{10}\text{Ne}$   D $^{18}_{8}\text{O}$

   Identify the similarity for each of the following pairs.
   a) A and C.
   b) A and D.
   c) B and C.
   d) B and D.
   e) Which two of the atoms or ions are isotopes of each other? Explain your reasoning.

**Exam Tip**
In your exam you'll have to look at the periodic table to find the nuclear symbol of an element. You usually won't be given it in the question like this.

**Tip:** Here we mean similarities in the numbers of protons, neutrons or electrons between the two atoms or ions.

## Practice Questions — Fact Recall

Q1 Name the three types of particle found in an atom.
Q2 Give the relative masses of these particles.
Q3 State where in the atom each of these particles would be found.
Q4 What is mass number?
Q5 What is atomic number?
Q6 How can you work out the number of neutrons an atom has?
Q7 What are isotopes?
Q8 Why do isotopes have the same chemical properties?
Q9 Explain why isotopes can have different physical properties.

# 2. Atomic Models

*The model of the atom is useful for understanding loads of ideas in chemistry. But it's just a model, and the accepted model of the atom has changed throughout history.*

## Changes to the atomic model

The model of the atom you're expected to know (the one on page 5) is the currently accepted model. It fits all the observations and evidence we have so far, so we assume it's true until someone shows that it's incomplete or wrong. In the past, completely different models were accepted, because they fitted the evidence available at the time.

Some ancient Greeks thought that all matter was made from indivisible particles. At the start of the 19th century John Dalton described atoms as solid spheres, and said that different types of sphere made up the different elements (see Figure 1).

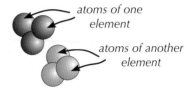

*Figure 1: Dalton's model of the atom.*

But as scientists did more experiments, our currently accepted models began to emerge, with modifications or refinements being made to take account of new evidence.

## Thomson's model

In 1897 J J Thomson did a whole series of experiments and concluded that atoms weren't solid and indivisible. His measurements of charge and mass showed that an atom must contain even smaller, negatively charged particles. He called these particles 'corpuscles' — we call them electrons. The 'solid sphere' idea of atomic structure had to be changed. The new model was known as the '**plum pudding model**' — a positively charged sphere with negative electrons embedded in it.

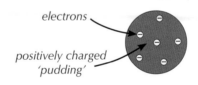

*Figure 2: Thomson's model of the atom.*

## Rutherford's model

In 1909 Ernest Rutherford and his students Hans Geiger and Ernest Marsden conducted the famous gold foil experiment. They fired alpha particles (which are positively charged) at an extremely thin sheet of gold. From the plum pudding model, they were expecting most of the alpha particles to be deflected very slightly by the positive 'pudding' that made up most of an atom. In fact, most of the alpha particles passed straight through the gold atoms, and a very small number were deflected backwards through more than 90°. This showed that the plum pudding model couldn't be right. So Rutherford came up with a model that could explain this new evidence — the **nuclear model of the atom**. In this model, there's a tiny, positively charged nucleus at the centre of the atom surrounded by a 'cloud' of negative electrons. Most of the atom's mass is concentrated at the centre and so most of the atom is empty space (see Figure 4).

*Figure 3: Thomson and Rutherford worked together at Cambridge University.*

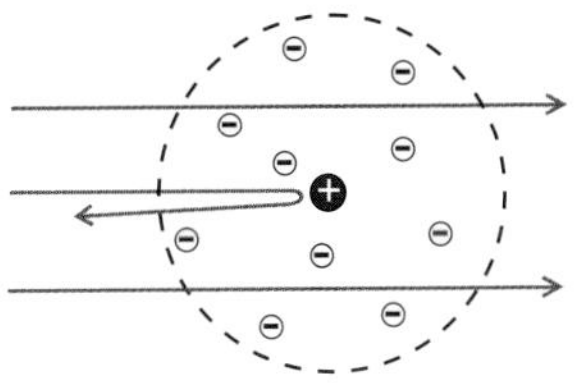

A few alpha particles are deflected very strongly by the nucleus.

Most of the alpha particles pass through empty space.

*Figure 4: Rutherford's model of the atom.*

**Tip:** This model is closer to the currently accepted model of an atom but still isn't quite right. Read on to find out why...

# Modifications to Rutherford's model

Rutherford's model seemed pretty convincing, but Henry Moseley discovered that the charge of the nucleus increased from one element to another in units of one. This led Rutherford to investigate the nucleus further. He finally discovered that it contained positively charged particles that he called protons. The charges of the nuclei of different atoms could then be explained — the atoms of different elements have a different number of protons in their nucleus. There was still one problem with the model — the nuclei of atoms were heavier than they would be if they just contained protons. Rutherford predicted that there were other particles in the nucleus, that had mass but no charge — and the neutron was eventually discovered by James Chadwick.

This is nearly always the way scientific knowledge develops — new evidence prompts people to come up with new, improved ideas. Then other people go through each new, improved idea with a fine-tooth comb as well — modern '**peer review**' is part of this process.

**Tip:** See page 5 for more on protons and neutrons.

**Tip:** See page 2 for more on 'peer review'.

# Bohr's model

The **Bohr model** (Figure 6) was a further improvement. Scientists realised that electrons in a 'cloud' around the nucleus of an atom, as Rutherford described, would quickly spiral down into the nucleus, causing the atom to collapse. Niels Bohr proposed a new model of the atom with four basic principles:

- Electrons only exist in fixed orbits (shells) and not anywhere in between.
- Each shell has a fixed energy.
- When an electron moves between shells electromagnetic radiation is emitted or absorbed.
- Because the energy of shells is fixed, the radiation will have a fixed frequency.

*Figure 5: Rutherford and Bohr worked together at the University of Manchester.*

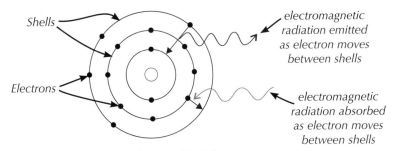

Shells

Electrons

electromagnetic radiation emitted as electron moves between shells

electromagnetic radiation absorbed as electron moves between shells

*Figure 6: Bohr's model of the atom.*

The frequencies of radiation emitted and absorbed by atoms were already known from experiments. The Bohr model fitted these observations.

The Bohr model also explained why some elements (the noble gases) are inert. Bohr said that the shells of an atom can only hold fixed numbers of electrons, and that an element's reactivity is due to its electrons. So, when an atom has full shells of electrons it's stable and does not react.

**Tip:** The term inert just means that it doesn't react with anything.

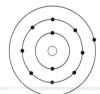

**Figure 7:** *Atomic structure of sodium (Bohr model).*

**Figure 8:** *Atomic structure of neon (Bohr model).*

Sodium only has 1 electron in its outer shell. This shell isn't full, so sodium is unstable and will react.

Neon (a noble gas) has full shells of electrons. This means the atom is stable, so neon will not react.

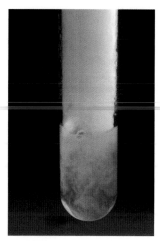

**Figure 9:** *Sodium reacts vigorously with water as it is unstable.*

## Other atomic models

We now know that the Bohr model is not perfect — but it's still widely used to describe atoms because it is simple and explains many observations from experiments, like bonding and ionisation energy trends. The most accurate model we have today involves complicated quantum mechanics — see Figure 10. Basically, you can never know where an electron is or which direction it's going in at any moment, but you can say how likely it is to be at a certain point in the atom. Oh, and electrons can act as waves as well as particles. But you don't need to worry about that.

**Tip:** Even though some of these models are outdated now you still need to learn about them. So make sure you know what each model is like and who came up with it.

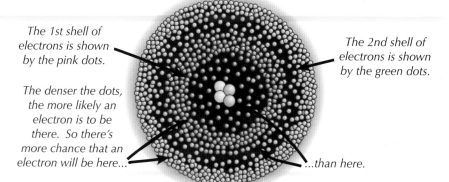

The 1st shell of electrons is shown by the pink dots.

The 2nd shell of electrons is shown by the green dots.

The denser the dots, the more likely an electron is to be there. So there's more chance that an electron will be here...

...than here.

**Figure 10:** *The quantum model of an atom.*

The **quantum model** might be more accurate, but it's a lot harder to get your head round and visualise. It does explain some observations that can't be accounted for by the Bohr model though. So scientists use whichever model is most relevant to whatever they're investigating.

### Practice Questions — Fact Recall

Q1 Describe how J J Thomson's model of the atom was different from Dalton's model.

Q2 What name was given to J J Thomson's model of the atom?

Q3 Name the scientists who conducted the gold foil experiment in 1909.

Q4 Explain how the gold foil experiment provided evidence that Dalton's model was wrong.

Q5 Describe Rutherford's model of the atom.

Q6 Describe the main features of Bohr's model of the atom.

Q7 Is the Bohr model a true representation of the structure of the atom?

# 3. Relative Mass

The actual mass of an atom is very, very tiny. Don't worry about exactly how tiny for now, but it's far too small to weigh. So, the mass of one atom is compared to the mass of carbon–12. This is its relative mass. You need to know about relative atomic mass, relative isotopic mass and relative molecular mass.

## Relative atomic mass

The **relative atomic mass**, $A_r$, is the average mass of an atom of an element on a scale where an atom of carbon-12 is exactly 12. The relative atomic mass of each element is shown in the periodic table (see Figure 1). Relative atomic mass is an average, so it's not usually a whole number.

## Relative isotopic mass

**Relative isotopic mass** is the mass of an atom of an isotope of an element on a scale where an atom of carbon-12 is exactly 12. Relative isotopic mass is usually a whole number (at AS level anyway).

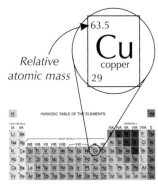

**Figure 1:** *Location of relative atomic masses on the periodic table.*

## Calculating relative atomic mass

You need to know how to calculate the relative atomic mass ($A_r$) of an element from its isotopic abundances. Different isotopes of an element occur in different quantities, or **isotopic abundances**. The relative atomic mass ($A_r$) of an element is the average mass of all its isotopes. If you've got the isotopic abundances as percentages, the easiest way to calculate the relative atomic mass is to imagine you have 100 atoms, and then find the average mass. Just follow these steps:

- Multiply each relative isotopic mass by its % relative isotopic abundance and add up the results.
- Divide by 100.

### Example
**Calculating the $A_r$ of chlorine**
The relative atomic mass of chlorine is the average mass of all chlorine atoms. 76% of the chlorine atoms found on Earth have a relative isotopic mass of 35, while 24% have a relative isotopic mass of 37. To calculate the relative atomic mass, just follow the steps above:

- Multiply each relative isotopic mass by its % relative isotopic abundance and add up the results:

  $(76 \times 35) + (24 \times 37) = 2660 + 888 = 3548$.

- Divide this by 100: $3548 \div 100 = 35.5$ (to 1 decimal place)

So the relative atomic mass of chlorine is 35.5.

You might be given your isotopic abundances in the form of a graph, such as a **mass spectrum**. Mass spectra are produced by mass spectrometers — devices which are used to find out what samples are made up of by measuring the masses of their components (see page 170).

**Learning Objectives:**
- Know that $^{12}C$ is used as the standard measurement of relative masses.
- Be able to define the terms relative isotopic mass and relative atomic mass, based on the $^{12}C$ scale.
- Be able to calculate the relative atomic mass of an element given the relative abundances of its isotopes.
- Know how spreadsheets can be used in calculating relative atomic masses from data.
- Be able to use the terms relative molecular mass and relative formula mass and calculate values from relative atomic masses.

**Specification Reference 1.1.1**

**Exam Tip**
You're often asked for the definition of relative atomic mass and relative isotopic mass. These are easy marks to get in the exam if you make the effort to learn them now.

**Tip:** The process of finding an average explains why the relative atomic mass is not usually a whole number.

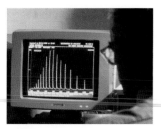

**Figure 2:** A mass spectrum being generated.

**Tip:** On mass spectra like this one you can treat the mass/charge ratio as the isotopic mass because the charge is usually just +1.

Sometimes the isotopic abundances on a mass spectrum might not be given as percentages, but the method for working out the $A_r$ is very similar:

- Multiply each relative isotopic mass by its relative abundance and add up the results.
- Then divide by the sum of the relative abundances.

**Example**

The graph on the right shows the mass spectrum for a sample of neon gas. You can use this mass spectrum to calculate the $A_r$ of neon.

- Multiply each relative isotopic mass by its relative isotopic abundance, and add up the results: $(20 \times 114) + (21 \times 0.2) + (22 \times 11.2) = 2530.6$
- Divide by the sum of the relative abundances: Sum of relative abundances = $114 + 0.2 + 11.2 = 125.4$
  $2530.6 \div 125.4 = 20.2$ (to 1 d.p.)

So the relative atomic mass of neon is 20.2.

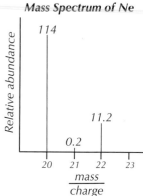

**Mass Spectrum of Ne**

**Tip:** Understanding how spreadsheets are used to make calculations easier is an important part of How Science Works. See pages 1-4 for more on How Science Works.

## Using spreadsheets to find $A_r$

Spreadsheets can be really handy when it comes to calculating the relative atomic mass of an element. This method is particularly useful when a large amount of data is being used. You can put the relative isotopic abundance data into a spreadsheet, then get the spreadsheet to work out the $A_r$ for you.

**Tip:** Spreadsheets are really useful but you won't be able to use them to work out atomic masses in your exam — so you'll need to know how to do the calculations yourself too.

**Example**

This spreadsheet contains data from the mass spectrum of zirconium.

|  | A | B | C | D |
|---|---|---|---|---|
| 1 | Relative Isotopic Mass | Relative Abundance | Relative Mass × Abundance | |
| 2 | 90 | 100.00 | 9000.00 | |
| 3 | 91 | 21.81 | 1984.71 | |
| 4 | 92 | 33.33 | 3066.36 | |
| 5 | 94 | 33.78 | 3175.32 | |
| 6 | 96 | 5.44 | 522.24 | |
| 7 | | 194.36 | 17748.63 | |
| 8 | | | | |
| 9 | Relative Atomic Mass = | | 91.31833 | |
| 10 | | | | |

In the red cells the spreadsheet has multiplied the numbers in column A by the numbers in column B to give the product of each relative isotopic mass and its relative abundance. In the purple cells, the spreadsheet has added up the numbers in the cells above to give the two totals you need to calculate the $A_r$. To work out the relative atomic mass, the sum in cell C7 is divided by the sum in B7. So the relative atomic mass of zirconium is 91.3, to 1 decimal place.

# Relative molecular mass

The **relative molecular mass**, $M_r$, is the average mass of a molecule on a scale where an atom of carbon-12 is exactly 12. To find the $M_r$, just add up the relative atomic mass values of all the atoms in the molecule.

**Tip:** Don't forget — you can find the relative atomic mass of an atom on the periodic table.

┌─ **Examples** ───────────────────────────────

**Calculating the relative molecular mass of $C_2H_6O$.**

In one molecule of $C_2H_6O$ there are 2 atoms of carbon, 6 of hydrogen and 1 of oxygen. The relative atomic masses ($A_r$) of each atom are shown in Figure 3.

$$M_r \text{ of } C_2H_6O = (2 \times 12) + (6 \times 1) + (1 \times 16) = 46$$

*6 H atoms*   *$A_r$ of H*   *2 C atoms*   *$A_r$ of C*   *1 O atom*   *$A_r$ of O*

**Calculating the relative molecular mass of $C_4H_{10}$.**

In one molecule of $C_4H_{10}$ there are 4 atoms of carbon and 10 of hydrogen.

$$M_r \text{ of } C_4H_{10} = (4 \times 12) + (10 \times 1) = 58$$

**Tip:** The molecular formula tells you how many of each atom there are in the molecule.

| Atom | $A_r$ |
|---|---|
| Carbon (C) | 12.0 |
| Hydrogen (H) | 1.0 |
| Oxygen (O) | 16.0 |
| Calcium (Ca) | 40.1 |
| Fluorine (F) | 19.0 |

***Figure 3:*** *Table of relative atomic masses.*

# Relative formula mass

**Relative formula mass** is the average mass of a formula unit on a scale where an atom of carbon-12 is exactly 12. It's used for compounds that are ionic (or giant covalent, such as $SiO_2$). To find the relative formula mass, just add up the relative atomic masses ($A_r$) of all the ions in the formula unit.

┌─ **Examples** ───────────────────────────────

**Calculating the relative formula mass of $CaF_2$.**

In $CaF_2$ there is one $Ca^{2+}$ ion and two $F^-$ ions. The $A_r$ of ions is the same as the $A_r$ of atoms of that element — the electrons make no difference to the mass.

*$A_r$ of Ca (there's only one calcium ion)*

$$M_r \text{ of } CaF_2 = 40.1 + (2 \times 19) = 78.1$$

*2 ions of F⁻*   *$A_r$ of F*

**Calculating the relative formula mass of $CaCO_3$.**

In $CaCO_3$ there is one $Ca^{2+}$ ion and one $CO_3^{2-}$ ion. The $CO_3^{2-}$ ion contains 1 carbon atom and 3 oxygen atoms, so the $A_r$ values of all these atoms need to be included in the calculation.

$$M_r \text{ of } CaCO_3 = 40.1 + 12 + (3 \times 16) = 100.1$$

**Tip:** Relative molecular mass and relative formula mass are basically the same thing — it's just that ionic compounds aren't made of molecules so they can't have a molecular mass. You work them out the same way though.

**Exam Tip**
It's really important that you can calculate relative molecular mass (and relative formula mass). It crops up in loads of different calculations so you need to be really confident that you can do it correctly.

## Practice Questions — Application

Q1 Find the relative atomic mass of the following elements:
  a) Rubidium
  b) Mercury
  c) Zinc

Q2 A sample of tungsten is 0.1% $^{180}W$, 26.5% $^{182}W$, 14.3% $^{183}W$, 30.7% $^{184}W$ and 28.4% $^{186}W$. Calculate the $A_r$ of tungsten.

Q3 A sample of zirconium is 51.5% $^{90}$Zr, 11.2% $^{91}$Zr, 17.1% $^{92}$Zr, 17.4% $^{94}$Zr and 2.8% $^{96}$Zr. Calculate the A$_r$ of zirconium.

Q4 The graphs below show the mass spectra for three elements. Use the data in the graphs to calculate the relative atomic mass of each of these elements:

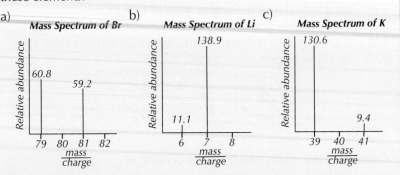

a) Mass Spectrum of Br
b) Mass Spectrum of Li
c) Mass Spectrum of K

**Tip:** You might also see mass ÷ charge as mass/charge or m/z.

**Tip:** There's a periodic table on page 274 — you might need it to answer these questions.

Q5 Find the relative molecular mass of the following compounds:

a) $NH_3$

b) $CO_2$

c) $C_2H_4O_6N_2$

Q6 Find the relative formula mass of the following compounds:

a) $CaCl_2$

b) $MgSO_4$

c) NaOH

## Practice Questions — Fact Recall

Q1 What is relative atomic mass?

Q2 What is relative isotopic mass?

Q3 a) How have computers made calculating relative atomic mass easier?

b) When is this particularly useful?

Q4 What is relative molecular mass?

Q5 What is relative formula mass?

# 4. The Mole

*Amount of substance is a really important idea in chemistry. It's all about working out exactly how much of a chemical you have and what amount of it is reacting with other chemicals. Then you can use that information in all sorts of calculations to do with things like mass, concentration and volume.*

## What is a mole?

Chemists often talk about 'amount of substance'. Basically, all they mean is 'number of particles'. Amount of substance is measured using a unit called the **mole** (mol for short) and given the symbol n. One mole is roughly $6 \times 10^{23}$ particles (the **Avogadro constant**, $N_A$). It doesn't matter what the particles are. They can be atoms, molecules, electrons, ions — anything.

**Examples**

**In the reaction $C + O_2 \rightarrow CO_2$:**

1 atom of carbon reacts with 1 molecule of oxygen to make 1 molecule of carbon dioxide, so 1 mole of carbon reacts with 1 mole of oxygen to make 1 mole of carbon dioxide.

**In the reaction $2Mg + O_2 \rightarrow 2MgO$:**

2 atoms of magnesium react with 1 molecule of oxygen to make 2 molecules of magnesium oxide, so 2 moles of magnesium react with 1 mole of oxygen molecules to make 2 moles of magnesium oxide.

Here's a nice simple formula for finding the number of moles from the number of atoms or molecules:

$$\text{Number of moles} = \frac{\text{Number of particles you have}}{\text{Number of particles in a mole}}$$

**Example**

I have $1.5 \times 10^{24}$ carbon atoms. How many moles of carbon is this?

$$\text{Number of moles} = \frac{1.5 \times 10^{24}}{6.02 \times 10^{23}} \approx 2.49 \text{ moles}$$

## Molar mass

**Molar mass**, M, is the mass of one mole of something. But the main thing to remember is that molar mass is just the same as the relative molecular mass, $M_r$ (or relative formula mass). The only difference is you stick a '$g \text{ mol}^{-1}$' for grams per mole on the end.

**Examples**

**Find the molar mass of $CaCO_3$.**

Relative formula mass, $M_r$, of $CaCO_3$ = $40.1 + 12 + (3 \times 16) = 100.1$
So the molar mass, M, is $100.1 \text{ g mol}^{-1}$ (i.e. 1 mole of $CaCO_3$ weighs 100.1 g).

**Find the molar mass of $Ni(OH)_2$.**

Relative formula mass, $M_r$, of $Ni(OH)_2$ = $58.7 + (2 \times (16 + 1)) = 92.7$
So the molar mass, M, is $92.7 \text{ g mol}^{-1}$ (i.e. 1 mole of $Ni(OH)_2$ weighs 92.7 g).

**Learning Objectives:**

- Be able to explain the term amount of substance.
- Know that a mole (symbol 'mol') is the unit for amount of substance.
- Know that the Avogadro constant, $N_A$, is the number of particles per mole ($6.02 \times 10^{23} \text{ mol}^{-1}$).
- Be able to define and use the term molar mass (units $g \text{ mol}^{-1}$) as the mass per mole of a substance.
- Be able to carry out calculations, using amount of substance in mol, involving mass.

**Specification Reference 1.1.2**

**Exam Tip**
Make sure you learn this formula — you won't be given it in the exam.

**Figure 1:** 1 mole of carbon.

**Tip:** Remember, to find relative formula mass, all you need to do is add up the relative atomic masses of all the atoms in the formula (see page 13).

# Calculations with moles

There's a formula that connects the molar mass of a substance to the number of moles of the substance that you have. It looks like this:

$$\text{Number of moles} = \frac{\text{mass of substance}}{\text{molar mass}}$$

**Exam Tip**
This formula crops up in all sorts of chemistry calculations — you'll definitely need to know it off by heart for your exams.

## Examples

**How many moles of aluminium oxide are present in 5.1 g of $Al_2O_3$?**

Molar mass of $Al_2O_3$ = $(2 \times 27.0) + (3 \times 16.0) = 102$ g mol$^{-1}$

Number of moles of $Al_2O_3$ = $\frac{5.1}{102} = 0.05$ moles

**How many moles of calcium bromide are present in 39.98 g of $CaBr_2$?**

Molar mass of $CaBr_2$ = $40.1 + (2 \times 79.9) = 199.9$ g mol$^{-1}$

Number of moles of $CaBr_2$ = $\frac{39.98}{199.9} = 0.2$ moles

**Tip:** The molar mass of a compound is the same as its $M_r$ — so this formula links moles and relative molecular mass too.

You can also rearrange the formula and use it to work out either the mass of a substance or its relative molecular mass:

## Examples

**What is the mass of 2 moles of NaF?**

Rearrange the formula to find mass (multiply both sides by molar mass):

mass of substance = number of moles × molar mass

Molar mass of NaF = $23 + 19 = 42$ g mol$^{-1}$
Mass of 2 moles of NaF = $2 \times 42 = 84$ g

**0.05 moles of a compound weighs 2.6 g. Find its relative molecular mass.**

Rearrange the formula to find molar mass:

molar mass = mass ÷ number of moles

Molar mass = $2.6 \div 0.05 = 52$ g mol$^{-1}$. So, relative molecular mass = 52.

**Tip:** If it helps you to remember how to rearrange the equation, you could use this formula triangle:

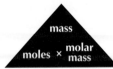

Just cover the thing you want to calculate to find the right formula.

(For example, if you cover mass it will tell you that to calculate mass you multiply moles by molar mass.)

## Practice Questions — Application

Q1 Look at this balanced equation: $4Na + O_2 \rightarrow 2Na_2O$
How many moles of $Na_2O$ are produced when 6 moles of Na react with 1.5 moles of $O_2$?

Q2 Find the molar mass of:
a) $F_2$        b) $CaCl_2$        c) $MgSO_4$

Q3 How many moles of sodium nitrate are present in 212.5 g of $NaNO_3$?

Q4 How many moles of zinc chloride are present in 15.5 g of $ZnCl_2$?

Q5 What is the mass of 2 moles of NaCl?

Q6 What is the mass of 0.25 moles of $MgCO_3$?

Q7 1.5 moles of a mystery compound weighs 66 g. Find its molar mass.

## Practice Questions — Fact Recall

Q1 a) How many particles are there in a mole?
    b) What's the name for this special number?

Q2 What is the molar mass of a chemical?

Q3 What's the formula that links molar mass and number of moles?

# 5. Concentration Calculations

*The amount of substance is closely linked to the volume of a substance and its concentration.  Read on to find out more...*

## Moles and concentration

The **concentration** of a solution is how many moles are dissolved per 1 $dm^3$ of solution.  The units are $mol\ dm^{-3}$ (or M).  A solution that has more moles per $dm^3$ than another is more concentrated.  A solution that has fewer moles per $dm^3$ than another is more dilute.  Here's the formula to find the number of moles:

$$\text{Number of moles} = \frac{\text{Concentration} \times \text{Volume (in cm}^3)}{1000}$$

$$\text{Or:  Number of moles} = \text{Concentration} \times \text{Volume (in dm}^3)$$

You need to be able to use these formulas to do calculations in the exam.

┌─ **Examples** ──────────────────────────

**How many moles of lithium chloride are present in 25 cm³ of a 1.2 mol dm⁻³ solution of LiCl?**

$$\text{Number of moles} = \frac{\text{concentration} \times \text{volume (in cm}^3)}{1000}$$

$$= \frac{1.2 \times 25}{1000} = 0.03 \text{ moles}$$

**A solution of Fe₂O₃ contains 0.2 moles of iron(III) oxide in 0.4 dm³. What is the concentration of the solution?**

Rearrange the formula to find concentration (divide both sides by volume):

$$\text{concentration} = \frac{\text{number of moles}}{\text{volume (in dm}^3)}$$

$$= \frac{0.2}{0.4} = 0.5 \text{ mol dm}^{-3}$$

**A 0.5 mol dm⁻³ solution of zinc sulfate contains 0.08 moles of ZnSO₄. What volume does the solution occupy?**

Rearrange the formula to find volume (divide both sides by volume):

$$\text{volume (in dm}^3) = \frac{\text{number of moles}}{\text{concentration}}$$

$$= \frac{0.08}{0.5} = 0.16 \text{ dm}^3$$

You might be asked to combine a concentration calculation with a molar mass calculation.  This just means using two formulas, one after the other.

┌─ **Example** ──────────────────────────

**What mass of sodium hydroxide needs to be dissolved in 50 cm³ of water to make a 2 mol dm⁻³ solution?**

First look at the question and see what information it gives you.  You've got concentration and volume — so you can work out number of moles.

**Learning Objectives:**

■ Be able to use the terms concentrated and dilute as qualitative descriptions for the concentration of a solution.

■ Be able to carry out calculations, using amount of substance in mol, involving:
(i) mass.
(ii) gas volume.
(iii) solution volume and concentration.

**Specification Reference 1.1.2**

**Tip:** 1 $dm^3$ is the same as 1000 $cm^3$ or 1 litre.

**Exam Tip**
You need to know all of the formulas in this section by heart — so look out for the formula boxes, and learn them.

**Tip:** This is another formula that you can stick in a formula triangle if it helps you:

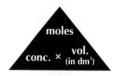

**Exam Tip**
Remember to watch out for the units in this type of calculation. Double-check whether the volume you've been given is in $cm^3$ or $dm^3$.

Number of moles = $\dfrac{\text{concentration} \times \text{volume}}{1000} = \dfrac{2 \times 50}{1000} = 0.1$ moles of NaOH

Then you can use this to work out the mass using the equation
number of moles = mass ÷ molar mass

Molar mass, M, of NaOH = 23 + 16 + 1 = 40 g mol$^{-1}$

Mass = number of moles × M = 0.1 × 40 = 4 g

*Figure 1: Potassium manganate solutions. The solution on the left is more concentrated and has more mol dm$^{-3}$ than the solution on the right, so is more darkly coloured.*

# Gas Volume

If temperature and pressure stay the same, one mole of any gas always has the same volume. At room temperature and pressure (r.t.p.), this happens to be 24 dm$^3$ (r.t.p. is 298 K (25 °C) and 100 kPa).

Here are two formulas for working out the number of moles in a volume of gas. Don't forget — only use them for r.t.p.

$$\text{number of moles} = \dfrac{\text{volume in dm}^3}{24}$$

$$\text{Or: number of moles} = \dfrac{\text{volume in cm}^3}{24\,000}$$

You need to be able to use these formulas to find numbers of moles and gas volumes.

┌ **Examples** ─────

**How many moles are there in 6 dm$^3$ of oxygen gas at r.t.p.?**

Number of moles = 6 ÷ 24
= 0.25 moles of oxygen molecules

**What volume, in cm$^3$, does 0.02 moles of hydrogen gas occupy at r.t.p.?**

Rearrange the formula to find volume (multiply both sides by 24 000):

Volume = number of moles × 24 000
= 0.02 × 24 000 = 480 cm$^3$

## Practice Questions — Application

Q1 How many moles of potassium phosphate are present in 50 cm$^3$ of a 2 mol dm$^{-3}$ solution?

Q2 How many moles of sodium chloride are present in 0.5 dm$^3$ of a 0.08 mol dm$^{-3}$ solution?

Q3 How many moles of silver nitrate are present in 30 cm$^3$ of a 0.7 mol dm$^{-3}$ solution?

Q4 A solution contains 0.25 moles of copper bromide in 0.5 dm$^3$. What is the concentration of the solution?

Q5 A solution contains 0.08 moles of lithium chloride in 0.75 dm$^3$. What is the concentration of the solution?

Q6 A solution contains 0.1 moles of iron oxide in 36 cm$^3$. What is the concentration of the solution?

Q7 A solution of calcium chloride contains 0.46 moles of $CaCl_2$. The concentration of the solution is 1.8 mol dm$^{-3}$. What volume does the solution occupy?

Q8 A solution of copper sulfate contains 0.01 moles of $CuSO_4$. The concentration of the solution is 0.55 mol dm$^{-3}$. What volume does the solution occupy?

Q9 The molecular formula of sodium oxide is $Na_2O$. What mass of sodium oxide would you have to dissolve in 75 cm$^3$ of water to make a 0.8 mol dm$^{-3}$ solution?

Q10 The molecular formula of cobalt bromide is $CoBr_2$. What mass of cobalt bromide would you have to dissolve in 30 cm$^3$ of water to make a 0.5 mol dm$^{-3}$ solution?

Q11 A solution is made by dissolving 4.08 g of a compound in 100 cm$^3$ of pure water. The solution has a concentration of 1.2 mol dm$^{-3}$. What is the molar mass of the compound?

Q12 How many moles are there in 2.4 dm$^3$ of carbon dioxide gas at r.t.p.?

Q13 How many moles are there in 0.65 dm$^3$ of carbon monoxide gas at r.t.p.?

Q14 How many moles are there in 3120 cm$^3$ of chlorine gas at r.t.p.?

Q15 What volume, in dm$^3$, does 0.21 moles of hydrogen chloride gas occupy at r.t.p.?

Q16 What volume, in dm$^3$, does 1.1 moles of fluorine gas occupy at r.t.p.?

Q17 What volume, in cm$^3$, does 0.028 moles of argon gas occupy at r.t.p.?

Q18 What volume, in cm$^3$, does 0.072 moles of nitrogen dioxide gas occupy at r.t.p.?

**Tip:** Concentration calculations come up a lot in the exam so we've given you loads of questions to help you suss it out.

**Tip:** There's more on calculating volumes of gases in reactions on page 29.

## Practice Questions — Fact Recall

Q1 Give the units of concentration.

Q2 Solution A has a concentration of 0.05 mol dm$^{-3}$, solution B has a concentration of 0.15 mol dm$^{-3}$. Which solution is more dilute?

Q3 What's the formula that links number of moles and concentration? (Write it out twice, once using each volume measurement.)

Q4 How many cm$^3$ are there in one dm$^3$?

Learning Objectives:

- Know that the empirical formula is the simplest whole number ratio of atoms of each element present in a compound.
- Know that the molecular formula is the actual number of atoms of each element in a molecule.

**Specification Reference 1.1.2**

# 6. Formulas

*Now for a few pages about chemical formulas. A formula tells you what atoms are in a compound. Useful, I think you'll agree. There are two types you need to know about — empirical formulas and molecular formulas.*

## Empirical and molecular formulas

You need to know what's what with empirical and molecular formulas. The **empirical formula** gives just the smallest whole number ratio of atoms in a compound. The **molecular formula** gives the actual numbers of atoms in a molecule. The molecular formula is made up of a whole number of empirical units.

--- Examples ---

This molecule is butane:

H—C—C—C—C—H (with H atoms above and below each carbon)

Butane contains 4 carbon (C) atoms and 10 hydrogen (H) atoms. So its molecular formula is $C_4H_{10}$.

Butane's empirical formula is $C_2H_5$. This means that the ratio of carbon atoms to hydrogen atoms in the molecule is 2 : 5. That's as much as you can simplify it.

This molecule is 1,2-dichlorocyclohexane:

1,2-dichlorocyclohexane contains 6 carbon (C) atoms, 10 hydrogen (H) atoms and two chlorine (Cl) atoms. So its molecular formula is $C_6H_{10}Cl_2$.

1,2-dichlorocyclohexane's empirical formula is $C_3H_5Cl$. This means that the ratio of carbon atoms to hydrogen atoms to chlorine atoms in the molecule is 3 : 5 : 1. That's as much as you can simplify it.

***Figure 1:*** *Molecular model of a molecule of butane.*

**Tip:** There's more information coming up on pages 22-25 about how you can use experimental data to work out empirical and molecular formulas.

If you know the empirical formula and the molecular mass of a compound, you can calculate its molecular formula. Just follow these steps:

1. Find the empirical mass (that's just the mass of the empirical formula).
2. Divide the molecular mass by the empirical mass. This tells you how many multiples of the empirical formula are in the molecular formula.
3. Multiply the empirical formula by that number to find the molecular formula.

**Tip:** Empirical mass is just like relative formula mass (see page 13).

There are a couple of examples on the next page to show you how it works.

**A molecule has an empirical formula of $C_4H_3O_2$, and a relative molecular mass of 166. Work out its molecular formula.**

1. Find the empirical mass — add up the relative atomic mass values of all the atoms in the empirical formula.

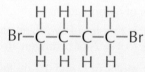

$$\text{empirical mass} = (4 \times 12) + (3 \times 1) + (2 \times 16) = 83$$

3 H atoms    $A_r$ of H

4 C atoms    $A_r$ of C    2 O atoms    $A_r$ of O

2. Divide the molecular mass by the empirical mass. The molecular mass is 166, so there are $(166 \div 83) = 2$ empirical units in the molecule.

3. The molecular formula is the empirical formula × 2, so the molecular formula = $C_8H_6O_4$.

> **Tip:** There's more on working out molecular formulas on page 24.

**The empirical formula of glucose is $CH_2O$. Its relative molecular mass is 180. Find its molecular formula.**

1. Find the empirical mass of glucose.
   empirical mass = $(1 \times 12) + (2 \times 1) + (1 \times 16) = 30$

2. Divide the molecular mass by the empirical mass. The molecular mass is 180, so there are $(180 \div 30) = 6$ empirical units in the molecule.

3. Molecular formula = $C_6H_{12}O_6$.

**Figure 2:** *Molecular model of a molecule of glucose.*

## Practice Questions — Application

**Q1** Benzene has the molecular formula $C_6H_6$. What is the empirical formula of benzene?

**Q2** A molecule contains 2 carbon atoms, 6 hydrogen atoms and 4 oxygen atoms. Give the molecular and empirical formulas of this molecule.

**Q3** The molecule below is 1,4-dibromobutane.

$$
\begin{array}{c}
\quad \text{H} \quad \text{H} \quad \text{H} \quad \text{H} \\
\quad | \quad | \quad | \quad | \\
\text{Br}-\text{C}-\text{C}-\text{C}-\text{C}-\text{Br} \\
\quad | \quad | \quad | \quad | \\
\quad \text{H} \quad \text{H} \quad \text{H} \quad \text{H}
\end{array}
$$

  a) What is the molecular formula of 1,2-dibromobutane?

  b) What is the empirical formula of 1,2-dibromobutane?

**Q4** A molecule has the empirical formula $C_4H_9$, and a molecular mass of 114. Find its molecular formula.

**Q5** A molecule has the empirical formula $C_3H_5O_2$, and a relative molecular mass of 146. Find its molecular formula.

**Q6** A molecule has the empirical formula $C_4H_6Cl_2O$, and a relative molecular mass of 423. Find its molecular formula.

## Practice Questions — Fact Recall

**Q1** What does the empirical formula of a compound tell you?

**Q2** What does the molecular formula of a compound tell you?

Learning Objective:
- Be able to calculate empirical and molecular formulas, using composition by mass and percentage compositions.

Specification Reference 1.1.2

# 7. Calculating Formulas

*You can work formulas out using experimental data or percentage compositions. You need to know how to calculate both empirical and molecular formulas, so here's how.*

## Calculating empirical formulas

There are two different ways of calculating empirical formulas you need to know about — calculating them from experimental data and calculating them from percentage compositions.

### Calculating empirical formulas from experimental data

You need to be able to work out empirical formulas from the masses of the products created in a reaction. To do this, just follow these steps:

1. Use the equation moles = mass $\div$ $M_r$ to work out how many moles of each product has been made.
2. Use the moles of each product made to work out how many moles of each atom you started with.
3. You can then write down the ratio of moles present at the start.
4. Divide by the smallest number of moles to get a whole number ratio.
5. This tells you the empirical formula.

**Exam Tip**
Make sure you write down all your working for calculation questions. You'll be more likely to spot any mistakes and if you do go wrong you might get some marks for the working.

─ Examples ───────────

**When a hydrocarbon is burnt in excess oxygen, 4.4 g of carbon dioxide and 1.8 g of water are made. What is the empirical formula of the hydrocarbon?**

1. The moles of $CO_2$ and $H_2O$ produced are:

$$\text{moles } CO_2 = \frac{\text{mass}}{M_r} = \frac{4.4}{12 + (16 \times 2)} = \frac{4.4}{44} = 0.1 \text{ moles}$$

$$\text{moles } H_2O = \frac{\text{mass}}{M_r} = \frac{1.8}{(2 \times 1) + 16} = \frac{1.8}{18} = 0.1 \text{ moles}$$

2. 1 mole of $CO_2$ contains 1 mole of carbon atoms, so you must have started with 0.1 moles of carbon atoms.

   1 mole of $H_2O$ contains 2 moles of hydrogen atoms, so you must have started with 0.2 moles (0.1 $\times$ 2) of hydrogen atoms.

3. If you started with 0.1 moles of C and 0.2 moles of H the C : H ratio is 0.1 : 0.2.

4. Dividing both sides by 0.1 (the smallest number of moles) gives a whole number C : H ratio of 1 : 2.

5. So the empirical formula of this hydrocarbon is $CH_2$.

**Tip:** A hydrocarbon is something that only contains hydrogen and carbon.

**Tip:** This method works because the only place the carbon in the carbon dioxide and the hydrogen in the water could have come from is the hydrocarbon.

Sometimes there might only be one product and you'll be told the mass of one of the reactants used instead. If this happens you can calculate the mass of the other reactant used with this equation:

**Tip:** This equation is just the rearranged version of:

mass of products = mass of reactants

$$\text{mass of reactant A} = \text{mass of product} - \text{mass of reactant B}$$

Once you know the mass of both reactants you can work out the moles of each reactant used and from there you can use points 4 and 5 above to find the empirical formula.

**2.4 g of magnesium ribbon burns in air to produce a white powder which has a mass of 4 g. What is the empirical formula of the white powder?**

If 2.4 g of magnesium has burnt to give 4 g of magnesium oxide then 4 − 2.4 = 1.6 g of oxygen must be added. So the moles of Mg and $O_2$ used are:

$$\text{moles Mg} = \frac{\text{mass}}{M_r} = \frac{2.4}{24.3} = 0.1 \text{ moles}$$

$$\text{moles O} = \frac{\text{mass}}{M_r} = \frac{1.6}{16} = 0.1 \text{ moles}$$

So the ratio of Mg to O is 0.1 : 0.1. Dividing both sides by 0.1 gives a whole number ratio of 1 : 1, so the empirical formula of magnesium oxide must be MgO.

**Figure 1:** *Magnesium ribbon burning in air.*

## Practice Questions — Application

**Q1** When a hydrocarbon is burnt in excess oxygen, 17.6 g of carbon dioxide and 10.8 g of water are made. What is the empirical formula of the hydrocarbon?

**Q2** When a hydrocarbon is burnt in excess oxygen, 3.52 g of carbon dioxide and 2.88 g of water are made. What is the empirical formula of the hydrocarbon?

**Q3** 5.52 g of sodium burns in air to produce 7.44 g of sodium oxide. What is the empirical formula of sodium oxide?

**Q4** 50.2 g of iron reacts with air to produce 69.4 g of an iron oxide. What is the empirical formula of this iron oxide?

## Calculating empirical formulas from percentage compositions

You need to know how to work out empirical formulas from the percentages of the different elements. Follow these steps each time:

1. Assume you've got 100 g of the compound — you can turn the percentages straight into masses. Then you can work out how many moles of each element are in 100 g of the compound.

2. Divide each number of moles by the smallest number of moles you found in step 1. This gives you the ratio of the elements in the compound.

3. Apply the numbers from the ratio to the formula.

**Tip:** Percentage compositions tell you what percentage of the mass of a molecule is made up of each element. So if a molecule contains 26% carbon by mass, 26% of the mass of that molecule is made up of carbon atoms.

**A compound is found to have percentage composition 56.5% potassium, 8.7% carbon and 34.8% oxygen by mass. Calculate its empirical formula.**

1. If you had 100 g of the compound you would have 56.5 g of potassium, 8.7 g of carbon and 34.8 g of oxygen. Use the formula, moles = mass ÷ $M_r$, to work out how many moles of each element that is.

   K: $\frac{56.5}{39.1}$ = 1.445 moles   C: $\frac{8.7}{12}$ = 0.725 moles   O: $\frac{34.8}{16}$ = 2.175 moles

2. Divide each number of moles by the smallest number (0.725 here).

   K: $\frac{1.445}{0.725}$ = 2.0      C: $\frac{0.725}{0.725}$ = 1.0      O: $\frac{2.175}{0.725}$ = 3.0

   This tells you that the ratio of K : C : O in the molecule is 2 : 1 : 3.

3. So you know the empirical formula's got to be $K_2CO_3$.

**Tip:** You should add up the percentages each time there's a question like this to make sure they add up to 100% and you haven't missed out any elements.

Sometimes you might only be given the percentage of some of the elements in the compound. Then you'll have to work out the percentages of the others.

─── Example ───

**An oxide of nitrogen contains 26% by mass of nitrogen. Calculate its empirical formula.**

1. The compound only contains nitrogen and oxygen, so if it is 26% N it must be $100 - 26 = 74\%$ O. So if you had 100 g of the compound you would have 26 g of nitrogen and 74 g of oxygen.

$$\text{N: } \frac{26}{14} = 1.86 \text{ moles} \qquad \text{O: } \frac{74}{16} = 4.63 \text{ moles}$$

2. Divide each number of moles by 1.86.

$$\text{N: } \frac{1.86}{1.86} = 1.0 \qquad \text{O: } \frac{4.63}{1.86} = 2.5$$

This tells you that the ratio of N : O in the molecule is 1 : 2.5.

3. All the numbers in an empirical formula have to be whole numbers, so you need to multiply the ratio by 2 to put it into its simplest whole number form: $2 \times (1 : 2.5) = 2 : 5$.

So the empirical formula is $N_2O_5$.

**Tip:** If you don't know one of the percentages, just take the percentages that you do know away from 100 to find it.

**Tip:** Being able to calculate empirical formulas is an important skill in chemistry. It's really useful when analysing the structures of compounds and might crop up in exam questions for later units, so make sure you understand it.

## Practice Questions — Application

Q1 A compound is found to have percentage composition 5.9% hydrogen and 94.1% oxygen by mass. Find its empirical formula.

Q2 A compound is found to have percentage composition 20.2% aluminium and 79.8% chlorine by mass. Find its empirical formula.

Q3 A compound is found to have percentage composition 8.5% carbon, 1.4% hydrogen and 90.1% iodine by mass. Find its empirical formula.

Q4 A compound containing only vanadium and chlorine is found to be 32.3% vanadium by mass. Find its empirical formula.

Q5 An oxide of chromium contains 31.58% by mass of oxygen. Find its empirical formula.

## Calculating molecular formulas

Once you know the empirical formula, you just need the molar mass and you can work out the molecular formula too. Dividing the molar mass by the mass of the empirical formula tells you what factor you need to scale the empirical formula up by to get the molecular formula.

**Tip:** See page 13 for more on finding relative molecular mass.

─── Example ───

**When 4.6 g of an alcohol, with molar mass 92 g mol⁻¹, is burnt in excess oxygen, it produces 8.8 g of carbon dioxide and 5.4 g of water. Calculate the empirical formula for the alcohol and then its molecular formula.**

First, find the empirical formula using the same steps as before:

$$\text{moles CO}_2 = \frac{\text{mass}}{M_r} = \frac{8.8}{12 + (16 \times 2)} = \frac{8.8}{44} = 0.2 \text{ moles}$$

1 mole of $CO_2$ contains 1 mole of carbon atoms, so you must have started with 0.2 moles of carbon atoms.

**Tip:** Alcohols contain carbon, hydrogen and oxygen.

$$\text{moles } H_2O = \frac{\text{mass}}{M_r} = \frac{5.4}{(2 \times 1) + 16} = \frac{5.4}{18} = 0.3 \text{ moles}$$

1 mole of $H_2O$ contains 2 moles of hydrogen atoms (H), so you must have started with 0.6 moles of hydrogen atoms.

To find the moles of oxygen coming from the alcohol you first need to find the mass of oxygen you started with. You can find this by using the moles of C and H that you calculated above to find the mass of C and H you started with and then take this away from the total mass of the alcohol:

Mass of C = no. of moles × $M_r$ = 0.2 × 12 = 2.4 g

Mass of H = no. of moles × $M_r$ = 0.6 × 1 = 0.6 g

Mass of alcohol = mass of C + mass of H + mass of O, so...

Mass of O = 4.6 − (2.4 + 0.6) = 1.6 g

$$\text{moles O in the alcohol} = \frac{\text{mass}}{M_r} = \frac{1.6}{16} = 0.1 \text{ moles}$$

You know the molar ratio. C : H : O = 0.2 : 0.6 : 0.1 = 2 : 6 : 1
So the empirical formula is $C_2H_6O$.

The mass of the empirical formula is (12 × 2) + (1 × 6) + 16 = 46 g

Divide the molar mass of the alcohol by this and you get 92 ÷ 46 = 2

So you need to scale the empirical formula up by 2 to get the molecular formula. So the molecular formula of the alcohol is $C_4H_{12}O_2$.

*Figure 2:* An alcohol burning in air.

**Tip:** You need to work out the mass of oxygen in this way because you don't know how much oxygen has come from the alcohol itself and how much has come from the air when the alcohol was burnt.

## Practice Questions — Application

**Q1** 3.1 g of phosphorus burns in air to produce 7.1 g of phosphorus oxide which has a molar mass of 284 g mol⁻¹. Calculate the empirical formula of phosphorus oxide and then its molecular formula.

**Q2** A hydrocarbon is found to have a percentage composition of 85.7% carbon and 14.3% hydrogen by mass. Find the molecular formula of this hydrocarbon given that it has a molar mass of 56 g mol⁻¹.

**Q3** An oxide of chlorine has a molar mass of 167 g mol⁻¹ and contains 42.5% chlorine by mass. Find its molecular formula.

**Q4** When 12.8 g of an alcohol, with molar mass 32 g mol⁻¹, is burnt in excess oxygen, it produces 17.6 g of $CO_2$ and 14.4 g of $H_2O$. Calculate the empirical and molecular formulas of the alcohol.

**Q5** When 2.64 g of an alcohol, with a molar mass 88 g mol⁻¹, is burnt in excess oxygen, it produces 2.16 g of $H_2O$ and 5.28 g of $CO_2$. Calculate the empirical and molecular formulas of the alcohol.

**Tip:** If the molar mass of the empirical formula is the same as the molar mass of your substance then the empirical formula is the same as the molecular formula.

**Learning Objective:**
- Be able to construct balanced chemical equations for reactions studied and for unfamiliar reactions given reactants and products.

**Specification Reference 1.1.2**

# 8. Balancing Equations

*Balancing equations is one of those topics that gets everywhere in chemistry. You'll have done this before, so it should look a bit familiar. Make sure you've got your head round it now though, because you'll definitely need it again.*

## How to balance equations

**Balanced equations** have the same number of each atom on both sides. They're.. well... you know... balanced. You can only add more atoms by adding whole compounds. You do this by putting a number in front of a compound or changing one that's already there. You can't mess with formulas — ever (e.g. you can change $H_2O$ to $2H_2O$, but never to $H_4O$).

---
**Examples**

**Balance the equation $H_2SO_4 + NaOH \rightarrow Na_2SO_4 + H_2O$.**

First you need to count how many of each atom you have on each side.

$$H_2SO_4 + NaOH \rightarrow Na_2SO_4 + H_2O$$

| $H = 3$ $Na = 1$ | $H = 2$ $Na = 2$ |
|---|---|
| $O = 5$ $S = 1$ | $O = 5$ $S = 1$ |

The left side needs 2 Na's, so try changing NaOH to 2NaOH:

$$H_2SO_4 + 2NaOH \rightarrow Na_2SO_4 + H_2O$$

| $H = 4$ $Na = 2$ | $H = 2$ $Na = 2$ |
|---|---|
| $O = 6$ $S = 1$ | $O = 5$ $S = 1$ |

Now the right side needs 4 H's, so try changing $H_2O$ to $2H_2O$:

$$H_2SO_4 + 2NaOH \rightarrow Na_2SO_4 + 2H_2O$$

| $H = 4$ $Na = 2$ | $H = 4$ $Na = 2$ |
|---|---|
| $O = 6$ $S = 1$ | $O = 6$ $S = 1$ |

Both sides have the same number of each atom — the equation is balanced.

**Balance the equation $C_2H_6 + O_2 \rightarrow CO_2 + H_2O$.**

First work out how many of each atom you have on each side.

$$C_2H_6 + O_2 \rightarrow CO_2 + H_2O$$

| $C = 2$ $H = 6$ | $C = 1$ $H = 2$ |
|---|---|
| $O = 2$ | $O = 3$ |

The right side needs 2 C's, so try $2CO_2$. It also needs 6 H's, so try $3H_2O$.

$$C_2H_6 + O_2 \rightarrow 2CO_2 + 3H_2O$$

| $C = 2$ $H = 6$ | $C = 2$ $H = 6$ |
|---|---|
| $O = 2$ | $O = 7$ |

The left side needs 7 O's, so try $3\frac{1}{2}O_2$ (you can use ½ to balance equations).

$$C_2H_6 + 3\frac{1}{2}O_2 \rightarrow 2CO_2 + 3H_2O$$

| $C = 2$ $H = 6$ | $C = 2$ $H = 6$ |
|---|---|
| $O = 7$ | $O = 7$ |

This balances the equation.

---

## Balancing ionic equations

In **ionic equations**, only the reacting particles are included. You don't have to worry about the rest of the stuff. First you make sure that both sides have the same number of atoms — just like a normal equation. Then you balance the charges by adding extra electrons.

## Examples

**Balance the ionic equation** $H_2O_2 \rightarrow O_2 + H^+$

Work out how many of each atom you have on each side.
$$H_2O_2 \rightarrow O_2 + H^+$$
$$O = 2 \quad H = 2 \mid O = 2 \quad H = 1$$

The right side needs 2 H's, so try $2H^+$:
$$H_2O_2 \rightarrow O_2 + 2H^+$$
$$O = 2 \quad H = 2 \mid O = 2 \quad H = 2$$

Now you need to balance the charges:

charges on left side | charges on right side
0 | $(2 \times 1+) = 2+$

The right side needs two extra electrons.
So the balanced ionic equation is: $H_2O_2 \rightarrow O_2 + 2H^+ + 2e^-$

**Figure 1:** *Hydrogen peroxide ($H_2O_2$) decomposing to produce oxygen gas.*

**Balance the ionic equation** $Cr_2O_7^{2-} + H^+ + e^- \rightarrow Cr^{3+} + H_2O$

Again, first work out how many of each atom you have on each side.
$$Cr_2O_7^{2-} + H^+ + e^- \rightarrow Cr^{3+} + H_2O$$
$$Cr = 2 \quad O = 7 \mid Cr = 1 \quad O = 1$$
$$H = 1 \qquad\qquad H = 2$$

The right side needs 2 Cr's, so try $2Cr^{3+}$. It also needs 7 O's, so try $7H_2O$.
$$Cr_2O_7^{2-} + H^+ + e^- \rightarrow 2Cr^{3+} + 7H_2O$$
$$Cr = 2 \quad O = 7 \mid Cr = 2 \quad O = 7$$
$$H = 1 \qquad\qquad H = 14$$

The left side needs 14 H's, so try $14H^+$.
$$Cr_2O_7^{2-} + 14H^+ + e^- \rightarrow 2Cr^{3+} + 7H_2O$$
$$Cr = 2 \quad O = 7 \mid Cr = 2 \quad O = 7$$
$$H = 14 \qquad\qquad H = 14$$

Now the charges just need balancing:

charges on left side | charges on right side
$(2-) + (14 \times 1+) + (1-) = 11+$ | $(2 \times 3+) = 6+$

The left side needs five additional electrons.
The balanced ionic equation is: $Cr_2O_7^{2-} + 14H^+ + 6e^- \rightarrow 2Cr^{3+} + 7H_2O$

**Tip:** The extra electrons are just there to balance charge — they're not atoms, so you don't need to include them in the atom balancing bit.

**Tip:** When you balance the charges, don't forget to multiply the charge by the number in front. One $H^+$ ion on its own has a charge of 1+, but 14 $H^+$ ions together carry a total charge of 14+.

## Practice Questions — Application

**Q1** Balance these equations:
a) $Mg + HCl \rightarrow MgCl_2 + H_2$
b) $S_8 + F_2 \rightarrow SF_6$
c) $Ca(OH)_2 + H_2SO_4 \rightarrow CaSO_4 + H_2O$
d) $Na_2CO_3 + HCl \rightarrow NaCl + CO_2 + H_2O$
e) $C_4H_{10} + O_2 \rightarrow CO_2 + H_2O$

**Q2** Balance these ionic equations:
a) $Ag \rightarrow Ag^{2+}$
b) $Br_2 \rightarrow Br^-$
c) $CrO_4^{2-} + H_2O \rightarrow CrO_2^- + OH^-$
d) $MnO_4^- + H^+ \rightarrow Mn^{2+} + H_2O$

# 9. Equations and Calculations

*Once you've made sure that an equation is balanced, you can use it to calculate all sorts of things — like how much product a reaction will make...*

## Calculating masses

You can use the balanced equation for a reaction to work out how much product you will get from a certain mass of reactant.

Here are the steps to follow:

1. Write out the balanced equation for the reaction.

2. Work out how many moles of the reactant you have.

3. Use the **molar ratio** from the balanced equation to work out the number of moles of product that will be formed from this much reactant.

4. Calculate the mass of that many moles of product.

**Tip:** The ratio of the moles of each reactant and product in a balanced chemical equation is called the molar ratio.

Here's a nice juicy example to help you get to grips with the method:

**Tip:** Don't forget — the big numbers in front of substances in the chemical equation show how many moles of each substance are reacting.

**Tip:** Look — it's that moles = mass ÷ $M_r$ formula yet again...

─ **Example** ───────────────────────

**Calculate the mass of iron(III) oxide produced if 28 g of iron is burnt in air.**

1. Write out the balanced equation: $2Fe_{(s)} + 1\frac{1}{2}O_{2(g)} \rightarrow Fe_2O_{3(s)}$

2. Work out how many moles of iron you have:
   $M_r$ of Fe = 55.8
   Moles = mass ÷ $M_r$ = 28 ÷ 55.8 = 0.5 moles of iron

3. The molar ratio of Fe : $Fe_2O_3$ is 2 : 1. This means that for every 2 moles of Fe that you have, you will produce 1 mole of $Fe_2O_3$. But you only have 0.5 moles of Fe here. So you will produce: 0.5 ÷ 2 = 0.25 moles of $Fe_2O_3$.

4. Now find the mass of 0.25 moles of $Fe_2O_3$:
   $M_r$ of $Fe_2O_3$ = (2 × 55.8) + (3 × 16) = 159.6
   Mass = moles × $M_r$ = 0.25 × 159.6 = 40 g of iron(III) oxide

──────────────────────────────────

You can use similar steps to work out how much of a reactant you had at the start of a reaction when you're given a certain mass of product:

**Tip:** <u>Reactants</u> are the chemicals you start with that get used up during a reaction. <u>Products</u> are the chemicals that are formed during a reaction.

─ **Example** ───────────────────────

**Hydrogen gas can react with nitrogen gas to give ammonia ($NH_3$). Calculate the mass of hydrogen needed to produce 6.8 g of ammonia.**

1. $N_{2(g)} + 3H_{2(g)} \rightarrow 2NH_{3(g)}$

2. $M_r$ of $NH_3$ = 14 + (3 × 1) = 17
   Moles = mass ÷ $M_r$ = 6.8 ÷ 17 = 0.4 moles of $NH_3$

3. From the equation: the molar ratio of $NH_3$ : $H_2$ is 2 : 3. So to make 0.4 moles of $NH_3$, you must need to start with (0.4 ÷ 2) × 3 = 0.6 moles of $H_2$

4. $M_r$ of $H_2$ = 2 × 1 = 2
   Mass = moles × $M_r$ = 0.6 × 2 = 1.2 g of hydrogen

──────────────────────────────────

**Tip:** Ammonia is produced from nitrogen and hydrogen by the Haber process. There's more about this on pages 194 and 198.

Q1  3.3 g of zinc is dissolved in hydrochloric acid, producing zinc chloride ($ZnCl_2$) and hydrogen gas.

   a) Write a balanced equation for this reaction.

   b) Calculate the number of moles of zinc in 3.3 g.

   c) How many moles of zinc chloride does the reaction produce?

   d) What mass of zinc chloride does the reaction produce?

Q2  A student burns some ethene gas ($C_2H_4$) in oxygen, producing carbon dioxide gas and 15 g of water.

   a) Write a balanced equation for this reaction.

   b) Calculate the number of moles of water in 15 g.

   c) How many moles of ethene did the student begin with?

   d) What mass of ethene did the student begin with?

Q3  Calculate the mass of barium carbonate ($BaCO_3$) produced if 4.58 g of barium chloride ($BaCl_2$) is reacted with sodium carbonate ($Na_2CO_3$).

**Figure 1:** *Zinc dissolving in hydrochloric acid.*

# Calculating gas volumes

It's pretty handy to be able to work out how much gas a reaction will produce, so that you can use large enough apparatus. Or else there might be a rather large bang. The first three steps of this method are the same as the method on the last page. Once you've found the number of moles of product, the final step is to put that number into one of the gas equations that you saw on page 18.

## Examples

**What volume of hydrogen gas is produced when 15 g of sodium is reacted with excess water at r.t.p.?**

1.  $2Na_{(s)} + 2H_2O_{(l)} \rightarrow 2NaOH_{(aq)} + H_{2(g)}$

2.  $M_r$ of Na = 23
    number of moles = mass ÷ $M_r$
    $$= 15 \div 23 = 0.65 \text{ moles of sodium}$$

3.  From the equation: the molar ratio of Na : $H_2$ is 2 : 1.
    So 0.65 moles of Na must produce (0.65 ÷ 2) = 0.325 moles of $H_2$.

At room temperature and pressure 1 mole of gas takes up 24 dm³.
Volume in dm³ = number of moles × 24
$$= 0.325 \times 24 = 7.8 \text{ dm}^3 \text{ of hydrogen gas}$$

**Tip:** 'Excess water' just means that all of the sodium will react.

**What volume of carbon dioxide is produced when 10 g of calcium carbonate reacts with excess hydrochloric acid at r.t.p.?**

1.  $CaCO_{3(s)} + 2HCl_{(aq)} \rightarrow CaCl_{2(aq)} + CO_{2(g)} + H_2O_{(l)}$

2.  $M_r$ of $CaCO_3$ = 40.1 + 12 + (3 × 16) = 100.1
    number of moles = mass ÷ $M_r$
    $$= 10 \div 100.1 = 0.1 \text{ moles of calcium carbonate}$$

3.  From the equation: the molar ratio of $CaCO_3$ : $CO_2$ is 1 : 1.
    So 0.1 moles of $CaCO_3$ must produce 0.1 moles of $CO_2$.

At room temperature and pressure 1 mole of gas takes up 24 dm³.
Volume in dm³ = number of moles × 24
$$= 0.1 \times 24 = 2.4 \text{ dm}^3 \text{ of carbon dioxide}$$

**Tip:** In these calculations you need to use the molar ratios which you get from the balanced equation. See page 28 for more on molar ratios.

# State symbols

**State symbols** are put after each compound in an equation. They tell you what state of matter things are in:

s = solid,    l = liquid,    g = gas,    aq = aqueous (solution in water).

**Exam Tip**
Make sure you include state symbols for the equations you write in the exam.

---
**Example**

$$CaCO_{3\ (s)} + 2HCl_{(aq)} \rightarrow CaCl_{2\ (aq)} + H_2O_{(l)} + CO_{2\ (g)}$$

*solid*        *aqueous*       *aqueous*     *liquid*     *gas*

---

## Practice Questions — Application

**Q1** Give the state symbols that you would use in an equation to show the state of the following substances.

a) a solution of magnesium chloride in water

b) a piece of magnesium metal

c) a measured amount of water

d) a solution of sodium nitrate in water

e) ethane gas

f) copper oxide powder

**Q2** 9 g of water is split apart to produce hydrogen gas and oxygen gas.

a) Write a balanced equation for this reaction.

b) Calculate the number of moles of water in 9 g.

c) How many moles of oxygen gas does the reaction produce?

d) What volume of oxygen gas will the reaction produce at r.t.p.?

**Q3** 7 g of zinc sulfide (ZnS) is burnt in oxygen. This produces solid zinc oxide (ZnO) and sulfur dioxide gas ($SO_2$).

a) Write a balanced equation for this reaction.

b) Calculate the number of moles of zinc sulfide in 7 g.

c) How many moles of sulfur dioxide gas does the reaction produce?

d) What volume of sulfur dioxide gas will the reaction produce at r.t.p.?

**Q4** A sample of hexane gas ($C_6H_{14}$) is cracked to give butane gas ($C_4H_{10}$) and ethene gas ($C_2H_4$). The mass of butane produced is 3 g.

a) Write a balanced equation for this reaction.

b) Calculate the number of moles of butane in 3 g.

c) How many moles of hexane gas were present in the sample?

d) What volume would this many moles of hexane gas occupy at r.t.p.?

**Q5** Magnesium metal will react with steam to produce solid magnesium oxide and hydrogen gas. Calculate the volume of steam needed to create 10 g of MgO at r.t.p.

# 10. Acids, Bases and Salts

*For AS Chemistry you need to know a bit about acids and bases.*
*This section is all about what acids and bases are and how they react*
*with each other to form salts.*

## What are acids and bases?

When mixed with water, all **acids** release hydrogen ions ($H^+$).

--- Examples ---

Sulfuric acid ($H_2SO_4$) releases hydrogen ions when it is mixed with water:

$$H_2SO_{4(l)} + water \rightarrow 2H^+_{(aq)} + SO_4^{2-}_{(aq)}$$

Hydrochloric acid (HCl) also releases hydrogen ions in water:

$$HCl_{(g)} + water \rightarrow H^+_{(aq)} + Cl^-_{(aq)}$$

Hydrogen atoms only contain one proton and one electron. So $H^+$ ions (which have lost the electron) are just protons. You never get $H^+$ ions by themselves in water — they're always combined with $H_2O$ to form hydroxonium ions ($H_3O^+$):

$$H^+_{(aq)} + H_2O_{(l)} \rightarrow H_3O^+_{(aq)}$$

**Bases** do the opposite of acids — they want to grab $H^+$ ions.

--- Example ---

Ammonia ($NH_3$) is a base and it can accept hydrogen ions, forming ammonium ions ($NH_4^+$):

$$NH_{3(aq)} + H^+_{(aq)} \rightarrow NH_4^+_{(aq)}$$

$OH^-$ ions act as bases and can accept hydrogen ions to form water:

$$OH^-_{(aq)} + H^+_{(aq)} \rightarrow H_2O_{(l)}$$

So, acids produce $H^+_{(aq)}$ ions in an aqueous solution — i.e. they're proton donors. Bases remove $H^+_{(aq)}$ ions from an aqueous solution — i.e. they're proton acceptors.

## Reactions of acids and bases

Acid molecules release their hydrogen ions, so other ions can hop into their places. You get a **salt** if the hydrogen ions are replaced by metal ions or ammonium ($NH_4^+$) ions. Different acids produce different salts:

- Sulfuric acid ($H_2SO_4$) produces salts called sulfates.
  These contain $SO_4^{2-}$ (sulfate) ions — e.g. $MgSO_4$ is magnesium sulfate.
- Hydrochloric acid (HCl) produces chlorides.
  These contain $Cl^-$ (chloride) ions — e.g. $MgCl_2$ is magnesium chloride.
- Nitric acid ($HNO_3$) produces nitrates.
  These contain $NO_3^-$ (nitrate) ions — e.g. $Mg(NO_3)_2$ is magnesium nitrate.

There are quite a few reactions of acids that produce salts...

### Acid-base reactions

When acids react with bases, they neutralise each other. The general formula for an acid-base reaction is:

$$Acid + Base \rightarrow Salt + Water$$

**Learning Objectives:**

- Be able to explain that an acid releases $H^+$ ions in aqueous solution.
- Be able explain that a base readily accepts $H^+$ ions from an acid. E.g. $OH^-$ forming $H_2O$ and $NH_3$ forming $NH_4^+$.
- Be able to explain that a salt is produced when the $H^+$ ion of an acid is replaced by a metal ion or $NH_4^+$.
- Know the formulae of the common acids (HCl, $H_2SO_4$ and $HNO_3$).
- Know that common bases are metal oxides, metal hydroxides and ammonia.
- Know that an alkali is a soluble base that releases $OH^-$ ions in aqueous solution.
- Know the formulae of the common alkalis (NaOH, KOH and $NH_3$).
- Be able to describe the reactions of an acid with carbonates, bases and alkalis, to form a salt.

**Specification Reference 1.1.3**

**Exam Tip**
You need to know the formulas for these three acids for the exam:
Sulfuric acid – $H_2SO_4$
Hydrochloric acid – HCl
Nitric acid – $HNO_3$

Metal oxides, metal hydroxides and ammonia are common bases. Metal oxides react with acids according to the following equation:

$$\text{Metal Oxide} + \text{Acid} \rightarrow \text{Salt} + \text{Water}$$

**Example**

Magnesium oxide (MgO) reacts with hydrochloric acid to form the salt magnesium chloride ($MgCl_2$) and water. The equation for this reaction is:

$$MgO_{(s)} + 2HCl_{(aq)} \rightarrow MgCl_{2(aq)} + H_2O_{(l)}$$

This is the ionic equation for the reaction:

$$O^{2-}_{(s)} + 2H^+_{(aq)} \rightarrow H_2O_{(l)}$$

In this reaction, the $O^{2-}$ ion accepts two $H^+$ ions which have been donated by the acid.

**Tip:** In this reaction magnesium ions are replacing the hydrogen ions in the acid to form a salt.

**Figure 1:** *Some common alkalis.*

Metal hydroxides are usually alkalis. An **alkali** is just a base that dissolves in water. Sodium hydroxide (NaOH) and potassium hydroxide (KOH) are the alkalis you're most likely to meet. Alkalis release $OH^-$ ions in water. These $OH^-$ ions accept $H^+$ ions (protons) from an acid to form water molecules. The general equation for this reaction is:

$$\text{Metal Hydroxide} + \text{Acid} \rightarrow \text{Salt} + \text{Water}$$

**Example**

Potassium hydroxide (KOH) reacts with hydrochloric acid to form the salt potassium chloride (KCl) and water. The equation for this reaction is:

$$KOH_{(aq)} + HCl_{(aq)} \rightarrow KCl_{(aq)} + H_2O_{(l)}$$

Here's the ionic equation for the reaction:

$$OH^-_{(aq)} + H^+_{(aq)} \rightarrow H_2O_{(l)}$$

The ionic equation shows that a proton is transferred from the acid to the hydroxide ion. This ionic equation is the same for all reactions between metal hydroxides and acids.

**Tip:** See pages 26-27 for more on ionic equations.

Ammonia, $NH_3$, is a base — in fact it dissolves in water, so aqueous ammonia is an alkali. It'll happily accept a proton from an acid to form an ammonium ion — this can then form an ammonium salt.

**Example**

Ammonia reacts with nitric acid to form ammonium nitrate ($NH_4NO_3$). The equation for this reaction is:

$$NH_{3\,(aq)} + HNO_{3\,(aq)} \rightarrow NH_4NO_{3\,(aq)}$$

The reaction of ammonia with sulfuric acid produces ammonium sulfate (($NH_4)_2SO_4$). Here's the equation:

$$2NH_{3\,(aq)} + H_2SO_{4\,(aq)} \rightarrow (NH_4)_2SO_{4\,(aq)}$$

The ionic equation for both these reactions is:

$$NH_{3\,(aq)} + H^+_{(aq)} \rightarrow NH_4^+_{(aq)}$$

The ionic equation is really useful because it applies to all reactions of ammonia with acids.

## Reactions of acids with metals

Salts are also produced when acids react with metals. But this time, hydrogen is produced instead of water, so the general equation is:

Metal + Acid → Metal Salt + Hydrogen

**Example**

Magnesium reacts with sulfuric acid to produce magnesium sulfate:

$$Mg_{(s)} + H_2SO_{4 (aq)} \rightarrow MgSO_{4 (aq)} + H_{2 (g)}$$

The ionic equation for this reaction is: $Mg_{(s)} + 2H^+_{(aq)} \rightarrow Mg^{2+}_{(aq)} + H_{2 (g)}$

## Reactions of acids with carbonates

When acids react with carbonates, a salt is produced along with water and carbon dioxide. Here's the general equation:

Metal Carbonate + Acid → Metal Salt + Carbon Dioxide + Water

**Example**

Sodium carbonate reacts with hydrochloric acid to produce sodium chloride, carbon dioxide and water:

$$Na_2CO_{3 (s)} + 2HCl_{(aq)} \rightarrow 2NaCl_{(aq)} + CO_{2 (g)} + H_2O_{(l)}$$

The ionic equation for this reaction is: $CO_3^{2-}_{(s)} + 2H^+_{(aq)} \rightarrow CO_{2 (g)} + H_2O_{(l)}$

*Figure 2:* *Magnesium ribbon reacting with acid. The solution fizzes because hydrogen gas is produced.*

*Figure 3:* *Sodium carbonate reacting with acid. It fizzes because carbon dioxide gas is produced.*

## Practice Questions — Application

Q1 Write an equation to show the reaction of hydrochloric acid with:
  a) copper(II) oxide (CuO) to give copper chloride ($CuCl_2$)
  b) sodium hydroxide (NaOH) to give sodium chloride (NaCl)
  c) magnesium carbonate ($MgCO_3$) giving magnesium chloride ($MgCl_2$)

Q2 Write an equation to show the reaction of sulfuric acid with:
  a) zinc oxide (ZnO) to give zinc sulfate ($ZnSO_4$)
  b) iron (Fe) to give iron(III) sulfate ($Fe_2(SO_4)_3$)
  c) calcium carbonate ($CaCO_3$) to give calcium sulfate ($CaSO_4$)

Q3 Write an equation to show the reaction of nitric acid with:
  a) aluminium oxide ($Al_2O_3$) to give aluminium nitrate ($Al(NO_3)_3$)
  b) potassium hydroxide (KOH) to give potassium nitrate ($KNO_3$)
  c) magnesium carbonate ($MgCO_3$) to give magnesium nitrate ($Mg(NO_3)_2$)

**Exam Tip**
If you're asked to describe what you'd see when a metal reacts with an acid, you need to say that the metal disappears (dissolves) and bubbles are produced.

## Practice Questions — Fact Recall

Q1 a) What is an acid?    b) What is a base?
Q2 Write down the molecular formula of:
  a) hydrochloric acid.  b) sulfuric acid.    c) nitric acid.
  d) sodium hydroxide.  e) potassium hydroxide.  f) ammonia.
Q3 What type of salt do each of the acids in Q2 form when they react?
Q4 What products are formed when an acid reacts with:
  a) a base?      b) a metal?      c) a metal carbonate?

- Be able to explain the terms anhydrous, hydrated and water of crystallisation.

- Be able to calculate the formula of a hydrated salt from given percentage composition, mass composition or experimental data.

**Specification Reference 1.1.3**

# 11. Anhydrous and Hydrated Salts

*Salts can come in two different forms — hydrated or anhydrous. Anhydrous salts don't contain water, hydrated salts do.*

## What are anhydrous and hydrated salts?

All solid salts consist of a **lattice** of positive and negative ions. In some salts, water molecules are incorporated in the lattice too — see Figure 1.

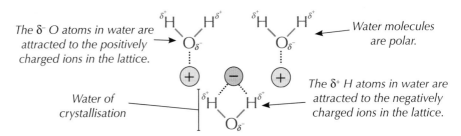

*The $\delta^-$ O atoms in water are attracted to the positively charged ions in the lattice.*

*Water molecules are polar.*

*The $\delta^+$ H atoms in water are attracted to the negatively charged ions in the lattice.*

*Water of crystallisation*

**Figure 1:** *A small part of a lattice in a hydrated salt.*

**Tip:** See page 69 for more on polar compounds and page 59 for more on lattice structures.

The water in a lattice is called **water of crystallisation**. A solid salt containing water of crystallisation is **hydrated**. A salt is **anhydrous** if it doesn't contain water of crystallisation.

One mole of a particular hydrated salt always has the same number of moles of water of crystallisation — its formula shows how many (it's always a whole number).

### Example

Hydrated copper sulfate has five moles of water for every mole of the salt. So its formula is $CuSO_4.5H_2O$ (see Figures 2 and 3). There's a dot between the $CuSO_4$ and the $H_2O$ to show that they are not joined by a covalent bond.

**Figure 2:** *Anhydrous copper sulfate ($CuSO_4$).*

**Figure 3:** *When water is added, $CuSO_4.5H_2O$ forms, which is blue in colour.*

## Finding the formulas of hydrated salts

Many hydrated salts lose their water of crystallisation when heated, to become anhydrous. If you know the mass of the salt when hydrated and anhydrous, you can work its formula out. Just follow these steps:

- First you find the mass of water lost by taking the mass of the anhydrous salt away from the mass of the hydrated salt.
- Then you find the number of moles of water lost.
- Next find the number of moles of anhydrous salt that's produced.
- Now you work out the ratio of moles of anhydrous salt to moles of water.
- Scale up or down so that your ratio is in the form 1 : n, round off your answer and you're done.

### Example

**Heating 3.210 g of hydrated magnesium sulfate, $MgSO_4.XH_2O$, forms 1.567 g of anhydrous magnesium sulfate. Find the value of X and write the formula of the hydrated salt.**

- The mass of water lost is $3.210 - 1.567 = 1.643$ g

**Tip:** To calculate the number of moles you'll need the equation:

$$moles = \frac{mass}{molar\ mass}$$

See page 16 for more on this.

- You can now calculate the moles of water present in the hydrated salt:

$$\text{moles } H_2O = \frac{\text{mass}}{M} = \frac{1.643}{16 + (2 \times 1)} = \frac{1.643}{18} = 0.0931 \text{ moles}$$

- And you can calculate the moles of anhydrous magnesium sulfate:

$$\text{moles } MgSO_4 = \frac{1.567}{24.3 + 32.1 + (4 \times 16)} = \frac{1.567}{120.4} = 0.0130 \text{ moles}$$

**Tip:** M here is the molar mass, which is the same as the molecular mass (see page 15 for a bit more explanation).

- So the ratio of $MgSO_4 : H_2O = 0.0130 : 0.0913$.

- Dividing both sides by 0.0130 gives a ratio of 1 : 7.02. This shows that there are 7.02 moles of water for every one mole of $MgSO_4$.

- X must be a whole number, and some errors are to be expected in any experiment, so you can safely round off your result to 1 : 7 — so the formula of the hydrated salt is $MgSO_4.7H_2O$.

You could also be given the percentage of the mass that is water. Then, you'd work out the formula by assuming you had 100 g of the hydrated salt and converting the percentages into masses.

*Figure 4:* Minerals are made from hydrated salts. This is turquoise, which is hydrated copper-aluminium phosphate $(CuAl_6(PO_4)_4(OH)_8.4H_2O)$.

### Example

**Hydrated $CaCl_2$ contains 49.3% $H_2O$ by mass. Find the formula of the hydrated salt.**

- If you had 100 g of hydrated $CaCl_2$ then 49.3 g would be water and 50.7 g (100 – 49.3) would be $CaCl_2$.

- Calculating the moles gives

$$\text{moles } CaCl_2 = \frac{\text{mass}}{M} = \frac{50.7}{40.1 + (2 \times 35.5)} = \frac{50.7}{111.1} = 0.456 \text{ moles}$$

$$\text{moles } H_2O = \frac{\text{mass}}{M} = \frac{49.3}{16 + (2 \times 1)} = \frac{49.3}{18} = 2.739 \text{ moles}$$

**Tip:** See page 23 for more on how to work out formulas using percentage composition.

- So the ratio of $CaCl_2 : H_2O = 0.456 : 2.739$. This is a ratio of 1 : 6 so the formula of the hydrated salt is $CaCl_2.6H_2O$.

## Practice Questions — Application

Q1 Heating 57.5 g of hydrated zinc sulfate ($ZnSO_4.XH_2O$) forms 32.3 g of anhydrous zinc sulfate. Find the value of **X** and write down the formula of the hydrated salt.

Q2 35.685 g of hydrated cobalt chloride ($CoCl_2.XH_2O$) contains 16.200 g of water. Find the value of **X** and write down the formula of the hydrated salt.

Q3 Hydrated $BaCl_2$ contains 14.74% $H_2O$ by mass. Find the formula of the hydrated salt.

Q4 Hydrated $Fe(NO_3)_3$ contains 30.87% $H_2O$ by mass. Find the formula of the hydrated salt.

**Exam Tip**
You can work out the formula of a hydrated salt from the molar mass too. All you have to do is find the molar mass of the anhydrous salt, take this away from the molar mass of the hydrated salt and divide the remaining mass by the molar mass of water to find out how many water molecules there are.

## Practice Questions — Fact Recall

Q1 What name is given to the water molecules in a lattice?

Q2 What does anhydrous mean?

Q3 How can a hydrated salt be converted into an anhydrous salt?

**Tip:** You can also do titrations the other way round — adding alkali to acid.

# 12. Titrations

*You can do a titration to find the concentration of an acid or an alkali. You'll almost certainly be asked to do one at some point during AS chemistry. And there are some more calculations to learn too.*

## Performing titrations

**Titrations** allow you to find out exactly how much acid is needed to neutralise a quantity of alkali. You measure out some alkali using a pipette (see Figure 2) and put it in a flask, along with some **indicator**, e.g. phenolphthalein. Add the acid to the alkali using a burette (see Figure 2) — open the tap to run acid into the alkali a little bit at a time. Every time you add some more acid, give the flask a swirl to make sure that the acid and the alkali are properly mixed.

First of all, do a rough titration to get an idea where the end point is. The end point of the titration is the exact point at which the indicator changes colour — at this point the amount of acid added is just enough to neutralise the alkali. Now do an accurate titration. Run the acid in to within 2 cm³ of the end point, then add the acid dropwise (a drop at a time). If you don't notice exactly when the solution changed colour you've overshot and your result won't be accurate. Record the amount of acid used to neutralise the alkali. It's best to repeat this process a few times, making sure you get the same answer each time. This will make sure your results are reliable.

**Figure 1:** *A student doing a titration. She is adding acid from the burette to the alkali in the flask. The alkali looks pink because it contains phenolphthalein.*

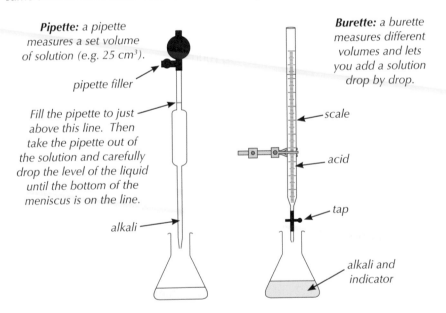

*Pipette: a pipette measures a set volume of solution (e.g. 25 cm³).*

*pipette filler*

*Fill the pipette to just above this line. Then take the pipette out of the solution and carefully drop the level of the liquid until the bottom of the meniscus is on the line.*

*alkali*

*Burette: a burette measures different volumes and lets you add a solution drop by drop.*

*scale*

*acid*

*tap*

*alkali and indicator*

**Figure 2:** *The apparatus needed for a titration.*

## Indicators

Indicators change colour at certain pHs. In titrations, indicators that change colour quickly over a very small pH range are used so you know exactly when the reaction has ended.

There are two main indicators for acid/alkali reactions that you need to know about:

- methyl orange — turns yellow to red when adding acid to alkali.
- phenolphthalein — turns pink to colourless when adding acid to alkali

**Figure 3:** *The colour changes observed with phenolphthalein (left) and methyl orange (right).*

# Calculating concentrations

You need to be able to use the results of a titration to calculate the concentration of acids and alkalis. There's more on concentration calculations on page 17.

---

## Examples

**25 cm³ of 0.5 M HCl was used to neutralise 35 cm³ of NaOH solution. Calculate the concentration of the sodium hydroxide solution in mol dm⁻³.**

First write a balanced equation and decide what you know and what you need to know:

$$HCl_{(aq)} + NaOH_{(aq)} \rightarrow NaCl_{(aq)} + H_2O_{(l)}$$

| | | |
|---|---|---|
| Volume: | 25 cm³ | 35 cm³ |
| Concentration: | 0.5 M | ? |

You know the volume and concentration of the HCl, so first work out how many moles of HCl you have:

$$\text{Number of moles HCl} = \frac{\text{concentration} \times \text{volume (cm}^3)}{1000}$$

$$= \frac{0.5 \times 25}{1000} = 0.0125 \text{ moles}$$

From the equation, you know 1 mole of HCl neutralises 1 mole of NaOH. So 0.0125 moles of HCl must neutralise 0.0125 moles of NaOH.

Now it's a doddle to work out the concentration of NaOH.

$$\text{Concentration of NaOH} = \frac{\text{moles of NaOH} \times 1000}{\text{volume (cm}^3)}$$

$$= \frac{0.0125 \times 1000}{35}$$

$$= 0.36 \text{ mol dm}^{-3}$$

Here's an example where it's an alkali being added to an acid instead.

**40 cm³ of 0.25 mol dm⁻³ KOH was used to neutralise 22 cm³ of HNO₃ solution. Calculate the concentration of the nitric acid in mol dm⁻³.**

Write out the balanced equation and the information that you have:

$$HNO_{3(aq)} + KOH_{(aq)} \rightarrow KNO_{3(aq)} + H_2O_{(l)}$$

| | | |
|---|---|---|
| Volume: | 22 cm³ | 40 cm³ |
| Concentration: | ? | 0.25 M |

You know the volume and concentration of the KOH, so now work out how many moles of KOH you have:

$$\text{Number of moles KOH} = \frac{\text{concentration} \times \text{volume (cm}^3)}{1000}$$

$$= \frac{0.25 \times 40}{1000} = 0.01 \text{ moles}$$

From the equation, you know 1 mole of KOH neutralises 1 mole of HNO₃. So 0.01 moles of KOH must neutralise 0.01 moles of HNO₃.

$$\text{Concentration of HNO}_3 = \frac{\text{moles of HNO}_3 \times 1000}{\text{volume (cm}^3)}$$

$$= \frac{0.01 \times 1000}{22}$$

$$= 0.45 \text{ mol dm}^{-3}$$

**Exam Tip**
With long wordy questions like this you might find it helpful to highlight the key bits of information in the question that you're likely to need.

**Tip:** The volumes in titrations are almost always in cm³ and not dm³ so you need to divide by 1000 when calculating the number of moles.

**Tip:** Remember, when you're using units of concentration, M and mol dm⁻³ are the same thing.

**Exam Tip**
Concentration calculations like this come up a lot in exams, so make sure you're confident with them.

Q1  28 cm³ of 0.75 mol dm⁻³ hydrochloric acid (HCl) was used to neutralise 40 cm³ of potassium hydroxide (KOH) solution.
   a)  Write a balanced equation for this reaction.
   b)  Calculate the number of moles of HCl used to neutralise the solution.
   c)  How many moles of KOH were neutralised by the HCl?
   d)  What was the concentration of the KOH solution?

Q2  15.3 cm³ of 1.5 mol dm⁻³ sodium hydroxide (NaOH) was used to neutralise 35 cm³ of nitric acid ($HNO_3$).
   a)  Write a balanced equation for this reaction.
   b)  Calculate the number of moles of NaOH used to neutralise the nitric acid.
   c)  How many moles of $HNO_3$ were neutralised by the NaOH?
   d)  What was the concentration of the $HNO_3$ solution?

Q3  12 cm³ of 0.5 mol dm⁻³ HCl solution was used to neutralise 24 cm³ of LiOH solution.  What was the concentration of the LiOH solution?

## Calculating volumes

You can use a similar method to find the volume of acid or alkali that you need to neutralise a solution.  You'll need to use the number of moles = (concentration × volume (cm³)) ÷ 1000 formula again, but this time rearrange it to find the volume:

$$\text{volume (cm}^3） = \frac{\text{number of moles} \times 1000}{\text{concentration}}$$

**Tip:** All of these calculations are just like the moles, concentration and volume ones back on page 17.  You just apply the same method to titrations.

---
**Example**

**20.4 cm³ of a 0.5 M solution of sodium carbonate reacts with 1.5 M nitric acid.  Calculate the volume of nitric acid required to neutralise the sodium carbonate.**

Like before, first write a balanced equation for the reaction and decide what you know and what you want to know:

$$Na_2CO_{3(aq)} + 2HNO_{3(aq)} \rightarrow 2NaNO_{3(aq)} + H_2O_{(l)} + CO_{2(g)}$$

Volume:   20.4 cm³           ?
Concentration:   0.5 M       1.5 M

Now work out how many moles of $Na_2CO_3$ you've got:

$$\text{Number of moles } Na_2CO_3 = \frac{\text{concentration} \times \text{volume (cm}^3）}{1000}$$

$$= \frac{0.5 \times 20.4}{1000} = 0.0102 \text{ moles}$$

1 mole of $Na_2CO_3$ neutralises 2 moles of $HNO_3$, so 0.0102 moles of $Na_2CO_3$ neutralises 0.0204 moles of $HNO_3$.

Now you know the number of moles of $HNO_3$ and the concentration, you can work out the volume:

$$\text{Volume of } HNO_3 = \frac{\text{number of moles} \times 1000}{\text{concentration}}$$

$$= \frac{0.0204 \times 1000}{1.5} = 13.6 \text{ cm}^3$$

**Tip:** See page 33 for more on the reactions of acids with metal carbonates.

And here's an example where you're finding the volume of alkali used.

---

**Example**

**18.2 cm³ of a 0.8 M solution HCl reacts with 0.3 M LiOH. Calculate the volume of lithium hydroxide required to neutralise the hydrochloric acid.**

Write out the balanced equation and the information that you have:

$$HCl_{(aq)} + LiOH_{(aq)} \rightarrow LiCl_{(aq)} + H_2O_{(l)}$$

| | | |
|---|---|---|
| *Volume:* | *18.2 cm³* | *?* |
| *Concentration:* | *0.8 M* | *0.3 M* |

Now work out how many moles of HCl you've got:

$$\text{Number of moles HCl} = \frac{\text{concentration} \times \text{volume (cm}^3)}{1000}$$

$$= \frac{0.8 \times 18.2}{1000} = 0.0146 \text{ moles}$$

1 mole of HCl neutralises 1 moles of LiOH, so 0.0146 moles of HCl neutralises 0.0146 moles of LiOH.

Now use this to work out the volume:

$$\text{Volume of LiOH} = \frac{\text{number of moles} \times 1000}{\text{concentration}}$$

$$= \frac{0.0146 \times 1000}{0.3} = 48.7 \text{ cm}^3$$

**Figure 4:** *A titration where an alkali is being added to an acid. The indicator in the flask is phenolphthalein, so the solution starts clear and turns pink at the endpoint.*

## Practice Questions — Application

Q1 18.8 cm³ of a 0.2 M solution of nitric acid ($HNO_3$) reacts with 0.45 M lithium hydroxide (LiOH) solution.
   a) Write a balanced equation for this reaction.
   b) Calculate the number of moles of $HNO_3$ present in the acid added.
   c) How many moles of LiOH were in the sample of the alkali?
   d) What volume of LiOH was required to neutralise the $HNO_3$ solution?

Q2 37.3 cm³ of a 0.42 mol dm⁻³ solution of potassium hydroxide (KOH) reacts with 1.1 mol dm⁻³ ethanoic acid ($CH_3COOH$) solution.
   a) Write a balanced equation for this reaction.
   b) Calculate the number of moles of KOH present in the alkali added.
   c) How many moles of $CH_3COOH$ were in the sample of the acid?
   d) What volume of $CH_3COOH$ was required to neutralise the KOH solution?

Q3 14 cm³ of a 1 M NaOH solution reacts with a 0.5 M HCl solution. What volume of HCl was required to neutralise the NaOH solution?

## Practice Questions — Fact Recall

Q1 Name the piece of equipment that you would use to measure out a set volume of alkali or acid for a titration.

Q2 When you are doing a titration, why do you swirl the flask after adding each drop?

Q3 What is the 'end point' of a titration?

Q4 State the colour change that you'll see if you add acid to a mixture of methyl orange and alkali.

# 13. Oxidation States

*Oxidation states are really useful in chemistry. They help you work out what's going on in chemical reactions. At AS level you need to know how to assign oxidation states to atoms in elements, compounds and ions. This is done using a simple set of rules. Read on to find out more...*

## Assigning oxidation states

Atoms use electrons to form bonds with other atoms. The **oxidation state** of an element tells you the total number of electrons it has donated or accepted when it is in a particular compound or ion. Oxidation states are also called oxidation numbers. There are lots of rules for working out oxidation states. Take a deep breath...

Uncombined elements have an oxidation state of 0. Elements just bonded to identical atoms also have an oxidation state of 0.

Examples

*Uncombined elements — oxidation state = 0*

*Elements bonded to identical elements — oxidation state = 0*

The oxidation state of a simple monatomic ion is the same as its charge.

Examples

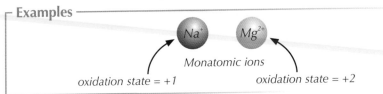

*Monatomic ions*

*oxidation state = +1*

*oxidation state = +2*

*Figure 1: Nuggets of gold, silver and copper. These are all uncombined elements with oxidation states of 0.*

**Tip:** Take a look at page 69 for more on electronegativity.

In compounds or compound ions, the overall oxidation state is just the ion charge (see Figure 2). Within an ion, the most electronegative element has a negative oxidation state (equal to its ionic charge). Other elements have more positive oxidation states.

Example

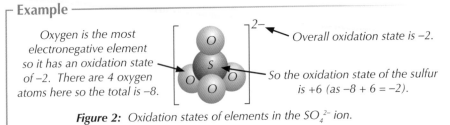

*Oxygen is the most electronegative element so it has an oxidation state of −2. There are 4 oxygen atoms here so the total is −8.*

*Overall oxidation state is −2.*

*So the oxidation state of the sulfur is +6 (as −8 + 6 = −2).*

*Figure 2: Oxidation states of elements in the $SO_4^{2-}$ ion.*

**Tip:** All atoms are treated as ions when you're finding oxidation states, even if they're covalently bonded.

The sum of the oxidation states for a neutral compound is 0 (see Figure 3).

Example

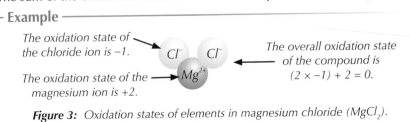

*The oxidation state of the chloride ion is −1.*

*The oxidation state of the magnesium ion is +2.*

*The overall oxidation state of the compound is $(2 \times -1) + 2 = 0$.*

*Figure 3: Oxidation states of elements in magnesium chloride ($MgCl_2$).*

Combined oxygen is nearly always –2, except in peroxides, where it's –1 (see Figure 4). Combined hydrogen is +1, except in metal hydrides where it is –1 and $H_2$ where it's 0 (see Figures 4 and 5).

**Tip:** There are other exceptions for combined oxygen — in $OF_2$ it's +2, and in $O_2F_2$ it's +1. And don't forget $O_2$, where it's 0.

### Examples

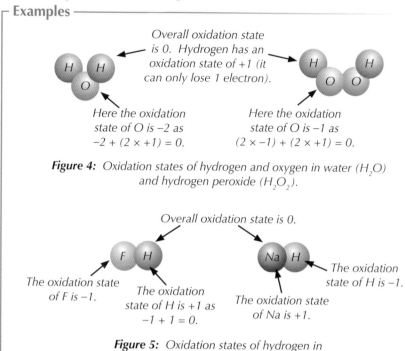

*Overall oxidation state is 0. Hydrogen has an oxidation state of +1 (it can only lose 1 electron).*

*Here the oxidation state of O is –2 as –2 + (2 × +1) = 0.*

*Here the oxidation state of O is –1 as (2 × –1) + (2 × +1) = 0.*

**Figure 4:** *Oxidation states of hydrogen and oxygen in water ($H_2O$) and hydrogen peroxide ($H_2O_2$).*

*Overall oxidation state is 0.*

*The oxidation state of F is –1.*

*The oxidation state of H is +1 as –1 + 1 = 0.*

*The oxidation state of Na is +1.*

*The oxidation state of H is –1.*

**Figure 5:** *Oxidation states of hydrogen in hydrogen fluoride (HF) and sodium hydride (NaH).*

**Exam Tip**
It's really important to remember the basic rules for working out oxidation states, as well as the exceptions — it's the kind of thing that could easily trip you up in exam questions.

# Finding oxidation states

You can work out oxidation numbers from formulas or systematic names.

### Finding oxidation states from formulas

In your exam, you may get a question asking you to work out the oxidation state of one element in a compound. To do this you just have to follow all the rules on the previous page and above and you'll be fine.

### Examples

**Find the oxidation state of Zn in $Zn(OH)_2$.**

- $Zn(OH)_2$ is neutral (it has no charge), so its overall oxidation state is 0.
- Oxygen's oxidation state is usually –2, and hydrogen's is usually +1.
- So the oxidation state of the $(OH)_2$ bit of the molecule is $2 \times (-2 + 1) = -2$.
- So the oxidation state of Zn in $Zn(OH)_2$ is $0 - (-2) = +2$.

### Finding oxidation states from systematic names

Sometimes, oxidation states aren't clear from the formula of a compound. In these cases, the oxidation number is attached as a Roman numeral. Whenever you see Roman numerals in a chemical name, it's an oxidation number and it applies to the element in front of it.

### Examples

Copper has oxidation state +2 in copper(II) sulfate.
Manganese has oxidation state +7 in a manganate(VII) ion ($MnO_4^-$).

**Figure 6:** *A bottle of copper(II) oxide. The Roman numerals show that the copper has an oxidation state of +2.*

This is particularly useful when looking at -ate ions. Ions with names ending in -ate (e.g. sulfate, nitrate, carbonate) contain oxygen, as well as another element. For example, sulfates contain sulfur and oxygen, nitrates contain nitrogen and oxygen... and so on. But sometimes the 'other' element in the ion can exist with different oxidation numbers, and so form different '-ate ions'. You can use the systematic names to work out which ions are present in the formulas.

— Examples —

In sulfate(VI) ions the sulfur has oxidation number +6. This is the $SO_4^{2-}$ ion.
In sulfate(IV) ions, the sulfur has oxidation number +4. This is the $SO_3^{2-}$ ion.

# Using oxidation states

If you know the oxidation states of the elements in a compound, you can use them to work out the systematic name for that compound or its formula.

## Working out systematic names

You might have to work out the systematic name for a compound, given its formula. To do this you have to find the oxidation states of the elements in the compound and then add in Roman numerals where needed.

— Example —

**What is the systematic name of $KNO_3$?**
This is potassium nitrate, but for the systematic name to be complete you need to give the oxidation number of the nitrogen. You know that potassium always forms $K^+$ ions, so the charge on the nitrate ion must be 1–. Each oxygen atom in the $NO_3^-$ ion has oxidation number –2. This gives $3 \times -2 = -6$. Then, since the ion has an overall oxidation number of –1, the nitrogen must be in the +5 state. So the compound is potassium nitrate(V).

**What is the systematic name of $Cu_2O$?**
This is copper oxide, but for the full systematic name you also need to give the oxidation number of the copper. You know that oxygen has an oxidation state of –2. The compound has no charge so the overall oxidation state of the compound is 0. So the oxidation state of the two copper atoms combined must be $0 - (-2) = +2$. There are two copper atoms in total so each has an oxidation state of $2 \div 2 = 1$. So this is copper(I) oxide.

## Working out formulas

You can also use oxidation numbers to work out the formula of a compound given its systematic name.

— Example —

**What is the formula of iron(III) oxide?**
Iron oxides contain iron and oxygen. Oxygen has an oxidation state of –2 and you can tell from the systematic name that the iron has an oxidation state of +3. So for the overall oxidation state to be 0 there must be 3 oxygen atoms (adding up to –6) and 2 iron atoms (adding up to +6). So the formula of iron(III) oxide is $Fe_2O_3$.

Working out the formula of compound ions is just the same except the oxidation numbers won't add up to 0 — they'll add up to the charge of the ion instead. You'll be told the charge of the ion in the question.

---

## Example

**Find the formula of a phosphate(III) ion given that it has a charge of 3–.**
As it's a phosphate ion it must contain phosphorus and oxygen. Oxygen has an oxidation state of –2 and you know from the systematic name that the phosphorus has an oxidation state of +3. The overall oxidation state of the ion is –3. So for the oxidation state to add up to –3 you need 3 oxygen atoms (giving a total of –6) and one phosphorus atom (+3). So the formula of a phosphate(III) ion is $PO_3^{3-}$.

**Exam Tip**
Don't forget to include the charge of the ion after you've worked out its formula. If you just put $PO_3$ here you wouldn't get any marks.

## Practice Questions — Application

**Q1** Give the oxidation states of the following ions.
a) $Na^+$     b) $F^-$     c) $Ca^{2+}$

**Q2** Give the overall oxidation states of the following ions.
a) $OH^-$     b) $CO_3^{2-}$     c) $NO_3^-$

**Q3** Work out the oxidation states of all the elements in the following compounds and compound ions.
a) $HCl$     b) $CO_3^{2-}$     c) $ClO_4^-$     d) $HSO_4^-$

**Q4** Work out the oxidation states of carbon in the following.
a) $CO$     b) $CCl_4$     c) $CaCO_3$     d) $C_3H_6$

**Q5** Work out the oxidation states of phosphorus in the following.
a) $P_4$     b) $PH_3$     c) $PO_4^{2-}$     d) $P_2F_4$

**Q6** a) What is the oxidation state of iron in iron(III) chloride?
b) What is the oxidation state of chlorine in chlorate(VII) ions?

**Q7** Give the systematic name of the following compounds.
a) $FeSO_4$     b) $MnCO_3$     c) $CuO$

**Q8** Give the formula of the following compounds and compound ions.
a) Copper(II) sulfate.
b) Iron(II) oxide.
c) Nitrate(III) ions with an overall charge of 1–.
d) Chromate(VI) ions with an overall charge of 2–.

**Exam Tip**
Finding oxidation states is easy when you know how. Just make sure you learn the rules for the exam and you'll be fine.

## Practice Questions — Fact Recall

**Q1** Give the oxidation state of an element bonded to an identical atom.
**Q2** What is the sum of the oxidation states for a neutral compound?
**Q3** What is the oxidation state of oxygen in a peroxide?
**Q4** Give the oxidation state of hydrogen in a metal hydride.

Unit 1: Module 1  Atoms and Reactions     43

- Be able to describe the terms oxidation and reduction in terms of electron transfer and changes in oxidation number.

- Know that metals generally form ions by losing electrons with an increase in oxidation number to form positive ions.

- Know that non-metals generally react by gaining electrons with a decrease in oxidation number to form negative ions.

- Be able to interpret and make predictions from redox equations in terms of oxidation numbers and electron loss/gain.

- Be able to describe the redox reactions of metals with dilute hydrochloric and dilute sulfuric acids.

**Specification Reference 1.1.4**

**Tip:** Now's your chance to learn the most famous memory aid thingy in the world...

OIL RIG
Oxidation Is Loss
Reduction Is Gain
(of electrons)

**Tip:** When an element is reduced, it's oxidation number is also reduced.

# 14. Redox Reactions

*This'll probably ring a bell from GCSE, but don't go thinking you know it all already — there's plenty to learn about redox reactions.*

## What are redox reactions?

A loss of electrons is called **oxidation**. A gain in electrons is called **reduction**. Reduction and oxidation happen simultaneously — hence the term "redox" reaction. An **oxidising agent** accepts electrons and gets reduced. A **reducing agent** donates electrons and gets oxidised.

Example

Here's a redox reaction between sodium and chlorine to form sodium chloride:

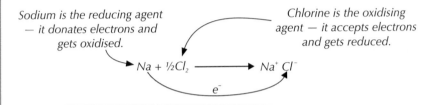

*Sodium is the reducing agent — it donates electrons and gets oxidised.*

*Chlorine is the oxidising agent — it accepts electrons and gets reduced.*

$$Na + \tfrac{1}{2}Cl_2 \longrightarrow Na^+Cl^-$$

$e^-$

## Changing oxidation states

Oxidation numbers go up or down as electrons are lost or gained.

- The oxidation number for an atom will increase by 1 for each electron lost.
- The oxidation number will decrease by 1 for each electron gained.

When metals form compounds, they generally donate electrons to form positive ions — this is accompanied by an increase in oxidation number. When non-metals form compounds, they generally gain electrons and form negative ions — this is accompanied by a decrease in oxidation number.

Examples

Zinc (a metal) can lose electrons to form $Zn^{2+}$ ions. When this happens, its oxidation number increases from 0 to +2.

Bromine (a non-metal) can gain an electron to form $Br^-$ ions. When this happens, its oxidation number decreases from 0 to −1.

In a redox reaction, some oxidation numbers will change — something will lose electrons and end up with an increased oxidation number and something will gain electrons and end up with a decreased oxidation number.

Example

In this reaction between iron(III) oxide and carbon(II) oxide (aka carbon monoxide), the products are the element iron and carbon(IV) oxide (more commonly known as carbon dioxide).

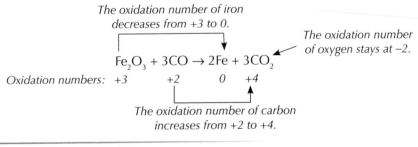

*The oxidation number of iron decreases from +3 to 0.*

*The oxidation number of oxygen stays at −2.*

$$Fe_2O_3 + 3CO \rightarrow 2Fe + 3CO_2$$

Oxidation numbers:   +3      +2      0     +4

*The oxidation number of carbon increases from +2 to +4.*

# Reactions of dilute acids with metals

On page 33 you saw how metals react with acids to produce a salt and hydrogen gas. Well this is a redox reaction. The metal atoms are oxidised, losing electrons and forming soluble metal ions. The hydrogen ions in solution are reduced, gaining electrons and forming hydrogen.

**Figure 1:** *Magnesium ribbon reacting with hydrochloric acid. The bubbles are the hydrogen gas molecules that are being formed.*

---

**Examples** ———————————

Magnesium reacts with dilute hydrochloric acid like this:

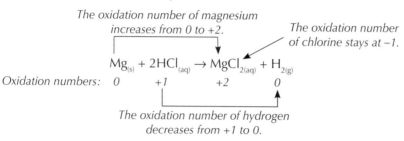

*The oxidation number of magnesium increases from 0 to +2.*

*The oxidation number of chlorine stays at –1.*

$$Mg_{(s)} + 2HCl_{(aq)} \rightarrow MgCl_{2(aq)} + H_{2(g)}$$

*Oxidation numbers:*    0      +1      +2      0

*The oxidation number of hydrogen decreases from +1 to 0.*

If you use sulfuric acid instead of hydrochloric acid, exactly the same processes of oxidation and reduction take place.

Potassium reacts with dilute sulfuric acid like this:

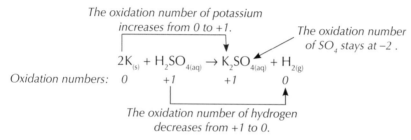

*The oxidation number of potassium increases from 0 to +1.*

*The oxidation number of SO$_4$ stays at –2 .*

$$2K_{(s)} + H_2SO_{4(aq)} \rightarrow K_2SO_{4(aq)} + H_{2(g)}$$

*Oxidation numbers:*    0      +1      +1      0

*The oxidation number of hydrogen decreases from +1 to 0.*

---

## Practice Questions — Application

**Q1** Describe the changes in oxidation state that occur in each of the following reactions between metals and acids.

a)   $Mg + H_2SO_4 \rightarrow MgSO_4 + H_2$

b)   $2V + 6HCl \rightarrow 2VCl_3 + 3H_2$

c)   $2Fe + 3H_2SO_4 \rightarrow Fe_2(SO_4)_3 + 3H_2$

**Q2** This is a redox reaction: $MnO_2 + 4HCl \rightarrow MnCl_2 + Cl_2 + 2H_2O$

a)   Describe the changes in oxidation state that occur in this reaction.

b)   Identify the oxidising and reducing agents in this reaction.

> **Tip:** If you're asked to describe the changes in oxidation state in a reaction you have to say which elements change oxidation states and what the change is.

## Practice Questions — Fact Recall

**Q1** What is oxidation?

**Q2** What is reduction?

**Q3** Describe the role of an oxidising agent in a redox reaction.

**Q4** Describe the role of a reducing agent in a redox reaction.

**Q5** What happens to the oxidation state when an atom loses an electron?

**Q6** What happens to the oxidation state when an atom gains an electron?

> **Tip:** The oxidation state of an atom doesn't always change when it reacts, so don't be alarmed if your answer is the same for the beginning and end of the reaction.

# Section Summary

Make sure you know...

- The relative masses and charges of protons, neutrons and electrons.
- How to describe the distribution of mass and charge within an atom (electrons orbit a central nucleus which is made up of protons and neutrons).
- That the mass (nucleon) number of an atom is the total number of protons and neutrons it contains.
- That the atomic or proton number of an atom is the number of protons it contains.
- How to work out the number of protons, neutrons and electrons in atoms and ions.
- That isotopes are atoms with the same number of protons but different numbers of neutrons.
- That the relative atomic mass of an element is its mass measured relative to carbon-12.
- That relative isotopic mass is the mass of an isotope of an element measured relative to carbon-12.
- How to calculate relative atomic mass from isotopic abundances.
- What the terms relative molecular mass and relative formula mass mean.
- That the term amount of substance means the number of particles.
- That amount of substance is measured using a unit called the mole (mol).
- That the Avogadro constant ($6 \times 10^{23}$) is the number of particles in one mole of a particular substance.
- That the molar mass is the mass of one mole of something and has the units $g\ mol^{-1}$.
- How to use the equation: no. of moles = mass of substance ÷ molar mass.
- How to carry out calculations using the amount of substance (in moles) and the volumes and concentrations of solutions.
- How the terms concentrated and dilute can be used to describe the concentration of a solution.
- How to carry out calculations using the amount of substance (in moles) and gas volumes.
- That the empirical formula gives the simplest whole number ratio of atoms of each element present in a compound.
- That the molecular formula gives the actual number of atoms of each element present in a molecule.
- How to calculate empirical and molecular formulas using mass and percentage compositions.
- How to construct balanced equations for chemical reactions.
- How to use balanced equations to determine stoichiometric relationships in calculations.
- That acids release protons in aqueous solution and bases release $OH^-$ ions in aqueous solution.
- The formulas of the common acids HCl, $H_2SO_4$ and $HNO_3$.
- That metal oxides, metal hydroxides and ammonia can all act as bases.
- That an alkali is a soluble base and that common alkalis include NaOH, KOH and $NH_3$.
- That a salt is produced when the $H^+$ ion in an acid is replaced by a metal ion or $NH_4^+$.
- That acids react with bases, alkalis, metals and metal carbonates to form salts.
- What the terms anhydrous, hydrated and water of crystallisation mean regarding salts.
- How to calculate the formula of a hydrated salt from mass compositions or percentage compositions.
- How to perform acid-base titrations and carry out structured titrations.
- How to calculate unknown concentrations and volumes using data collected from a titration.
- How to assign oxidation states to atoms in elements, compounds and ions.
- That oxidation is a loss of electrons and reduction is a gain in electrons.
- How to use Roman numerals to determine the oxidation state of an element in a compound.
- How to write formulas using oxidation states.
- How the oxidation state of an element changes when it is oxidised or reduced.
- That metals usually lose electrons in reactions while non-metals generally gain electrons.
- How to describe the redox reactions of metals with dilute HCl and $H_2SO_4$.

# Exam-style Questions

**1**    The element silicon (atomic number 14) is commonly used in the production of electronics. There are three stable isotopes of silicon, $^{28}Si$, $^{29}Si$ and $^{30}Si$.

**(a) (i)** What are isotopes?

*(2 marks)*

**(ii)** Fill in the table below to show how many protons, neutrons and electrons each isotope of silicon contains.

| | Protons | Neutrons | Electrons |
|---|---|---|---|
| $^{28}Si$ | | | |
| $^{29}Si$ | | | |
| $^{30}Si$ | | | |

*(2 marks)*

**(b)**    The three isotopes of silicon are found naturally with the following isotopic abundances: $^{28}Si$ : 92.23%, $^{29}Si$ : 4.67% and $^{30}Si$ : 3.1%.

**(i)** Define the term relative atomic mass.

*(3 marks)*

**(ii)** Calculate the relative atomic mass of silicon.
Give your answer to 2 decimal places.

*(2 marks)*

**(c)**    Silicon is most commonly found as silicon dioxide ($SiO_2$).

**(i)** State the oxidation state of silicon in $SiO_2$.

*(1 mark)*

**(ii)** Give the systematic name of silicon dioxide.

*(1 mark)*

**(d)**    Silicon dioxide reacts with sodium hydroxide (NaOH) as shown by the equation below:

$$SiO_2 + 2NaOH \rightarrow Na_2SiO_3 + H_2O$$

**(i)** Use your knowledge of oxidation states to determine whether the reaction above is a redox reaction. Explain you answer.

*(2 marks)*

**(ii)** Calculate the relative formula mass of $Na_2SiO_3$.

*(1 mark)*

**2**    Atoms are made up of protons, neutrons and electrons.

**(a)**    Complete the table below to show the relative masses and charges of the three subatomic particles.

| | Mass | Charge |
|---|---|---|
| Proton | | +1 |
| Neutron | 1 | |
| Electron | | |

*(1 mark)*

**(b)**    The structure of the atom was investigated by Ernest Rutherford in 1909. He fired alpha particles at a thin sheet of gold and observed what happened to them.

    **(i)**    What happened to most of the alpha particles?

        What does this show about the structure of the atom?

*(2 marks)*

    **(ii)**  What happened to a few alpha particles?

        What does this show about the structure of the atom?

*(2 marks)*

**(c)**    Atoms make up elements.  How many atoms are there in 5.0 g of gold?

*(2 marks)*

**3**    Alcohols contain the elements carbon, hydrogen and oxygen.
When 9.0 g of an unknown alcohol is burnt in air, 17.6 g of $CO_2$ and 9.0 g of $H_2O$ are produced.

**(a)**    Define the term empirical formula.

*(1 mark)*

**(b) (i)**  Calculate how many moles of $CO_2$ and $H_2O$ are produced when this alcohol is burnt.

*(2 marks)*

    **(ii)**  Calculate the mass of carbon, hydrogen and oxygen present in the alcohol.

*(3 marks)*

    **(iii)** Deduce the empirical formula of this alcohol.

*(2 marks)*

    The unknown alcohol has a molar mass of 90 g $mol^{-1}$.

**(c) (i)**  Define the term molecular formula.

*(1 mark)*

    **(ii)**  Deduce the molecular formula of this alcohol.

*(2 marks)*

**4**    This question is about the reactions of acids.

**(a)**    When an acid is added to a base, a neutralisation reaction occurs.
In a titration, 26.0 cm³ of 0.600 mol dm⁻³ hydrochloric acid was needed
to exactly neutralise 20.0 cm³ of a sodium hydroxide solution.

**(i)**    Write an equation for the reaction between hydrochloric acid and
sodium hydroxide.

*(1 mark)*

**(ii)**    Calculate how many moles of hydrochloric acid were added to the
sodium hydroxide solution.

*(2 marks)*

**(iii)**    Calculate the concentration of the sodium hydroxide solution used
in this titration.

*(2 marks)*

**(b)**    Acids react with metals to produce salts.  When aluminium (Al) reacts
with hydrochloric acid, aluminium(III) chloride is produced.

**(i)**    What is the oxidation state of aluminium in aluminium(III) chloride?

*(1 mark)*

**(ii)**    Use your knowledge of oxidation states to work out the chemical formula
of aluminium(III) chloride.

*(1 mark)*

**(iii)**    What would you see when this reaction takes place?

*(2 marks)*

**(c)**    The reactions of acids with metals are redox reactions.  Below is the
reaction of sodium with sulfuric acid:

$$2Na + H_2SO_4 \rightarrow Na_2SO_4 + H_2$$

**(i)**    How does the oxidation state of sodium change during this reaction?

*(1 mark)*

**(ii)**    What is the role of sodium in this reaction?

*(1 mark)*

**(d)**    The reaction of dilute nitric acid with calcium produces a salt called
calcium(II) nitrate ($Ca(NO_3)_2$).  Hydrated calcium(II) nitrate
contains 30.5% water by mass.

**(i)**    Define the term anhydrous.

*(1 mark)*

**(ii)**    The hydrated salt has the formula $Ca(NO_3)_2.xH_2O$.  Find the value of **x**.

*(4 marks)*

## Learning Objectives:

- State the number of orbitals making up s-, p- and d-subshells, and the number of electrons that occupy s-, p- and d-subshells.

- State the number of electrons that can fill the first four shells.

- Describe an orbital as a region that can hold up to two electrons, with opposite spins.

- Describe the shapes of s and p orbitals.

- Describe the relative energies of s-, p- and d-orbitals for the shells 1, 2, 3 and the 4s and 4p orbitals;

- Deduce the electron configurations of atoms, given the atomic number, up to Z = 36, and ions, given the atomic number and ionic charge, limited to s and p blocks up to Z = 36.

- Classify the elements into s, p and d blocks.

**Specification Reference 1.2.1**

**Tip:** Don't get confused by notation like 2s or 4f. The letter shows what type of sub-shell it is, the number shows what shell it's in. So 3p means a p sub-shell in the 3rd electron shell.

# 1. Electronic Structure

*Electronic structure is all about how electrons are arranged in atoms.*

## Electron shells

In the currently accepted model of the atom, electrons have fixed energies. They move around the nucleus in certain regions of the atom called **shells** or **energy levels**. Each shell is given a number called the principal quantum number. The further a shell is from the nucleus, the higher its energy and the larger its principal quantum number — see Figure 1.

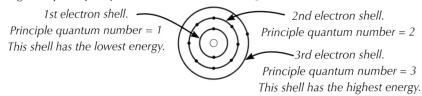

*1st electron shell.*
*Principle quantum number = 1*
*This shell has the lowest energy.*

*2nd electron shell.*
*Principle quantum number = 2*

*3rd electron shell.*
*Principle quantum number = 3*
*This shell has the highest energy.*

***Figure 1**: A sodium atom.*

These shells are divided up into **sub-shells**. Different electron shells have different numbers of sub-shells, which each have a different energy. Sub-shells can be s sub-shells, p sub-shells, d sub-shells or f sub-shells.

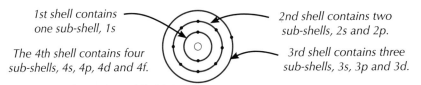

*1st shell contains one sub-shell, 1s*

*2nd shell contains two sub-shells, 2s and 2p.*

*The 4th shell contains four sub-shells, 4s, 4p, 4d and 4f.*

*3rd shell contains three sub-shells, 3s, 3p and 3d.*

***Figure 2**: A sodium atom.*

These sub-shells have different numbers of **orbitals** which can each hold up to 2 electrons. The table below shows the number of orbitals and electrons in each sub-shell. You can use it to work out how many electrons each shell can hold.

| Sub-shell | Number of orbitals | Maximum electrons |
|-----------|--------------------|--------------------|
| s | 1 | 2 |
| p | 3 | 6 |
| d | 5 | 10 |
| f | 7 | 14 |

**Example**

The third shell contains 3 sub-shells: 3s, 3p and 3d.

- An s sub-shell contains 1 orbital, so can hold 2 electrons (1 × 2).
- A p sub-shell contains 3 orbitals, so can hold 6 electrons (3 × 2).
- A d sub-shell contains 5 orbitals, so can hold 10 electrons (5 × 2).

So the total number of electrons the third shell can hold is 2 + 6 + 10 = 18

The table on the right shows the number of electrons that the first four electron shells can hold.

| Shell | Sub-shells | Total number of electrons | |
|-------|-----------|--------------------------|---|
| 1st | 1s | 2 | = 2 |
| 2nd | 2s 2p | 2 + (3 × 2) | = 8 |
| 3rd | 3s 3p 3d | 2 + (3 × 2) + (5 × 2) | = 18 |
| 4th | 4s 4p 4d 4f | 2 + (3 × 2) + (5 × 2) + (7 × 2) | = 32 |

**Exam Tip**
Make sure you learn how many electrons each electron shell can hold — you won't get far with electronic structures if you don't know these numbers.

# Orbital shape

An orbital is the bit of space that an electron moves in (see Figure 3). Orbitals within the same sub-shell have the same energy. If there are two electrons in an orbital, they must 'spin' in opposite directions — this is called spin-pairing.

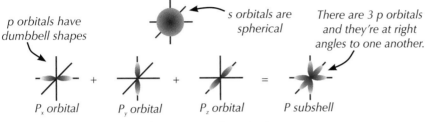

*p orbitals have dumbbell shapes*

*s orbitals are spherical*

*There are 3 p orbitals and they're at right angles to one another.*

$P_x$ orbital    +    $P_y$ orbital    +    $P_z$ orbital    =    P subshell

**Figure 3:** *s and p orbitals.*

**Tip:** Electrons have a property called 'spin'. Spin just has to do with the momentum that an electron has (and that's all you need to know about it for AS level). Two electrons in the same orbital will have opposite spins — one is called 'down' and the other 'up'.

# Showing electron configurations

The number of electrons that an atom or ion has, and how they are arranged, is called its **electron configuration**. Electron configurations can be shown in different ways. For example, an atom of neon has 10 electrons — two electrons are in the 1s sub-shell, two are in the 2s sub-shell and six are in the 2p sub-shell. You can show this electron configuration in three different ways...

### 1. Sub-shell notation

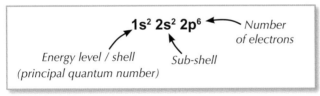

$1s^2\ 2s^2\ 2p^6$ ← *Number of electrons*

*Energy level / shell (principal quantum number)*    *Sub-shell*

**Tip:** Dumbbell-shaped just means it looks like this:

So if you're asked to draw the shape of a p-orbital, draw this.

### 2. Arrows in boxes

Each of the boxes represents one orbital. Each of the arrows represents one electron. The up and down arrows represent the electrons spinning in opposite directions. Two electrons can only occupy the same orbital if they have opposite spin.

| 1s | 2s | 2p |
|----|----|------|
| ↑↓ | ↑↓ | ↑↓ ↑↓ ↑↓ |

**Exam Tip**
In the exam you'll only have to do electron configurations up to the d-subshell (so don't worry about the f-subshell).

### 3. Energy level diagrams

These show the energy of the electrons in different orbitals, as well as the number of electrons and their arrangement.

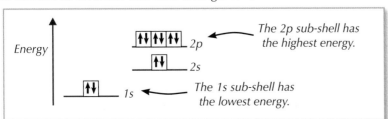

*The 2p sub-shell has the highest energy.*

*The 1s sub-shell has the lowest energy.*

**Exam Tip**
You need to know how to show electron configurations using sub-shell notation, arrows in boxes and energy level diagrams — any of them could come up in the exam.

# Working out electron configurations

You can figure out most electronic configurations pretty easily, so long as you know a few simple rules:

## Rule 1

Electrons fill up the lowest energy sub-shells first.

**Example**

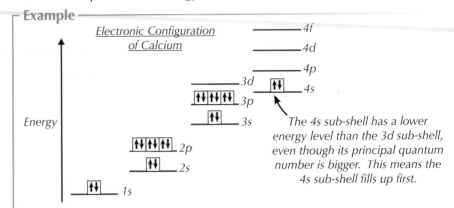

*Electronic Configuration of Calcium*

*The 4s sub-shell has a lower energy level than the 3d sub-shell, even though its principal quantum number is bigger. This means the 4s sub-shell fills up first.*

## Rule 2

Electrons fill orbitals singly before they start sharing.

**Examples**

## Rule 3

For the configuration of ions from the s and p blocks of the periodic table, just add or remove the electrons to or from the highest energy occupied sub-shell.

**Examples**

Mg atom:   $1s^2 \, 2s^2 \, 2p^6 \, 3s^2$       Cl atom:   $1s^2 \, 2s^2 \, 2p^6 \, 3s^2 \, 3p^5$

$Mg^{2+}$ ion:   $1s^2 \, 2s^2 \, 2p^6$        $Cl^-$ ion:   $1s^2 \, 2s^2 \, 2p^6 \, 3s^2 \, 3p^6$

### Shortened electron configurations

Noble gas symbols in square brackets, such as [Ar], are sometimes used in electron configurations. For example, calcium ($1s^2 \, 2s^2 \, 2p^6 \, 3s^2 \, 3p^6 \, 4s^2$) can be written as $[Ar]4s^2$, where $[Ar] = 1s^2 \, 2s^2 \, 2p^6 \, 3s^2 \, 3p^6$.

# Electronic structure and chemical properties

The number of outer shell electrons decides the chemical properties of an element. You can use the Periodic Table to help you work them out.

- The s block elements (Groups 1 and 2) have 1 or 2 outer shell electrons. These are easily lost to form positive ions with an inert gas configuration. E.g. Na — $1s^2 \, 2s^2 \, 2p^6 \, 3s^1 \rightarrow Na^+$ — $1s^2 \, 2s^2 \, 2p^6$ (the electronic configuration of neon).

- The elements in Groups 5, 6 and 7 (in the p block) can gain 1, 2 or 3 electrons to form negative ions with an inert gas configuration. E.g. O — $1s^2 \, 2s^2 \, 2p^4 \rightarrow O^{2-}$ — $1s^2 \, 2s^2 \, 2p^6$. Groups 4 to 7 can also share electrons when they form covalent bonds.

*Figure 4: Elements can be classified as s block elements, p block elements or d block elements depending on where they are in the Periodic Table and which sub-shell their highest energy electrons are in.*

- Group 0 (the inert gases) have completely filled s and p sub-shells and don't need to bother gaining, losing or sharing electrons — their full sub-shells make them inert.
- The d block elements (which include the transition metals) tend to lose s and d electrons to form positive ions.

## Practice Questions — Application

**Q1** Use sub-shell notation to show the full electron configurations of the elements listed below.

a) Lithium                 b) Titanium

c) Gallium               d) Nitrogen

**Q2** Draw arrows in boxes to show the electron configurations of the elements listed below.

a) Calcium               b) Nickel

c) Sodium                d) Oxygen

**Q3** Draw energy level diagrams to show the electron configurations of the elements listed below.

a) Magnesium          b) Argon

c) Carbon                d) Arsenic

**Q4** Use sub-shell notation to show the electron configurations of the ions listed below.

a) $Na^+$                   b) $O^{2-}$

c) $Al^{3+}$                  d) $Cl^-$

**Q5** Which elements have the electron configurations given below?

a) $[Ar]3d^{10}\,4s^2\,4p^5$

b) $[Ne]3s^2\,3p^3$

c) $[Ar]3d^3\,4s^2$

**Exam Tip**
Writing electron configurations using noble gas symbols can save you loads of time. Just make sure you've got your head round sub-shell notation before you start to use it — otherwise you're likely to get confused. And if a question asks you to give the <u>full</u> configuration then make sure that's what you do.

## Practice Questions — Fact Recall

**Q1** How many orbitals does a p sub-shell contain?

**Q2** How many electrons can a p sub-shell hold?

**Q3** How many electrons can the 3rd electron shell hold in total?

**Q4** Describe the shape of:

a) an s-orbital.         b) a p-orbital.

**Q5** What does "electron configuration" mean?

**Q6** Which electron shells are filled up first?

**Q7** The electron configuration shown here is wrong. Explain why.

**Q8** Describe the ions that Group 5, 6 and 7 elements usually form.

**Learning Objectives:**

- Define the terms first ionisation energy and successive ionisation energy.

- Explain that ionisation energies are influenced by nuclear charge, electron shielding and the distance of the outermost electron from the nucleus.

- Predict from successive ionisation energies of an element: the number of electrons in each shell of an atom, and the group of the element.

**Specification Reference 1.2.1**

# 2. Ionisation Energies

*More stuff on electron configurations coming up. The title may be ionisation energies, but it's still all about electrons and how they're arranged.*

## Ionisation

When electrons have been removed from an atom or molecule, it's been ionised. The energy you need to remove the first electron is called the **first ionisation energy**.

> The first ionisation energy is the energy needed to remove 1 electron from each atom in 1 mole of gaseous atoms to form 1 mole of gaseous 1+ ions.

You have to put energy in to ionise an atom or molecule, so it's an endothermic process. You can write equations for this process — here's the equation for the first ionisation of oxygen:

$$O_{(g)} \rightarrow O^+_{(g)} + e^- \qquad \text{1st ionisation energy} = +1314 \text{ kJ mol}^{-1}$$

Here are a few rather important points about ionisation energies:

- You must use the gas state symbol, (g), because ionisation energies are measured for gaseous atoms.

- Always refer to 1 mole of atoms, as stated in the definition, rather than to a single atom.

- The lower the ionisation energy, the easier it is to form an ion.

**Tip:** An endothermic process is one that takes in heat — see page 179 for more on this.

## Factors affecting ionisation energy

A high ionisation energy means there's a high attraction between the electron and the nucleus. There are three things that can affect ionisation energy:

### 1. Nuclear charge

The more protons there are in the nucleus, the more positively charged the nucleus is and the stronger the attraction for the electrons.

### 2. Distance from the nucleus

Attraction falls off very rapidly with distance. An electron close to the nucleus will be much more strongly attracted than one further away.

### 3. Shielding

As the number of electrons between the outer electrons and the nucleus increases, the outer electrons feel less attraction towards the nuclear charge. This lessening of the pull of the nucleus by inner shells of electrons is called shielding.

**Tip:** You can only really see the effect of nuclear charge on ionisation energy if you're looking at atoms with outer electrons that are the same distance from the nucleus and with equal shielding effects.

This only really happens when you're looking at elements in the same period of the Periodic Table.

--- Example ---

*There are only two electrons between the nucleus and the outer electron in a lithium atom.*

*There are ten electrons between the nucleus and the outer electron in a sodium atom — the shielding effect is greater.*

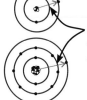

*The distance between the nucleus and the electron being removed is greater in the sodium atom.*

**Figure 1:** *A lithium atom and a sodium atom.*

This means that lithium has a higher first ionisation energy (519 kJ mol⁻¹) than sodium (496 kJ mol⁻¹). (The shielding and the distance from the nucleus have a bigger effect than the nuclear charge in this example.)

# Successive ionisation energies

You can remove all the electrons from an atom, leaving only the nucleus. Each time you remove an electron, there's a **successive ionisation energy**. These are called second ionisation energy, third ionisation energy... and so on. For example, the **second ionisation energy** is the energy needed to remove 1 electron from each ion in 1 mole of gaseous 1+ ions to form 1 mole of gaseous 2+ ions.

And here's the equation for the second ionisation of oxygen :

$$O^+(g) \rightarrow O^{2+}(g) + e^-$$   2nd ionisation energy = +3388 kJ mol$^{-1}$

**Exam Tip**
Make sure you learn the definitions of first and successive ionisation energies — it's really common to get an exam question on them.

# Ionisation energies and shell structure

If you have the successive ionisation energies of an element you can work out the number of electrons in each shell of the atom and which element the group is in. A graph of successive ionisation energies provides evidence for the shell structure of atoms (see Figure 2).

**Tip:** This is an example of how real-life data (the successive ionisation energies of an atom) can provide evidence for a theory (the electronic structure of the atom). See page 3 for more.

HOW SCIENCE WORKS

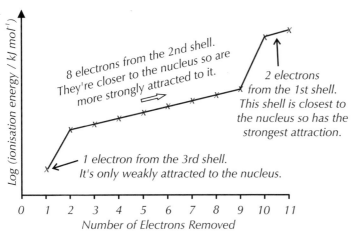

*Figure 2:* Successive ionisation energies of sodium.

**Tip:** The y-axis of this graph has a log (logarithmic) scale. Log scales go up in powers of a number (e.g. 1, 10, 100, etc.) rather than in units (1, 2, 3, etc.). Log scales are often used for graphs like this because ionisation energy values have such a huge range.

Within each shell, successive ionisation energies increase. This is because electrons are being removed from an increasingly positive ion — there's less repulsion amongst the remaining electrons, so they're held more strongly by the nucleus. The big jumps in ionisation energy happen when a new shell is broken into — an electron is being removed from a shell closer to the nucleus.

Graphs like the one in Figure 2 can tell you which group of the periodic table an element belongs to. Just count how many electrons are removed before the first big jump to find the group number.

┌ Example ───────────────────────────────────
In Figure 2, one electron is removed before the first big jump — sodium is in Group 1.
└

These graphs can be used to predict the electronic structure of an element. Working from right to left, count how many points there are before each big jump to find how many electrons are in each shell, starting with the first.

┌ Example ───────────────────────────────────
Working from right to left in Figure 2, the graph has 2 points on the right-hand side, then a jump, then 8 points, a jump, and 1 final point. Sodium has 2 electrons in the first shell, 8 in the second and 1 in the third.
└

Q1 a) Write an equation for the first ionisation energy of chlorine.

b) Write an equation for the second ionisation energy of chlorine.

Q2 The graph below shows the successive ionisation energies of an element.

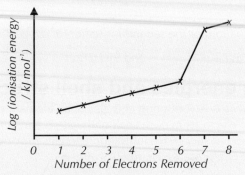

a) Which group is this element in?

b) State the number of electrons it has in each shell.

c) Name the element.

Q3 a) Sketch a graph showing the successive ionisation energies of magnesium.

b) Explain the shape of the graph.

Q4 The first ionisation energy of beryllium is 900 kJ mol$^{-1}$. The first ionisation energy of boron is 801 kJ mol$^{-1}$. Explain why there is a difference between these ionisation energies.

Q5 The first ionisation energy of aluminium is 578 kJ mol$^{-1}$. The first ionisation energy of silicon is 786 kJ mol$^{-1}$. Explain why there is a difference between these ionisation energies.

Q6 The first ionisation energy of lithium is 519 kJ mol$^{-1}$. The second ionisation energy is 7298 kJ mol$^{-1}$ and the third ionisation energy is 11815 kJ mol$^{-1}$.

Explain why the difference between the first and second ionisation energies is much greater than the difference between the second and third ionisation energies.

**Exam Tip**
If you get a question like this in the exam asking you to compare ionisation energies, make sure you remember the 3 factors that affect ionisation energy. Work out how the factors differ between each element, and you should have a very good idea of your answer.

Q1 Define first ionisation energy.

Q2 How does the number of protons affect the first ionisation energy?

Q3 Give two other factors that affect the first ionisation energy.

Q4 Define second ionisation energy.

Q5 Explain why successive ionisation energies increase within each shell of an atom.

# 3. Ionic Bonding

*When different elements join or bond together, you get a compound.*
*There are two main types of bonding in compounds — ionic and covalent.*
*First up is ionic bonding.*

## Ions

Ions are formed when electrons are transferred from one atom to another.
The simplest ions are single atoms which have either lost or gained 1, 2 or 3
electrons so that they've got a full outer shell.

┌─ **Examples** ─────────────────────────────────────

### The sodium ion

A sodium atom (Na) loses 1 electron to form a sodium ion ($Na^+$) —
see Figure 1.

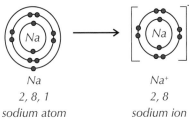

Na
*2, 8, 1*
*sodium atom*

$Na^+$
*2, 8*
*sodium ion*

**Figure 1:** *Formation of a sodium ion.*

This can be shown by the equation: $Na \rightarrow Na^+ + e^-$.

### The chloride ion

A chlorine atom (Cl) gains 1 electron to form a chloride ion ($Cl^-$) —
see Figure 2.

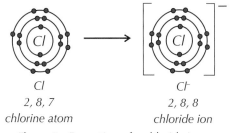

Cl
*2, 8, 7*
*chlorine atom*

$Cl^-$
*2, 8, 8*
*chloride ion*

**Figure 2:** *Formation of a chloride ion.*

This can be shown by the equation: $Cl + e^- \rightarrow Cl^-$.

### Other examples:

A magnesium atom (Mg) loses 2 electrons to form a magnesium ion ($Mg^{2+}$),
shown by the equation: $Mg \rightarrow Mg^{2+} + 2e^-$.
An oxygen atom (O) gains 2 electrons to form an oxide ion ($O^{2-}$), shown by
the equation: $O + 2e^- \rightarrow O^{2-}$.

You don't have to remember what ion each element forms — nope, for many
of them you just look at the Periodic Table. Elements in the same group all
have the same number of outer electrons. So they have to lose or gain the
same number to get the full outer shell that they're aiming for. And this means
that they form ions with the same charges. Figure 3 shows the ions formed by
the elements in different groups.

**Learning Objectives:**

- Predict ionic charge from the position of an element in the Periodic Table.

- State the formulae for the following ions: $NO_3^-$, $CO_3^{2-}$, $SO_4^{2-}$ and $NH_4^+$.

- Describe the term ionic bonding as electrostatic attraction between oppositely charged ions.

- Construct 'dot-and-cross' diagrams, to describe ionic bonding.

- Describe giant ionic lattices with strong ionic bonding, i.e. as in NaCl.

- Describe, interpret and/or predict physical properties, including melting and boiling points, electrical conductivity and solubility of ionic structures.

- Deduce the type of structure and bonding present from given information.

**Specification Reference 1.2.2**

**Tip:** The notation '2, 8, 1' shows the electron configuration of an atom or ion. There's more about how to work them out on page 52.

**Tip:** Equations that show the formation of ions need to be <u>balanced</u> — have a look back at pages 26-27 for how to balance ionic equations.

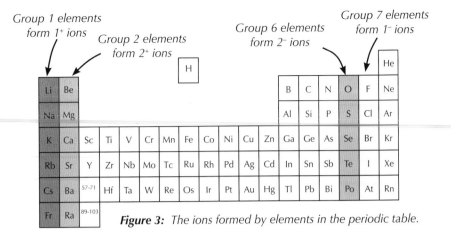

Group 1 elements form 1⁺ ions

Group 2 elements form 2⁺ ions

Group 6 elements form 2⁻ ions

Group 7 elements form 1⁻ ions

**Figure 3:** The ions formed by elements in the periodic table.

**Exam Tip**
Make sure you know how to find the charges on different ions from the periodic table — you never know when it'll come in handy in the exam.

Not all ions are made from single atoms. There are lots of ions that are made up of a group of atoms with an overall charge. These are called **compound ions**. You need to remember the formulas of these ones:

| Nitrate | Carbonate | Sulfate | Ammonium |
|---|---|---|---|
| $NO_3^-$ | $CO_3^{2-}$ | $SO_4^{2-}$ | $NH_4^+$ |

# Ionic compounds

**Electrostatic attraction** holds positive and negative ions together — it's very strong. When atoms are held together like this, it's called ionic bonding. So, an **ionic bond** is an electrostatic attraction between two oppositely charged ions. When oppositely charged ions form an ionic bond you get an ionic compound. The formula of a compound tells you what ions that compound has in it. The positive charges in the compound balance the negative charges exactly — so the total overall charge is zero. This is a dead handy way of checking the formula. You can use 'dot-and-cross' diagrams to show how ionic bonding works in ionic compounds.

**Figure 4:** The reaction between sodium and chlorine to form sodium chloride.

┌─ **Examples** ─────────────────────────────

**Sodium chloride**
The formula of sodium chloride is NaCl. It just tells you that sodium chloride is made up of $Na^+$ ions and $Cl^-$ ions (in a 1:1 ratio). In NaCl, the single positive charge on the $Na^+$ ion balances the single negative charge on the $Cl^-$ ion (see Figure 5).

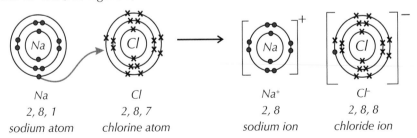

| Na | Cl | $Na^+$ | $Cl^-$ |
|---|---|---|---|
| 2, 8, 1 | 2, 8, 7 | 2, 8 | 2, 8, 8 |
| sodium atom | chlorine atom | sodium ion | chloride ion |

**Figure 5:** Formation of sodium chloride from a sodium atom and a chlorine atom.

Here the dots represent the Na electrons and the crosses represent the Cl electrons. All electrons are really identical, but this is a good way of following their movement.

## Magnesium oxide

Magnesium oxide, MgO, is another example of an ionic compound. The formation of magnesium oxide involves the transfer of two electrons — see Figure 6. The formula tells you that magnesium oxide is made up of $Mg^{2+}$ ions and $O^{2-}$ ions in a 1:1 ratio.

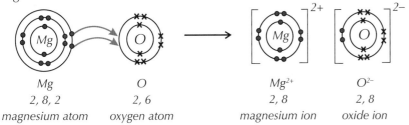

| Mg | O | $Mg^{2+}$ | $O^{2-}$ |
| 2, 8, 2 | 2, 6 | 2, 8 | 2, 8 |
| magnesium atom | oxygen atom | magnesium ion | oxide ion |

**Figure 6:** Formation of magnesium oxide from a magnesium atom and an oxygen atom.

**Figure 7:** Magnesium is burned in oxygen to form magnesium oxide.

## Magnesium chloride

Magnesium chloride ($MgCl_2$) is different again. In this compound, the 2+ charge on the $Mg^{2+}$ ion balances the two individual charges on the two $Cl^-$ ions — see Figure 8.

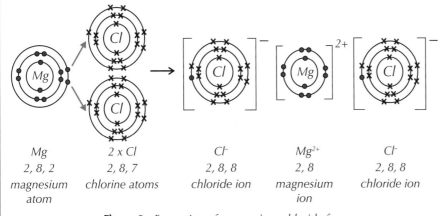

| Mg | 2 x Cl | $Cl^-$ | $Mg^{2+}$ | $Cl^-$ |
| 2, 8, 2 | 2, 8, 7 | 2, 8, 8 | 2, 8 | 2, 8, 8 |
| magnesium atom | chlorine atoms | chloride ion | magnesium ion | chloride ion |

**Figure 8:** Formation of magnesium chloride from a magnesium atom and two chlorine atoms.

**Figure 9:** Magnesium chloride.

# Giant ionic lattices

Ionic crystals are **giant lattices** of ions. A lattice is just a regular structure. The structure's called 'giant' because it's made up of the same basic unit repeated over and over again. The sodium chloride lattice is cube shaped (see Figures 10 and 11).

The Na⁺ and Cl⁻ ions alternate.

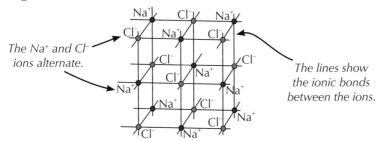

The lines show the ionic bonds between the ions.

**Figure 10:** The structure of sodium chloride.

**Figure 11:** Crystals of sodium chloride (table salt).

Different ionic compounds have different shaped structures, but they're all still giant lattices.

# Behaviour of ionic compounds

The structure of ionic compounds decides their physical properties — things like their electrical conductivity, melting point and solubility.

## Electrical conductivity

Ionic compounds conduct electricity when they're molten or dissolved — but not when they're solid. The ions in a liquid are free to move (and they carry a charge). In a solid they're fixed in position by the strong ionic bonds.

## Melting and boiling points

Ionic compounds have high melting and boiling points. The giant ionic lattices are held together by strong electrostatic forces. It takes loads of energy to overcome these forces, so melting and boiling points are very high (801 °C and 1413 °C respectively for sodium chloride).

## Solubility

Ionic compounds tend to dissolve in water. Water molecules are polar — part of the molecule has a small negative charge, and the other bits have small positive charges (see page 69). The water molecules pull the ions away from the lattice and cause it to dissolve.

**Figure 12:** *Water doesn't conduct electricity (see top). When the ionic compound sodium chloride is added to the water (above), it dissolves and the free Na$^+$ and Cl$^-$ ions allow a current to flow.*

## Practice Questions — Application

Q1  Use the periodic table to give the charge on the following ions:

 a) Bromide        b) Potassium        c) Beryllium

Q2  a) Write an equation to show a sulfur atom forming an ion.

 b) Draw a 'dot and cross' diagram to show a sulfur atom forming an ion.

Q3  Calcium reacts with iodine to form an ionic compound.

 a) What is the charge on a calcium ion?

 b) What is the charge on an iodide ion?

 c) Give the formula of calcium iodide.

Q4  Fluorine forms ionic bonds with lithium.

 a) Give the formula of the compound formed.

 b) Describe how an ionic bond forms between a fluorine atom and a lithium atom.

 c) Draw a 'dot and cross' diagram to show the formation of an ionic bond between fluorine and lithium.

## Practice Questions — Fact Recall

Q1  What effect does electrostatic attraction have on oppositely charged ions?

Q2  Explain what an ionic lattice is.

Q3  Draw the structure of sodium chloride.

Q4  Explain why ionic compounds conduct electricity when molten.

Q5  Magnesium oxide is an ionic compound. Apart from electrical conductivity when molten or dissolved, describe three physical properties you would expect magnesium oxide to have.

# 4. Covalent Bonding

*Ionic bonding done — now it's on to covalent bonding.*

## Molecules

**Molecules** are the smallest parts of compounds that can take part in chemical reactions. They're formed when two or more atoms bond together — it doesn't matter if the atoms are the same or different. Chlorine gas ($Cl_2$), carbon monoxide (CO), water ($H_2O$) and ethanol ($C_2H_5OH$) are all molecules. Molecules are held together by strong covalent bonds — a covalent bond is a shared pair of electrons. Most of the time the atoms end up with eight electrons in their outer shells. This is good for the atoms — it's a very stable arrangement.

### Single bonds

In covalent bonding, two atoms share electrons, so they've both got full outer shells of electrons. Both the positive nuclei are attracted electrostatically to the shared electrons.

**Examples**

Two chlorine atoms (Cl) bond covalently to form a molecule of chlorine ($Cl_2$) — see Figure 1. (These diagrams don't show all the electrons — just the ones in the outer shells.)

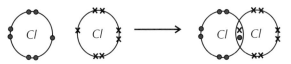

A chlorine molecule can also be drawn as:

Cl—Cl

**Figure 1:** *Formation of a molecule of chlorine.*

The diagrams below show other examples of covalent molecules.

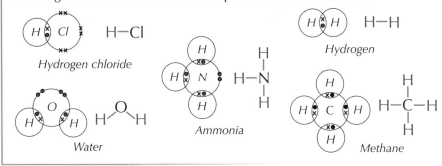

Hydrogen chloride    H—Cl

Hydrogen    H—H

Water

Ammonia    H—N

Methane    H—C—H

### Double and triple bonds

Atoms in covalent molecules don't just form single bonds — double or even triple covalent bonds can form too. This means that the atoms are sharing more than one pair of electrons.

**Examples**

**Double bonds**

In molecules of $O_2$ and $CO_2$ each oxygen atom shares two pairs of electrons with another atom. So, both molecules contain double bonds.

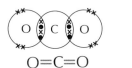

O=C=O

O=O

**Triple bonds**

When a molecule of nitrogen ($N_2$) forms, the nitrogen atoms share three pairs of electrons. So, each molecule of nitrogen contains one triple bond.

N≡N

**Learning Objectives:**

- Describe the term covalent bond as a shared pair of electrons.
- Construct 'dot-and-cross' diagrams to describe: single covalent bonding, e.g. as in $H_2$, $Cl_2$, HCl, $H_2O$, $NH_3$, $CH_4$, $BF_3$ and $SF_6$; multiple covalent bonding, e.g. as in $O_2$, $N_2$ and $CO_2$; dative covalent (coordinate) bonding, e.g. as in $NH_4^+$; plus molecules and ions analogous to them.
- Describe, interpret and/or predict physical properties, including melting and boiling points, electrical conductivity and solubility in terms of covalent bonding and molecules.
- Describe giant covalent lattices, i.e. as in diamond and graphite.
- Deduce the type of structure and bonding present from given information.

**Specification Reference 1.2.2**

**Exam Tip**
Be ready to draw any of these 'dot-and-cross' diagrams in the exam — any of them could come up and it's easy if you can remember them.

## Special cases

There are always a few pesky exceptions to make life that bit trickier.
For example, a few compounds contain atoms with fewer than 8 electrons
in their outer shell.

### Example

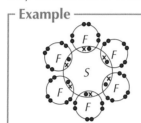

In boron trifluoride, boron only
has 6 electrons in its outer shell.

And a few compounds can use d orbitals to 'expand the octet'. This means
they contain atoms with more than 8 electrons in their outer shell.

### Example

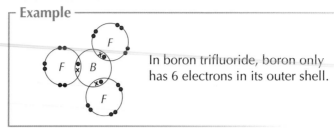

In sulfur hexafluoride, sulfur has
12 electrons in its outer shell.

***Figure 2:*** *A molecular model
of sulfur hexafluoride.*

## Dative covalent bonding

In a normal single covalent bond, atoms share a pair of electrons — with
one electron coming from each atom. In **dative covalent**, also known as
**coordinate**, bonding, one of the atoms provides both of the shared electrons.

### Example

**The ammonium ion**

The ammonium ion ($NH_4^+$) is formed by dative covalent bonding.
It forms when the nitrogen atom in an ammonia molecule donates
a pair of electrons to a proton ($H^+$) — see Figure 3.

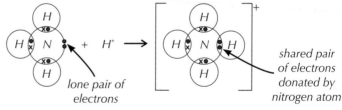

***Figure 3:*** *Dative bonding in $NH_4^+$.*

**Tip:** Once a dative
bond has formed, it's
no different to a normal
covalent bond.

Dative covalent bonding can also be shown in diagrams by an arrow,
pointing away from the 'donor' atom (see Figure 4).

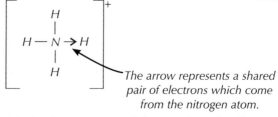

The arrow represents a shared
pair of electrons which come
from the nitrogen atom.

***Figure 4:*** *An alternative way of showing dative bonding in $NH_4^+$.*

# Behaviour of simple covalent compounds

**Simple covalent compounds** have strong bonds within molecules but weak forces between the molecules. Their physical properties, such as electrical conductivity, melting point and solubility, are determined by the bonding in the compound.

### Electrical conductivity

Simple covalent compounds don't conduct electricity because there are no free ions or electrons to carry the charge.

### Melting and boiling points

Simple covalent compounds have low melting and boiling points because the weak forces between molecules are easily overcome.

### Solubility

Some simple covalent compounds dissolve in water depending on how polarised the molecules are (see page 69 for more on polarisation).

**Tip:** All the examples on page 61 are simple covalent compounds — strong bonds exist within the molecules, but not between them.

# Giant covalent structures

Giant covalent structures have a huge network of covalently bonded atoms. (They're sometimes called **macromolecular** structures.) Carbon atoms can form this type of structure because they can each form four strong, covalent bonds. There are two types of giant covalent carbon structure you need to know about, graphite and diamond.

### Graphite

The carbon atoms in graphite are arranged in sheets of flat hexagons covalently bonded with three bonds each (see Figure 5). The fourth outer electron of each carbon atom is delocalised. The sheets of hexagons are bonded together by weak van der Waals forces (see pages 70-71).

**Tip:** 'Delocalised' means an electron isn't attached to a particular atom — it can move around between atoms.

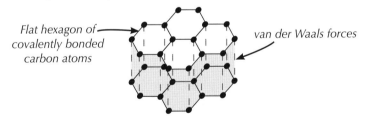

Flat hexagon of covalently bonded carbon atoms

van der Waals forces

***Figure 5:*** *The structure of graphite.*

Graphite's structure means it has certain properties:

- The weak bonds between the layers in graphite are easily broken, so the sheets can slide over each other — graphite feels slippery and is used as a dry lubricant and in pencils.

- The 'delocalised' electrons in graphite are free to move along the sheets, so an electric current can flow.

- The layers are quite far apart compared to the length of the covalent bonds, so graphite has a low density and is used to make strong, lightweight sports equipment.

- Because of the strong covalent bonds in the hexagon sheets, graphite has a very high melting point (it sublimes at over 3900 K).

- Graphite is insoluble in any solvent. The covalent bonds in the sheets are too difficult to break.

***Figure 6:*** *A graphite pencil being used to lubricate a zip fastening.*

**Tip:** 'Sublimes' means it changes straight from a solid to a gas, skipping out the liquid stage.

## Diamond

Diamond is also made up of carbon atoms. Each carbon atom is covalently bonded to four other carbon atoms (see Figure 7). The atoms arrange themselves in a tetrahedral shape — its crystal lattice structure.

**Tip:** Tetrahedral is a molecular shape — see pages 65-68 for more on shapes of molecules.

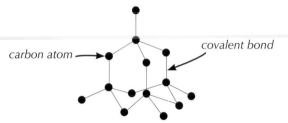

*Figure 7: The structure of diamond.*

Because of its strong covalent bonds:

- Diamond has a very high melting point — it actually sublimes at over 3800 K.
- Diamond is extremely hard — it's used in diamond-tipped drills and saws.
- Vibrations travel easily through the stiff lattice, so it's a good thermal conductor.
- It can't conduct electricity — all the outer electrons are held in localised bonds.
- Like graphite, diamond won't dissolve in any solvent.

**Tip:** You can 'cut' diamond to form gemstones (see Figure 8). Its structure makes it refract light a lot, which is why it sparkles.

*Figure 8: A cut and polished diamond. Oooh, sparkly.*

## Practice Questions — Fact Recall

Q1 How is a covalent bond formed?

Q2 Draw a 'dot-and-cross' diagram to show the formation of a chlorine molecule.

Q3 Explain what a triple covalent bond is.

Q4 Draw a 'dot-and-cross' diagram to show the bonding in $BF_3$.

Q5 What is a dative covalent bond?

Q6 Give another name for dative covalent bonding.

Q7 In a diagram of a molecule with a dative covalent bond, what does the arrow show?

Q8 Chlorine ($Cl_2$) is a simple covalent molecule.

    a) Explain why chlorine has a very low melting point.

    b) Would you expect chlorine to conduct electricity? Explain your answer.

Q9 Describe the structure of diamond.

# 5. Shapes of Molecules

*There's a lot of variation in molecular shape and you need to understand how to work out the shape of any molecule or molecular ion. Don't worry though, the next few pages have lots of advice to help you along.*

## Electron pair repulsion

Molecules and molecular ions come in loads of different shapes. The shape depends on the number of pairs of electrons in the outer shell of the central atom. Pairs of electrons can be shared in a covalent bond or can be unshared. Shared electrons are called bonding pairs, unshared electrons are called **lone pairs** or non-bonding pairs.

Electrons are all negatively charged, so it's pretty obvious that electron pairs will repel each other as much as they can. This sounds straightforward, but the type of electron pair affects how much it repels other electron pairs. Lone pairs repel more than bonding pairs. So, the greatest angles are between lone pairs of electrons, and bond angles between bonding pairs are often reduced because they are pushed together by lone pair repulsion. This is known by the long-winded name '**Valence-Shell Electron-Pair Repulsion Theory**'. Figure 1 shows the electron pairs in water.

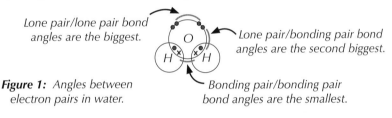

*Lone pair/lone pair bond angles are the biggest.*

*Lone pair/bonding pair bond angles are the second biggest.*

*Bonding pair/bonding pair bond angles are the smallest.*

**Figure 1:** *Angles between electron pairs in water.*

## Drawing shapes of molecules

It can be tricky to draw molecules showing their shapes — but one way to do it is to show which way the bonds are pointing. In a molecule diagram, use wedges to show a bond pointing towards you, and a broken (or dotted) line to show a bond pointing away from you (see Figure 2).

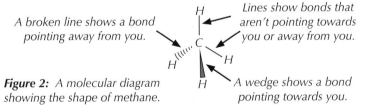

*A broken line shows a bond pointing away from you.*

*Lines show bonds that aren't pointing towards you or away from you.*

*A wedge shows a bond pointing towards you.*

**Figure 2:** *A molecular diagram showing the shape of methane.*

## Calculating the number of electron pairs

To work out the shape of a molecule or an ion you need to know how many lone pairs and how many bonding pairs of electrons are on the central atom. Follow these steps:

1. Find the central atom — it's the one all the other atoms are bonded to.

2. Work out how many electrons are in the outer shell of the central atom. Use the periodic table to do this.

3. The formula of the molecule or ion will tell you how many atoms are bonded to the central atom so you can work out the number of electrons donated to the central atom by other atoms.

### Learning Objectives:

- Explain that the shape of a simple molecule is determined by repulsion between electron pairs surrounding a central atom.

- State that lone pairs of electrons repel more than bonded pairs.

- Explain the shapes of, and bond angles in, molecules and ions with up to six electron pairs (including lone pairs) surrounding a central atom, e.g. as in $BF_3$ (trigonal planar), $CH_4$ and $NH_4^+$ (tetrahedral), $SF_6$ (octahedral), $NH_3$ (pyramidal), $H_2O$ (non-linear), $CO_2$ (linear).

- Predict the shapes of, and bond angles in, molecules and ions.

**Specification Reference 1.2.2**

**Tip:** If you're dealing with an ion don't forget to take into account its charge so you know how many electrons it's gained or lost.

4. Add up the electrons and divide by 2 to find the number of electron pairs. If you're dealing with an ion, you need to take into account its charge, as it will affect the number of electrons involved in the bonding.

5. Compare the number of electron pairs to the number of bonds to find the number of lone pairs and the number of bonding pairs.

─ Examples ──────────────────────────

**Carbon tetrafluoride, $CF_4$**

1. The central atom in this molecule is carbon.

2. Carbon's in Group 4 — so it has four electrons in its outer shell.

3. There are four covalent bonds bonding the central atom to fluorine atoms, so there are four electrons coming from the fluorine atoms.

4. There are 8 electrons in total, so there are 4 electron pairs.

5. 4 pairs of electrons are involved in bonding the fluorine atoms to the carbon so there must be four bonding pairs of electrons. That accounts for all the electrons — there are no lone pairs (see Figure 3).

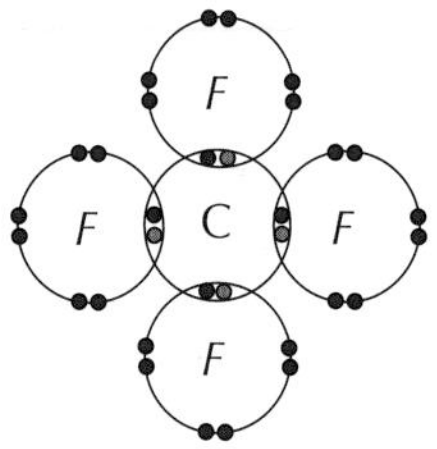

**Tip:** Elements that are in Group 7 (e.g. fluorine) can form one covalent bond with another atom to complete their outer shell. See pages 61-64 for more on covalent bonding.

***Figure 3:*** *A molecule of $CF_4$.*

**Phosphorus trihydride, $PH_3$**

1. The central atom in this molecule is phosphorus.

2. It's in Group 5 — so it has five electrons in its outer shell.

3. Phosphorus forms three covalent bonds with hydrogen, so there are three electrons coming from the hydrogen atoms.

4. There are 8 electrons in total which means 4 electron pairs.

5. Three electron pairs are involved in bonding with the hydrogen atoms (bonding pairs) and so there's one lone pair of electrons (see Figure 4).

**Tip:** The number of bonds the central atom forms is also called its coordination number.

**Tip:** A hydrogen atom will form one covalent bond with another atom to complete its outer shell.

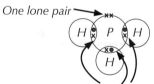

*One lone pair*

*Three bonding pairs*

***Figure 4:*** *Electron pairs in a molecule of $PH_3$.*

# Working out the shapes of molecules

Once you know how many electron pairs are on the central atom, you can work out the shape of the molecule.

### Central atoms with two electron pairs

Molecules with two electron pairs have a bond angle of 180° and have a **linear** shape. This is because the pairs of bonding electrons want to be as far away from each other as possible.

**Tip:** You need to know how to calculate the number of electron pairs before you try and learn this bit. Make sure you've got that sorted before you go any further.

─ Examples ──────────────────────────

**Beryllium chloride, $BeCl_2$**

Beryllium has two bonding pairs of electrons and no lone pairs so the bond angle in $BeCl_2$ is 180° and it has a linear shape.

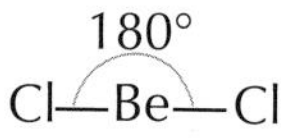

180°
Cl—Be—Cl

### Carbon dioxide, $CO_2$

Carbon has four bonding pairs of electrons (found in two carbon-oxygen double bonds). You treat the double bonds like single bonds so $CO_2$ will have a linear shape.

$$O = C = O$$

180°

*Figure 5:* A molecular model of carbon dioxide, showing it to be a linear molecule with a bond angle of 180°.

## Central atoms with three electron pairs

Molecules that have three electron pairs around the central atom don't always have the same shape — the shape depends on the combination of bonding pairs and lone pairs of electrons. If there are three bonding pairs of electrons the repulsion of the charge clouds is the same between each pair and so the bond angles are all 120°. The shape of the molecule is **trigonal planar**.

─ Example ─────────────────

**Boron trifluoride, $BF_3$**

The central boron atom has three bonding pairs of electrons, so the bond angle in $BF_3$ is 120° and it has a trigonal planar shape.

**Exam Tip**
You'll be expected to know all of the bond angles for the shapes of molecules in your exam — so make sure you learn them.

If there are two bonding pairs of electrons and one lone pair in a molecule you'll get a squished trigonal planar shape which is called **non-linear**. The bond angle will be a bit less than 120°.

## Central atoms with four electron pairs

If there are four pairs of bonding electrons and no lone pairs on a central atom, all the bond angles are 109.5° — the charge clouds all repel each other equally. The shape of the molecule is **tetrahedral**.

─ Examples ─────────────────

**Methane, $CH_4$**

The carbon atom has four bonding pairs of electrons so the shape of $CH_4$ is tetrahedral.

**Tip:** It might help you to think of wedges as bonds that stick out of the page, broken lines as bonds that point behind the page and straight lines as bonds that are flat against the page.

**Ammonium ion, $NH_4^+$**

The nitrogen atom has four bonding pairs of electrons so the shape of $NH_4^+$ is tetrahedral.

If there are three bonding pairs of electrons and one lone pair, the lone-pair/bonding-pair repulsion will be greater than the bonding-pair/bonding-pair repulsion and so the angles between the atoms will change. There'll be smaller bond angles between the bonding pairs of electrons and larger angles between the lone pair and the bonding pairs. The bond angle is 107° and the shape of the molecules is **trigonal pyramidal**.

─ Example ─────────────────

**Ammonia, $NH_3$**

The nitrogen has three bonding pairs of electrons and a lone pair, so the shape of $NH_3$ is trigonal pyramidal.

*Figure 6:* A molecular model of ammonia, showing it to be a trigonal pyramidal shape.

If there are two bonding pairs of electrons and two lone pairs of electrons the lone-pair/lone-pair repulsion will squish the bond angle even further. The bond angle is 104.5° and the shape of the molecules is **non-linear**.

┌─ Example ─────────────────────

**Water, $H_2O$**

The oxygen atom has two bonding pairs shared with hydrogen atoms and two lone pairs, so the shape of $H_2O$ is non-linear (bent).

$$H \overset{\times\times\,\,\times\times}{\underset{104.5°}{\diagdown O \diagup}} H$$

### Central atoms with five or six electron pairs

Some central atoms can use d orbitals and can 'expand the octet' — which means they can have more than eight bonding electrons. A molecule with five bonding pairs will be **trigonal bipyramidal**. Repulsion between the bonding pairs means that three of the atoms will form a trigonal planar shape with bond angles of 120° and the other two atoms will be at 90° to them.

┌─ Example ─────────────────────

**Phosphorus pentachloride, $PCl_5$**

The phosphorus atom has five bonding pairs so it has a trigonal bipyramidal shape.

A molecule with six bonding pairs will be **octahedral**. All of the bond angles in the molecule are 90°.

┌─ Example ─────────────────────

**Sulfur hexafluoride, $SF_6$**

Sulfur has six bonding pairs making its shape **octahedral**.

## Practice Questions — Application

Q1 a) How many electron pairs are on the central atom of an $H_2S$ molecule?

   b) How many lone pairs does a molecule of $H_2S$ have?

   c) Draw and name the shape of an $H_2S$ molecule.

   d) Give the bond angle between bonding pairs in $H_2S$.

Q2 a) Draw and name the shape of a molecule of $AsH_3$.

   b) Give the bonding pair/bonding pair bond angle in $AsH_3$.

Q3 Draw and name the shape of a molecule of $CCl_2F_2$. Explain your answer.

## Practice Questions — Fact Recall

Q1 What is the bond angle between electron pairs in a trigonal planar molecule?

Q2 How many electron pairs are on the central atom in a tetrahedral molecule?

Q3 Name the structure that a molecule will have if it has six bonding pairs on the central atom.

# 6. Polarisation

*Polarisation of bonds occurs because of the nature of different atomic nuclei — some are just more attractive than others.*

## Electronegativity

Very few compounds come even close to being purely ionic. Only bonds between atoms of a single element, like diatomic gases such as hydrogen ($H_2$) or oxygen ($O_2$), can be purely covalent. So really, most compounds come somewhere in between the two extremes — meaning they've often got ionic and covalent properties, e.g. covalent hydrogen chloride gas molecules dissolve to form hydrochloric acid, which is an ionic solution.

The ability of an atom to attract the bonding electrons in a covalent bond is called **electronegativity**. Electronegativity is measured on the Pauling Scale. A higher number means an element is better able to attract the bonding electrons. Fluorine is the most electronegative element. Oxygen, nitrogen and chlorine are also very strongly electronegative — see Figure 1.

## Polar and non-polar bonds

The covalent bonds in diatomic gases (e.g. $H_2$, $Cl_2$) are non-polar because the atoms have equal electronegativities and so the electrons are equally attracted to both nuclei (see Figure 2). Some elements, like carbon and hydrogen, have pretty similar electronegativities, so bonds between them are essentially non-polar.

*shared electrons*

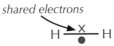

**Figure 2:** *A non-polar covalent bond in a hydrogen molecule.*

In a covalent bond between two atoms of different electronegativities, the bonding electrons are pulled towards the more electronegative atom. This makes the bond polar (see Figure 3).

'δ' (delta) means 'slightly', so 'δ+' means 'slightly positive'.

'δ–' means 'slightly negative'. It shows that chlorine is more electronegative than hydrogen.

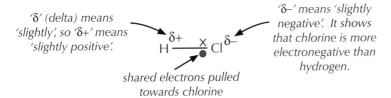

shared electrons pulled towards chlorine

**Figure 3:** *A polar covalent bond in a hydrogen chloride molecule.*

In a polar bond, the difference in electronegativity between the two atoms causes a **dipole**. A dipole is a difference in charge between the two atoms caused by a shift in electron density in the bond. So what you need to remember is that the greater the difference in electronegativity, the more polar the bond.

| Element | Electronegativity (Pauling Scale) |
|---------|-----------------------------------|
| H | 2.1 |
| C | 2.5 |
| N | 3.0 |
| Cl | 3.0 |
| O | 3.5 |
| F | 4.0 |

**Figure 1:**
*The electronegativity of different elements.*

**Exam Tip**
You don't need to learn the electronegativity values — if you need them you'll be given them in the exam.

**Tip:** It's really, really important that you get your head around the relationship between electronegativity, polarisation and dipoles. Differences in the <u>electronegativity</u> of atoms <u>cause</u> bonds to become <u>polarised</u>, which results in a <u>dipole</u> — a <u>difference in charge</u> between the two atoms.

## Practice Questions — Fact Recall

Q1 Chlorine is more electronegative than hydrogen. Explain what this means.

Q2 Explain why the H — F bond is polarised.

Q3 What is a dipole?

# 7. Intermolecular Forces

- Describe intermolecular forces based on permanent dipoles, as in hydrogen chloride, and induced dipoles (van der Waals' forces), as in the noble gases.

- Describe structures as simple molecular lattices, i.e. as in $I_2$ and ice.

- Describe hydrogen bonding, including the role of a lone pair, between molecules containing –OH and –NH groups, i.e. as in $H_2O$, $NH_3$ and analogous molecules.

- Describe and explain the anomalous properties of $H_2O$ resulting from hydrogen bonding, e.g. the density of ice compared with water and its relatively high freezing point and boiling point.

- Deduce the type of structure and bonding present from given information.

**Specification Reference 1.2.2**

*Molecules don't just exist independently — they can interact with each other. And you need to know how they interact.*

## What are intermolecular forces?

Intermolecular forces are forces between molecules. They're much weaker than covalent, ionic or metallic bonds. There are three types you need to know about: induced dipole-dipole or van der Waals forces (this is the weakest type), permanent dipole-dipole forces and hydrogen bonding (this is the strongest type).

## Van der Waals forces

Van der Waals forces cause all atoms and molecules to be attracted to each other. Electrons in charge clouds are always moving really quickly. At any particular moment, the electrons in an atom are likely to be more to one side than the other. At this moment, the atom would have a temporary dipole. This dipole can cause another temporary dipole in the opposite direction on a neighbouring atom (see Figure 1). The two dipoles are then attracted to each other. The second dipole can cause yet another dipole in a third atom. It's kind of like a domino rally. Because the electrons are constantly moving, the dipoles are being created and destroyed all the time. Even though the dipoles keep changing, the overall effect is for the atoms to be attracted to each other.

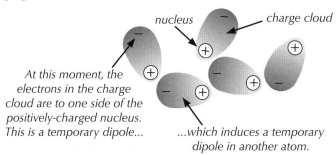

*At this moment, the electrons in the charge cloud are to one side of the positively-charged nucleus. This is a temporary dipole...*

*...which induces a temporary dipole in another atom.*

**Figure 1:** *Temporary dipoles in a liquid resulting in van der Waals forces.*

**Tip:** If a temporary dipole has been caused by another temporary dipole it can be called an induced dipole.

**Example**

Van der Waals forces are responsible for holding iodine molecules together in a lattice. Iodine atoms are held together in pairs by strong covalent bonds to form molecules of $I_2$ (see Figure 2). But the molecules are then held together in a simple molecular lattice arrangement by weak van der Waals attractions (see Figure 3).

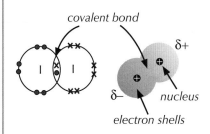

**Figure 2:** *A dot-and-cross diagram and a diagram showing electron density in a molecule of iodine.*

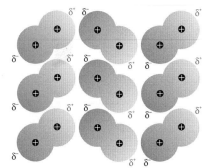

**Figure 3:** *Lattice of iodine molecules held together by van der Waals forces.*

Not all van der Waals forces are the same strength — larger molecules have larger electron clouds, meaning stronger van der Waals forces. Molecules with greater surface areas also have stronger van der Waals forces because they have a more exposed electron cloud.

When you boil a liquid, you need to overcome the intermolecular forces, so that the particles can escape from the liquid surface. It stands to reason that you need more energy to overcome stronger intermolecular forces, so liquids with stronger van der Waals forces will have higher boiling points. Van der Waals forces affect other physical properties, such as melting point and viscosity too.

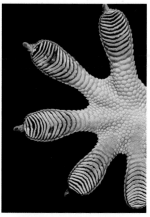

**Figure 4:** *The adhesive ability of a gecko's foot is thought to be due to van der Waals forces.*

---

**Example**

As you go down the group of noble gases, the number of electrons increases. Van der Waals forces are the only forces between noble gas atoms, so the boiling points of the gases depend on them. As the number of electrons increases, the van der Waals forces increase, and therefore so do the boiling points (see Figure 5).

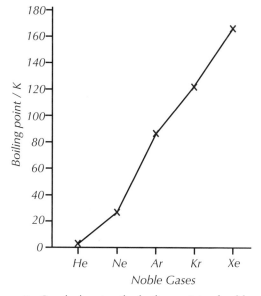

**Figure 5:** *Graph showing the boiling points of noble gases.*

---

**Tip:** Remember — there are van der Waals forces between all molecules.

**Figure 6:** *Johannes Diderik van der Waals (1837-1923), a Dutch physicist who was the first to understand the importance of the intermolecular forces that are now named after him.*

# Permanent dipole-dipole forces

The δ+ and δ– charges on polar molecules cause weak electrostatic forces of attraction between molecules. These are called permanent dipole-dipole forces.

---

**Example**

Hydrogen chloride gas has polar molecules due to the difference in electronegativity of hydrogen and chlorine.

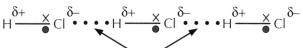

*The molecules have weak electrostatic forces between them because of the shift in electron density.*

**Figure 7:** *Permanent dipole-dipole forces in hydrogen chloride gas.*

---

**Exam Tip**
When you're drawing dipoles in the exam, make sure you include the δ+ and δ– symbols to show the charges.

If you put an electrostatically charged rod next to a jet of a polar liquid, like water, the liquid will move towards the rod. It's because polar liquids contain molecules with permanent dipoles. It doesn't matter if the rod is positively or negatively charged. The polar molecules in the liquid can turn around so the oppositely charged end is attracted towards the rod (see Figures 8 and 9).

**Figure 8:** A charged glass rod bends water.

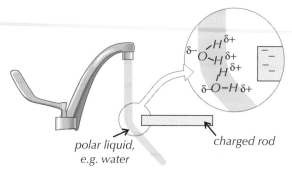

polar liquid, e.g. water

charged rod

**Figure 9:** Dipoles in a stream of water cause it to move towards a charged glass rod.

**Tip:** Charge density is just a measure of how much positive or negative charge there is in a certain volume.

# Hydrogen bonding

Hydrogen bonding only happens when hydrogen is covalently bonded to fluorine, nitrogen or oxygen. Hydrogen has a high charge density because it's so small and fluorine, nitrogen and oxygen are very electronegative. The bond is so polarised that the hydrogen of one molecule forms a weak bond with the fluorine, nitrogen or oxygen of another molecule. Molecules which have hydrogen bonding are usually organic, containing -OH or -NH groups.

**Exam Tip**
Hydrogen bonding is a special case scenario — it only happens in specific molecules. In the exam, you could be asked to compare intermolecular forces in different substances, so you'll need to know the different intermolecular forces and their relative strengths. Don't forget that not <u>every</u> molecule with hydrogen in it makes hydrogen bonds.

┌ **Examples** ──────────────────────────────

Water and ammonia both have hydrogen bonding (see Figures 10 and 11).

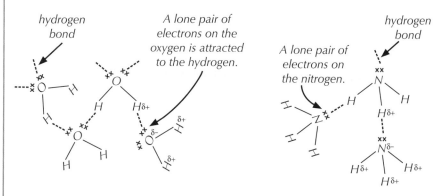

**Figure 10:** Hydrogen bonding in water.

**Figure 11:** Hydrogen bonding in ammonia.

**Exam Tip**
If you're asked to draw a diagram to show hydrogen bonding you'll need to include the lone pairs of electrons on the electronegative atom (O, N or F). You may also have to show the partial charges — the $\delta+$ goes on the H atom and the $\delta-$ goes on the electronegative atom.

Hydrogen bonding has a huge effect on the properties of substances. They are soluble in water and have higher boiling and freezing points than non-polar molecules of a similar size. Water and ammonia have very high boiling points if you compare them with other hydrides in their groups, because of the extra energy needed to break the H bonds — see Figure 12.

In ice, molecules of $H_2O$ are held together in a simple molecular lattice by hydrogen bonds. And because hydrogen bonds are relatively long, ice is less dense than liquid water.

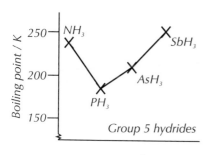
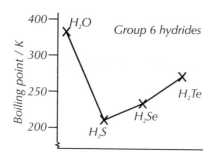

**Figure 12:** *Graph showing the boiling points of Group 5 and 6 hydrides.*

## Practice Questions — Application

Q1 What intermolecular force(s) exist(s) in $H_2$?

Q2 The table in Figure 13 shows the electronegativity values of some elements.

a) Use the table to explain why there are hydrogen bonds between $H_2O$ molecules but not between HCl molecules.

b) Identify one other element from the table that would form hydrogen bonds when covalently bonded to hydrogen.

c) What is the strongest type of intermolecular force between molecules of HCl?

d) Name one other element from the table that would not form hydrogen bonds when covalently bonded to hydrogen.

Q3 Hydrogen has an electronegativity value of 2.1 on the Pauling scale, nitrogen has a value of 3.0 and phosphorus has a value of 2.2.

a) The boiling point of $NH_3$ is –33 °C and the boiling point of $PH_3$ is –88 °C. Explain why the boiling point of $PH_3$ is lower.

b) Arsenic (As) has an electronegativity value of 2.18. Would you expect the boiling point of $AsH_3$ to be higher or lower than that of $NH_3$?

| Element | Electronegativity (Pauling Scale) |
|---------|-----------------------------------|
| H | 2.1 |
| C | 2.5 |
| Cl | 3.0 |
| O | 3.5 |
| F | 4.0 |

**Figure 13:**
*The electronegativity of different elements.*

## Practice Questions — Fact Recall

Q1 What is the weakest type of intermolecular force?

Q2 Describe the bonding within and between iodine molecules.

Q3 What are permanent dipole-dipole forces?

Q4 a) What is the strongest intermolecular force in ammonia?

b) Draw a diagram to show this intermolecular force between two ammonia molecules.

Q5 Name the strongest intermolecular force in water.

Q6 Explain why ice is less dense that liquid water.

## Learning Objectives:

- Describe metallic bonding as the attraction of positive ions to delocalised electrons.
- Describe structures as giant metallic lattices.
- Describe, interpret and/or predict physical properties, including melting and boiling points, electrical conductivity and solubility in terms of metallic bonding.
- Deduce the type of structure and bonding present from given information.

**Specification Reference 1.2.2**

# 8. Metallic Bonding

*You'll be familiar with metallic bonding from GCSE, but there's more to know...*

## Metallic bonding

Metal elements exist as **giant metallic lattice structures**. The outermost shell of electrons of a metal atom is delocalised — the electrons are free to move about the metal. This leaves a positive metal ion, e.g. $Na^+$, $Mg^{2+}$, $Al^{3+}$. The positive metal ions are attracted to the delocalised negative electrons. They form a lattice of closely packed positive ions in a sea of delocalised electrons — this is metallic bonding (see Figure 1).

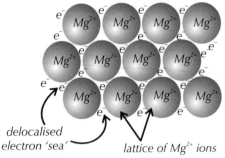

*delocalised electron 'sea'*            *lattice of $Mg^{2+}$ ions*

**Figure 1:** Metallic bonding in magnesium.

Metallic bonding explains the properties of metals — for example, their melting and boiling points, their ability to be shaped, their conductivity and their solubility.

## Melting and boiling points

The number of delocalised electrons per atom affects the melting and boiling points. The more there are, the stronger the bonding will be and the higher the melting and boiling points. $Mg^{2+}$ has two delocalised electrons per atom, so it's got higher melting and boiling points than $Na^+$, which only has one. The size of the metal ion and the lattice structure also affect the melting and boiling points.

## Ability to be shaped

As there are no bonds holding specific ions together, the metal ions can slide over each other when the structure is pulled, so metals are malleable (can be shaped, see Figure 2) and ductile (can be drawn into a wire).

## Conductivity

The delocalised electrons can pass kinetic energy to each other, making metals good thermal conductors. Metals are good electrical conductors because the delocalised electrons can carry a current.

## Solubility

Metals are insoluble, except in liquid metals, because of the strength of the metallic bonds.

**Figure 2:** *Magnesium shaped into a ribbon.*

---

### Practice Questions — Fact Recall

Q1  Describe the structure of magnesium.

Q2  What type of bonding can be found in magnesium?

Q3  Explain the following:

    a)  Copper can be drawn into wires.

    b)  Copper is a good thermal conductor.

# Section Summary

**Make sure you know...**

- How many electrons each of the first four shells in atoms can contain.
- How many orbitals make up the s-, p- and d- subshells and how many electrons go in each of them.
- That an orbital is the bit of space that an electron moves in and that each orbital can hold up to two electrons with opposite spins.
- What shapes the s- and p-orbitals are.
- The relative energy levels of the s-, p- and d-orbitals of the first 4 electron shells.
- What the s-block, d-block and p-block of the periodic table are.
- How to work out electron configurations from the periodic table.
- What first ionisation energy and successive ionisation energies are.
- How nuclear charge, electron shielding and the distance of the electron from the nucleus affect ionisation energies.
- How to use successive ionisation energies to work out the number of electrons in each shell of an atom and which group the atom is in.
- That electrostatic attraction holds ions together and that this is called ionic bonding.
- How to use the periodic table to work out the charge on an ion.
- The formulas of the compound ions $NO_3^-$, $CO_3^{2-}$, $SO_4^{2-}$ and $NH_4^+$.
- How to draw dot-and-cross diagrams to show ionic bonding.
- How the structure of ionic compounds decides their physical properties — their electrical conductivity, melting and boiling points and solubility.
- That covalent bonds form when atoms share pairs of electrons.
- How single, double and triple covalent bonds form between atoms.
- That dative (or coordinate) covalent bonds form when one atom donates both the shared electrons in a bond.
- How the structure of covalent compounds decides their physical properties — their electrical conductivity, melting and boiling points and solubility.
- What a giant covalent (macromolecular) lattice is.
- The structures of graphite and diamond and how the structures determine their properties.
- How the repulsion between electron pairs on a central atom affects the shape of simple molecules.
- How to predict the shapes of molecules that have central atoms with 2, 3, 4, 5 and 6 electron pairs, including their bond angles and shape names.
- That electronegativity is the ability to attract the bonding electrons in a covalent bond.
- How differences in electronegativities between bonding atoms causes polarisation.
- The difference between polar and non-polar bonds.
- The relative strengths of permanent dipole-dipole forces, van der Waals forces and hydrogen bonds.
- What permanent dipole-dipole forces and van der Waals forces are, and what causes them.
- How hydrogen bonds form and their effect on the properties of compounds.
- What metallic bonding is and how to recognise giant metallic lattice structures.
- How the structure of metals decides their physical properties — their conductivity, melting and boiling points, ability to be shaped and solubility.

# Exam-style Questions

**1**      The Group 5 elements include nitrogen, phosphorus, arsenic and antimony.
They can form covalent bonds with hydrogen.

     **(a)**      Which block of the periodic table are the Group 5 elements found in?

*(1 mark)*

     **(b)**      The graph below shows the boiling points of some Group 5 hydrides.

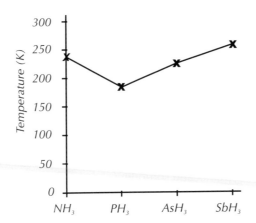

         **(i)**    Explain the trend in boiling points shown by the graph for $PH_3$, $AsH_3$ and $SbH_3$.

*(3 marks)*

         **(ii)**   Suggest what the trend in melting point would be for $PH_3$, $AsH_3$ and $SbH_3$.

*(1 mark)*

     **(c)**      Name the strongest type of intermolecular force found in $NH_3$.

*(1 mark)*

**2**      Carbon can form lots of different structures and can combine with other elements to form lots of different compounds.

     **(a)**      Graphite and diamond contain only carbon atoms.

         **(i)**    Both substances have the same type of structure. Name this structure.

*(1 mark)*

         **(ii)**   Describe the structures and bonding of graphite and diamond.

*(5 marks)*

         In your answer, you should use appropriate technical terms, spelled correctly.

         **(iii)** Explain why graphite can conduct electricity but diamond cannot.

*(2 marks)*

**(b) (i)** State the type of intermolecular forces found between molecules of methane, $CH_4$.

*(1 mark)*

**(ii)** Explain why the boiling point of diamond is much higher than the boiling point of methane.

*(2 marks)*

**3** Fluorine is a Group 7 element.  This question is about its properties and reactions.

**(a)** The table below shows the successive ionisation energies of fluorine.

| ionisation number | 1st | 2nd | 3rd | 4th | 5th | 6th | 7th | 8th | 9th |
|---|---|---|---|---|---|---|---|---|---|
| ionisation energy $(kJ\ mol^{-1})$ | 1681 | 3374 | 6050 | 8407 | 11022 | 15164 | 17868 | 92038 | 106434 |

**(i)** Give the meaning of the term first ionisation energy.

*(3 marks)*

**(ii)** Write an equation, including state symbols, to show the third ionisation energy of fluorine.

*(1 mark)*

**(iii)** Use the table to explain how you know that the first 7 electrons removed are in a different shell to the 8th and 9th electrons.

*(3 marks)*

**(iv)** Explain why the first ionisation energy of fluorine is higher than the first ionisation energy of chlorine.

*(3 marks)*

**(b)** Fluorine can form covalent bonds with sulfur, $S_8$, to produce the molecule $SF_6$.

**(i)** Suggest an equation for the formation of $SF_6$.

*(1 mark)*

**(ii)** Draw a dot-and-cross diagram to show the bonding in $SF_6$.
Use your diagram to explain the shape of the molecule.

*(5 marks)*

**(c)** A fluorine ion, $F^-$, can react with $BF_3$ to form the $BF_4^-$ ion.  A dative covalent bond forms between $F^-$ and $BF_3$.

**(i)** State the bond angle in $BF_3$.

*(1 mark)*

**(ii)** Explain what is meant by the term dative covalent bond.

*(1 mark)*

**(iii)** Predict the shape of the $BF_4^-$ ion.  Explain your answer.

*(3 marks)*

**4**     The table below shows the electronegativities of some elements.

| Element | C | H | Cl | O | F |
|---|---|---|---|---|---|
| Electronegativity (Pauling Scale) | 2.5 | 2.1 | 3.0 | 3.5 | 4.0 |

**(a) (i)**   Define the term electronegativity.

*(2 marks)*

**(ii)**   Explain how electronegativity can give rise to permanent dipole-dipole forces.

*(3 marks)*

**(b) (i)**   Use the information in the table to name the strongest intermolecular forces in HCl, $CH_4$ and HF.

*(3 marks)*

**(ii)**   Draw a diagram to show the strongest intermolecular forces between HF molecules. Include partial charges and all lone pairs.

*(3 marks)*

**(iii)**   Explain why the only forces between $Cl_2$ molecules are van der Waals forces.

*(1 mark)*

**5**     Calcium is a metallic element which can react to form ionic bonds with negatively charged ions.

**(a)**     Draw a labelled diagram to show the structure and bonding in calcium metal and explain why calcium is able to conduct electricity.

*(3 marks)*

**(b)**     Calcium can react with oxygen to form the ionic compound calcium oxide, CaO.

**(i)**   State what is meant by the term ionic compound.

*(2 marks)*

**(ii)**   Complete the electron configuration of a calcium ion, $Ca^{2+}$.

$1s^2\ 2s^2\ 2p^6$ ...............................................................

*(1 mark)*

**(iii)**   Draw a dot-and-cross diagram to show the bonding in CaO.
Show the outer electrons only.

*(2 marks)*

**(c)**     Calcium can also form the ionic compound calcium carbonate.

**(i)**   State the formula of the carbonate ion.

*(1 mark)*

**(ii)**   Calcium carbonate decomposes when heated to form calcium oxide and carbon dioxide.
State the shape and bond angle of a molecule of carbon dioxide.
Explain why carbon dioxide has this shape.

*(4 marks)*

# 1. The Periodic Table

**Learning Objectives:**

- Understand the work of Döbereiner, Newlands, Mendeleev, Moseley, Seaborg and others in developing the periodic table.
- Know that in the periodic table, elements are arranged by increasing atomic (proton) number.
- Know that elements are arranged in groups that have similar physical and chemical properties.
- Be able to explain that atoms of elements in a group have similar outer shell electron configurations, resulting in similar properties.

**Specification Reference 1.3.1**

*You'll remember from GCSE that the periodic table isn't just arranged how it is by chance. There are well-thought-out reasons behind it, and you can find out lots of stuff from it, not least about the numbers of electron shells and electrons each element has. Read on....*

## Grouping the elements

In the early 1800s, there were only two ways to categorise elements — by their physical and chemical properties and by their **relative atomic mass**. (The modern periodic table is arranged by proton number, but back then, they knew nothing about protons or electrons. The only thing they could measure was relative atomic mass.)

In 1817, Johann Döbereiner attempted to group similar elements — these groups were called Döbereiner's triads. He saw that chlorine, bromine and iodine had similar characteristics. He also realised that other properties of bromine (e.g. atomic weight) fell halfway between those of chlorine and iodine. He found other such groups of three elements (e.g. lithium, sodium and potassium), and called them triads. It was a start.

An English chemist called John Newlands had the first good stab at making a table of the elements in 1863. He noticed that if he arranged the elements in order of mass, similar elements appeared at regular intervals — every eighth element was similar. He called this the law of octaves, and he listed some known elements in rows of seven so that the similar elements lined up in columns — see Figure 1.

Elements arranged in rows of seven.

| | 1 | 2 | 3 | 4 | 5 | 6 | 7 |
|---|---|---|---|---|---|---|---|
| | Li | Be | B | C | N | O | F |
| | Na | Mg | Al | Si | P | S | Cl |

Similar elements in columns.

**Figure 1:** *The arrangement of elements by John Newlands.*

The problem was, the pattern broke down on the third row, with many transition metals like Fe, Cu and Zn messing it up completely.

## Mendeleev's table

In 1869, Russian chemist Dmitri Mendeleev produced a much better table, which wasn't far off the one we have today. He arranged all the known elements by atomic mass (like Newlands did), but the clever thing he did was to leave gaps in the table where the next element didn't seem to fit. By putting in gaps, he could keep elements with similar chemical properties in the same group — see Figure 3.

He also predicted the properties of undiscovered elements that would go in the gaps. When elements were later discovered (e.g. germanium, scandium and gallium) with properties that matched Mendeleev's predictions, it showed that clever old Mendeleev had got it right.

**Tip:** The development of the periodic table is another example of 'peer review'. See page 2 for more.

**Tip:** The discovery of the missing elements was good evidence that Mendeleev was on the right lines.

*Figure 2: Dmitri Mendeleev (1834-1907) was a Russian chemist who developed the periodic table.*

| | Group 1 | Group 2 | Group 3 | Group 4 | Group 5 | Group 6 | Group 7 |
|---|---|---|---|---|---|---|---|
| 1 | H | | | | | | |
| 2 | Li | Be | B | C | N | O | F |
| 3 | Na | Mg | Al | Si | P | S | Cl |
| 4 | K | Ca | ? | Ti | V | Cr | Mn |
| | Cu | Zn | ? | ? | As | Se | Br |
| 5 | Rb | Sr | Y | Zr | Nb | Mo | ? |
| | Ag | Cd | In | Sn | Sb | Te | I |
| 6 | Cs | Ba | La | ? | Ta | W | ? |
| | Au | Hg | Tl | Pb | Bi | ? | ? |

*Figure 3: Dmitri Mendeleev's table of elements. The question marks show gaps in the table which were later filled when new elements were discovered.*

# The modern periodic table

The modern periodic table is pretty much the one produced by Henry Moseley in 1914. He arranged the elements according to atomic number rather than by mass. This fixed a few elements that Mendeleev had put out of place using atomic mass. He also added the noble gases (Group 0) which had been discovered in the 1890s. The final big change was a result of the work of Glenn Seaborg. He suggested how the f-block elements fit into the periodic table (though they're usually shown separated from the main part of the table). The modern periodic table is shown in Figure 4.

**Tip:** Henry Moseley also did lots of work on the structure of the atom — see page 9 for more.

**Tip:** The atomic number is the number of protons in the nucleus — so it's also known as the proton number.

**Exam Tip**
You'll be given a periodic table in your exam, so you'll have a copy to refer to. It's a good idea to be familiar with how it works <u>before</u> you go into the exam though.

**Tip:** When you arrange elements by atomic number, there are a few that no longer go in order of atomic mass. For example, Ar would go after K if you put the elements in order of atomic mass. But Ar comes before K in the modern periodic table.

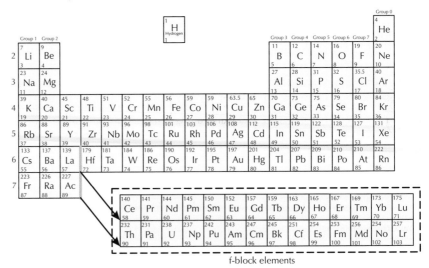

*Figure 4: The modern periodic table.*

### Periods and rows

The modern periodic table is arranged into **periods** (rows) and **groups** (columns). All the elements within a period have the same number of electron shells (if you don't worry about the sub-shells).

**Tip:** The elements of Period 1 (hydrogen and helium) both have 1 electron shell.

┌─ Example ───────────────────────────────
The elements in Period 2 all have 2 electron shells:

*The first three elements in Period 2.*    *All have two electron shells.*

All the elements within a group have the same number of electrons in their outer shell. This means they have similar physical and chemical properties. The group number tells you the number of electrons in the outer shell.

**Examples**

Group 1 elements have 1 electron in their outer shell:

As a result the elements in Group 1 all have similar properties. For example, they all react strongly with water (see Figure 5).

Group 4 elements have 4 electrons in their outer shell and so on.

*Figure 5:  The Group 1 elements potassium, sodium and lithium all react strongly with water.*

# Electron configurations

You can use the periodic table to work out electron configurations. The period number tells you how many electron shells the element has and the group number tells you how many electrons an element has in its outer electron shell. But to make things even easier the periodic table can be split into an s block, d block and p block (see Figure 6). Doing this shows you which sub-shells all the electrons go into.

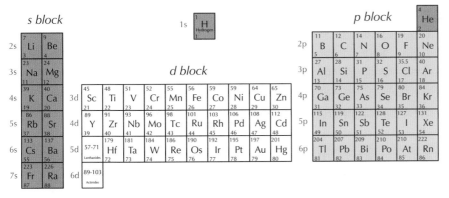

*Figure 6:  The periodic table showing the s block, p block and d block.*

### s-block elements

The s-block elements have an outer shell electron configuration of $s^1$ or $s^2$.

**Examples**

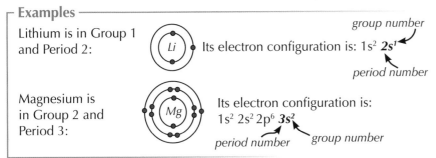

Lithium is in Group 1 and Period 2:   Its electron configuration is: $1s^2$ $2s^1$ ← group number ← period number

Magnesium is in Group 2 and Period 3:   Its electron configuration is: $1s^2\ 2s^2\ 2p^6\ 3s^2$ ← period number, group number

### p-block elements

The p-block elements have an outer shell configuration of $s^2p^1$ to $s^2p^6$.

**Exam Tip**
You won't get a periodic table split up like this in the exam so you need to remember what the different blocks are.

**Tip:** If you can't remember what sub-shells are, don't know what the electron configuration of an element shows, or can't quite get your head around what all this $1s^2\ 2s^2\ 2p^6$ business is, then have a look back at pages 50 and 51 — it's all explained in more detail there.

Chlorine is in Group 7 and Period 3:

Its electron configuration is:

$2 + 5 = 7$ = group number

$1s^2\ 2s^2\ 2p^6\ \mathbf{3s^2\ 3p^5}$

*period number*

## d-block elements

The d-block elements have electron configurations in which d sub-shells are being filled. They're a bit trickier — you don't always write the sub-shells in the order they're filled.

**Tip:** Watch out for the fact that 3d is on the same row as 4s and 4p in the periodic table. Remember that the 4s sub-shell is of lower energy than the 3d sub-shell so it fills first. Sneaky.

**Example**

The electron configuration of cobalt is: $1s^2\ 2s^2\ 2p^6\ 3s^2\ 3p^6\ \mathbf{3d^7}\ 4s^2$

*Even though the 3rd sub-shell fills last in cobalt, it's not written at the end of the line.*

When you've got the periodic table labelled with the shells and sub-shells, it's pretty easy to read off the electron structure of any element by starting at the top and working your way across and down until you get to your element.

**Tip:** It doesn't really matter how you work out the electron configurations of elements, whether you use the rules on page 52 or whether you read them off the periodic table like on this page. The important thing is that you get them right — so find a method you're happy with and stick with it.

**Example**

To work out the electron structure of phosphorus (P), you can use the periodic table to see that it's in Group 5 and Period 3. Starting with Period 1, the electron configuration of a full shell is $1s^2$. For Period 2 it's $2s^2\ 2p^6$. However, phosphorus' outer shell is only partially filled — it's got 5 outer electrons in the configuration $3s^2\ 3p^3$.

So:    Period 1 — $1s^2$

Period 2 — $2s^2\ 2p^6$

Period 3 — $3s^2\ 3p^3$

The full electron structure of phosphorus is: $1s^2\ 2s^2\ 2p^6\ 3s^2\ 3p^3$.

## Practice Questions — Application

Q1  How many electron shells do atoms of the following elements have?

    a) Sulfur, S        b) Bromine, Br        c) Rubidium, Rb

Q2  How many electrons are in the outer shell of atoms of these elements?

    a) Selenium, Se   b) Aluminium, Al   c) Potassium, K

Q3  Work out the electron configurations of the following elements:

    a) Sodium, Na     b) Calcium, Ca      c) Chlorine, Cl

**Tip:** Don't forget that for d-block elements, the sub-shells aren't written in the order that they're filled.

    d) Arsenic, As     e) Vanadium, V     f) Scandium, Sc

## Practice Questions — Fact Recall

Q1  a) How did Mendeleev arrange the elements in his version of the periodic table?

    b) How are elements arranged in the modern periodic table?

Q2  a) What is a period?

    b) What is a group?

Q3  Explain why elements in a group have similar chemical properties.

# 2. Periodic Trends

*Periodic trends are patterns in the periodic table — and you have to know the reasons for them.*

## Periodicity

Periodicity is an important idea in chemistry. It's all to do with the trends in repeating physical and chemical properties of elements across the periodic table — things like melting point, boiling point, atomic radius and ionisation energy.

## Melting and boiling points

If you look at how the melting and boiling points change across the periods, the trend isn't immediately obvious. The melting and boiling points of the Period 2 and 3 elements generally increase from the first to the fourth elements in the period, but then decrease from the fourth to the eighth elements (see Figures 1 and 2).

**Figure 1:** *The trend in boiling points across Periods 2 and 3.*

**Figure 2:** *The trend in melting points across Periods 2 and 3.*

Once you start looking at the bond strengths and structures of the elements in Periods 2 and 3, the reasons for the trends become clear.

### Metals

For the metals (Li and Be, Na, Mg and Al), melting and boiling points increase across the period because the metal-metal bonds get stronger. The bonds get stronger because the metal ions have a greater charge, an increasing number of **delocalised electrons** and a decreasing ionic radius. This leads to a higher **charge density**, which attracts the ions together more strongly (see Figure 3).

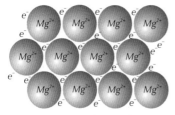

*The magnesium ions have a larger radius and a charge of 2+ so there are two delocalised electrons for each ion...*

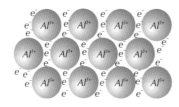

*...whereas the aluminium ions have a smaller radius and a charge of 3+ so there are three delocalised electrons for each ion.*

**Figure 3:** *The structures of magnesium and aluminium.*

**Learning Objectives:**

- Know that elements in periods show repeating trends in physical and chemical properties and this is known as periodicity.

- Be able to describe the trends in melting points, boiling points, atomic radii and electron configurations across Periods 2 and 3.

- Be able to explain variations in melting and boiling points across Periods 2 and 3 in terms of structure and bonding.

- Be able to describe and explain the trend in first ionisation energies of elements across a period.

- Be able to interpret data on melting points, boiling points, electron configurations, atomic radii and first ionisation energies to demonstrate periodicity.

- Be able to describe and explain the decrease in first ionisation energies down a group in terms of increasing atomic radius and increasing electronic shielding outweighing increasing nuclear charge.

**Specification Reference 1.3.1**

**Tip:** The charge density is the amount of charge in relation to the size of an ion. Smaller ions have greater charge densities than larger ions with the same charge.

## Macromolecular structures

The elements with macromolecular structures (B and C, Si) have strong covalent bonds linking all their atoms together — see Figure 4. A lot of energy is needed to break these bonds. So, for example, carbon (as graphite or diamond) and silicon have the highest melting and boiling points in their periods.

**Tip:** The structure of silicon should look familiar — it's similar to diamond (page 64). There's a good reason — carbon and silicon are both in Group 4, so have the same number of electrons in their outer shell.

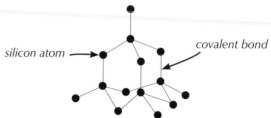

silicon atom ⟶

covalent bond

*Figure 4:* The structure of silicon.

## Simple molecular structures

Next come the simple molecular substances ($N_2$, $O_2$ and $F_2$, $P_4$, $S_8$ and $Cl_2$). Their melting and boiling points depend upon the strength of the van der Waals forces between their molecules. Van der Waals forces are weak and easily overcome so these elements have low melting and boiling points.

**Tip:** See page 70 for lots more about van der Waals forces.

More atoms in a molecule mean stronger van der Waals forces. For example, in Period 3 sulfur is the biggest molecule ($S_8$), so it's got higher melting and boiling points than phosphorus or chlorine — see Figure 5.

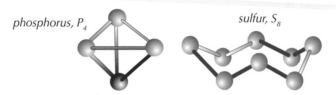

phosphorus, $P_4$

sulfur, $S_8$

*Figure 5:* The structures of phosphorus and sulfur.

The noble gases (neon and argon) have the lowest melting and boiling points because they exist as individual atoms (they're monatomic) resulting in very weak van der Waals forces.

*Figure 6:* Sulfur (yellow powder) and phosphorus (stored under water) are solids at room temperature.

# Atomic radius

Atomic radius decreases across a period. Figure 7 shows this trend in Periods 2 and 3. As the number of protons increases, the positive charge of the nucleus increases. This means electrons are pulled closer to the nucleus, making the atomic radius smaller (see Figure 8). The extra electrons that the elements gain across a period are added to the outer energy level so they don't really provide any extra **shielding** effect (shielding works with inner shells mainly).

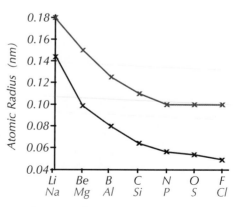

*Figure 7:* The atomic radii of the first seven elements in Periods 2 and 3.

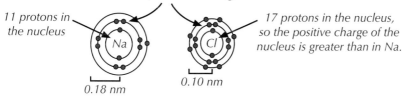

Na and Cl have the same number of electrons in the
first and second shells, so the shielding is the same.

11 protons in
the nucleus

17 protons in the nucleus,
so the positive charge of the
nucleus is greater than in Na.

0.18 nm

0.10 nm

**Figure 8:** *The atomic radii of sodium and chlorine.*

**Figure 9:** *Cut sodium metal.*

# Ionisation energy

You saw on page 54 that there are three main things that affect the size of
ionisation energies:

- Atomic radius — the further the outer shell electrons from the
  nucleus, the lower the ionisation energy.

- Nuclear charge — the more protons in the nucleus, the higher
  the ionisation energy.

- Electron shielding — the more inner shells there are, the more
  shielding there is, and the lower the ionisation energy.

### Trend in ionisation energy across a period

As you move across a period, the general trend is for the ionisation energies
to increase — i.e. it gets harder to remove the outer electrons. This is
because the number of protons is increasing, which means a stronger nuclear
attraction. All the extra electrons are at roughly the same energy level,
even if the outer electrons are in different orbital types. This means there's
generally little extra shielding effect or extra distance to lessen the attraction
from the nucleus.

> **Tip:** Shielding is when
> the inner electrons
> effectively 'screen' the
> outer electrons from
> the pull of the nucleus.
> Look back at page 54
> for more on shielding.

┌─ Examples ─────────────────

In Period 2 the first ionisation energies generally increase from lithium to
neon and in Period 3 the first ionisation energies generally increase from
sodium to argon (see Figure 10).

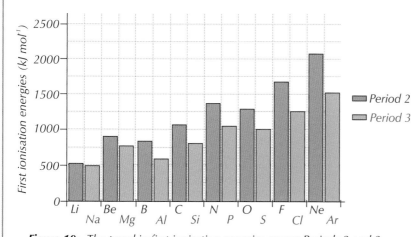

**Figure 10:** *The trend in first ionisation energies across Periods 2 and 3.*

In both cases this is because the number of protons increases across the
period, so the nuclear attraction is stronger and the outer electrons get more
difficult to remove.

> **Tip:** If you've got a keen
> eye you'll have noticed
> that there are dips in the
> trend between Groups
> 2 and 3 and Groups 5
> and 6. You don't need
> to know why at AS
> level. If you're asked for
> the trend in ionisation
> energy in your exam,
> just say it generally
> increases across a period.

> **Exam Tip**
> There's no need to
> memorise the graphs
> in this section, but you
> do need to know their
> shapes and be able to
> explain them.

## Trend in ionisation energy down a group

As you go down a group in the periodic table, ionisation energies generally fall, i.e. it gets easier to remove outer electrons (see Figure 11).

This is because elements further down a group have extra electron shells compared to ones above. The extra shells mean that the outer electrons are further away from the nucleus, which greatly reduces the attraction to the nucleus. The extra inner shells also shield the outer electrons from the attraction of the nucleus. Both of these factors make it easier to remove outer electrons, resulting in a lower ionisation energy. The positive charge of the nucleus does increase as you go down a group (due to the extra protons), but this effect is overridden by the effect of the extra shells.

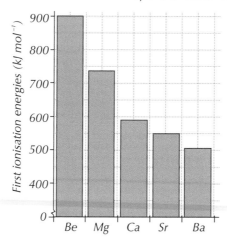

**Figure 11:** First ionisation energies of the first five elements of Group 2.

## Practice Questions — Application

Q1 a) Explain why the boiling point of lithium is higher than the boiling point of nitrogen.

  b) Explain why the boiling point of beryllium is higher than that of lithium.

Q2 a) Explain why magnesium has a higher melting point than sodium.

  b) Explain why sulfur has a higher melting point than phosphorus.

Q3 The melting point of silicon is 1414 °C and the melting point of phosphorus is 44 °C.

  a) Explain why the melting point of phosphorus is lower than the melting point of silicon.

  b) Name a Period 3 element with a lower melting point than phosphorus.

Q4 a) Explain why the atomic radius of aluminium is larger than the atomic radius of sulfur.

  b) Name a Period 3 element with a larger atomic radius than aluminium.

Q5 Boron has an atomic radius of 90 pm. The atomic radius of beryllium is 112 pm.

  a) Explain why boron has a smaller atomic radius than beryllium.

  b) Suggest an element in Period 2 which has a larger atomic radius than beryllium.

Q6 Use your knowledge of periodic trends to answer the following:

a) Would you expect calcium to have a higher or lower boiling point than potassium? Explain your answer.

b) Would you expect strontium to have a larger or smaller atomic radius than rubidium? Explain your answer.

c) Would you expect bromine to have a higher or lower first ionisation energy than selenium? Explain your answer.

## Practice Questions — Fact Recall

Q1 Define the term periodicity.

Q2 Describe the trend in melting and boiling points that occurs across Period 2 of the periodic table.

Q3 a) Describe the trend in atomic radius that occurs across Period 3 of the periodic table.

b) Explain this trend.

Q4 a) Describe the general trend in ionisation energy across a period of the periodic table.

b) Explain this trend.

Q5 Explain why first ionisation energies decrease down a group.

**Exam Tip**
If you're asked about a specific trend, it might help you to roughly sketch out the shape of the relevant graph. That way you'll easily be able to see how the values for the elements compare to each other.

- Be able to explain the trend in reactivity of Group 2 elements down the group.

- Be able to describe the redox reactions of the Group 2 elements Mg–Ba with oxygen and water.

- Be able to describe the action of water on oxides of elements in Group 2 and state the approximate pH of any resulting solution.

- Be able to describe the thermal decomposition of the carbonates of elements in Group 2 and the trend in their ease of decomposition.

- Be able to interpret and make predictions from the chemical and physical properties of Group 2 elements and compounds.

- Be able to explain the use of $Ca(OH)_2$ in agriculture to neutralise acid soils and the use of $Mg(OH)_2$ in some indigestion tablets as an antacid.

**Specification Reference 1.3.2**

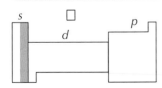

**Figure 2:** *The s, p and d blocks of the periodic table (see page 81 for more). Group 2 is highlighted in grey.*

**Tip:** These reactions are redox reactions. See page 44 for more on this.

# 3. Group 2 — The Alkaline Earth Metals

*The alkaline earth metals are in the s block of the periodic table. You have to know some trends in their properties as you go down Group 2 and some of the reactions of Group 2 elements and their compounds.*

## Trend in reactivity down Group 2

When Group 2 elements react they lose electrons, forming positive ions (cations). The easier it is to lose electrons (i.e. the lower the first and second ionisation energies), the more reactive the element. So because ionisation energy decreases down the group, reactivity increases down the group.

## Reactions of Group 2 elements

Group 2 elements all have two electrons in their outer shell ($s^2$). They can lose their two outer electrons to form 2+ ions. Their ions then have every atom's dream electronic structure — that of a **noble gas** (see Figure 1).

| Element | Electronic structure | Ion | Electronic structure |
|---------|---------------------|-----|---------------------|
| Be | $1s^2\,2s^2$ | $Be^{2+}$ | $1s^2$ |
| Mg | $1s^2\,2s^2\,2p^6\,3s^2$ | $Mg^{2+}$ | $1s^2\,2s^2\,2p^6$ |
| Ca | $1s^2\,2s^2\,2p^6\,3s^2\,3p^6\,4s^2$ | $Ca^{2+}$ | $1s^2\,2s^2\,2p^6\,3s^2\,3p^6$ |

**Figure 1:** *Electronic structures of Group 2 atoms and ions.*

So, when Group 2 elements react, they are oxidised from a state of 0 to +2.

$$M \rightarrow M^{2+} + 2e^-$$

Oxidation state:        $0 \rightarrow +2$

---
**Examples**

$Mg \rightarrow Mg^{2+} + 2e^-$     $Ca \rightarrow Ca^{2+} + 2e^-$     $Be \rightarrow Be^{2+} + 2e^-$

Oxidation number:    0     +2         0     +2        0     +2

---

### Reactions with water

The Group 2 metals react with water to give a metal hydroxide and hydrogen.

$$M_{(s)} + 2H_2O_{(l)} \rightarrow M(OH)_{2\,(aq)} + H_{2\,(g)}$$

Oxidation state:     0                $\rightarrow$ +2

In this equation, M is used to represent any Group 2 metal.

---
**Example**

Calcium reacts with water to form calcium hydroxide and hydrogen.

$$Ca_{(s)} + 2H_2O_{(l)} \rightarrow Ca(OH)_{2\,(aq)} + H_{2\,(g)}$$

Oxidation state:    0             $\rightarrow$ +2

The hydrogen gas forms bubbles in the solution.

---

The elements react more readily down the group because the ionisation energies decrease (see Figure 3). See pages 54-55 for more on ionisation energies.

| Group 2 element | 1st ionisation energy / kJ mol⁻¹ | Rate of reactivity with water |
|---|---|---|
| Be | 900 | doesn't react |
| Mg | 738 | VERY slow |
| Ca | 590 | steady |
| Sr | 550 | fairly quick |
| Ba | 503 | rapid |

**Figure 3:** *Comparison of first ionisation energies and reactivity with water for Group 2 elements.*

**Figure 4:** *Magnesium (left) and calcium (right) reacting with water. Calcium is more reactive so reacts quicker.*

## Reactions with oxygen

When Group 2 metals burn in oxygen, you get solid white oxides. Here's the general equation for the reaction of a Group 2 metal (M) with oxygen.

$$2M_{(s)} + O_{2\,(g)} \rightarrow 2MO_{(s)}$$

### Examples

Calcium burns in air to produce calcium oxide (CaO). The equation for this reaction is:

$$2Ca_{(s)} + O_{2\,(g)} \rightarrow 2CaO_{(s)}$$

Beryllium burns in air to produce beryllium oxide (BeO).
Here's the equation:

$$2Be_{(s)} + O_{2\,(g)} \rightarrow 2BeO_{(s)}$$

As with the other reactions of Group 2 elements, during this reaction the oxidation state of the Group 2 element increases from 0 to +2.

**Figure 5:** *Calcium burns in air, producing an orange flame.*

The oxides of the Group 2 metals react readily with water to form metal hydroxides, which dissolve. The hydroxide ions, OH⁻, make these solutions strongly alkaline (e.g. pH 12 - 13).

### Example

Calcium oxide reacts with water to form calcium hydroxide. The calcium hydroxide then dissolves in the water, releasing OH⁻ ions and Ca²⁺ ions. So,

$$CaO_{(s)} + H_2O_{(l)} \rightarrow Ca^{2+}_{(aq)} + 2OH^-_{(aq)}$$

The OH⁻ ions make the solution strongly alkaline.

**Tip:** It's because their oxides form alkaline solutions that the Group 2 elements are also known as the alkaline earth metals.

Magnesium oxide is an exception — it only reacts slowly and the hydroxide isn't very soluble. The oxides form more strongly alkaline solutions as you go down the group, because the hydroxides get more soluble.

# Thermal decomposition of carbonates

Thermal decomposition is when a substance breaks down (decomposes) when heated. The more thermally stable a substance is, the more heat it will take to break it down. Group 2 carbonates decompose to form the oxide and carbon dioxide. The general equation for this reaction is:

$$MCO_{3\,(s)} \rightarrow MO_{(s)} + CO_{2\,(g)}$$

**Figure 6:** Thermal decomposition of calcium carbonate.

**Tip:** Calcium carbonate minerals are found in many different types of rock, including marble, limestone and chalk.

---Examples---

Calcium carbonate ($CaCO_3$) decomposes to give calcium oxide and carbon dioxide. The equation for this reaction is:

$$CaCO_{3\ (s)} \rightarrow CaO_{(s)} + CO_{2\ (g)}$$

Strontium carbonate ($SrCO_3$) decomposes to give strontium oxide (SrO) and carbon dioxide. The equation for this reaction is:

$$SrCO_{3\ (s)} \rightarrow SrO_{(s)} + CO_{2\ (g)}$$

The tendency for a Group 2 carbonate to decompose is measured in terms of **thermal stability**. The greater the thermal stability of the carbonate, the less likely it is to undergo thermal decomposition. Thermal stability increases down the group. So, it'd take more heat to decompose, say, calcium carbonate than magnesium carbonate — see Figure 7.

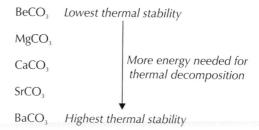

$BeCO_3$    *Lowest thermal stability*

$MgCO_3$

$CaCO_3$        *More energy needed for thermal decomposition*

$SrCO_3$

$BaCO_3$    *Highest thermal stability*

**Figure 7:** *The trend in thermal stability of the Group 2 carbonates.*

**Figure 8:** *A tractor spreading slaked lime to neutralise acid soil.*

# Uses of Group 2 compounds

Group 2 elements are known as the **alkaline earth metals**, and many of their common compounds are used for neutralising acids. Here are a couple of common examples:

- Calcium hydroxide (slaked lime, $Ca(OH)_2$) is used in agriculture to neutralise acid soils. It has to be used in moderation though, otherwise the soils will become too alkaline to support crop growth.
- Magnesium hydroxide ($Mg(OH)_2$) is used in some indigestion tablets as an **antacid** — this neutralises excess stomach acid.

In both cases, the ionic equation for the neutralisation is:

$$H^+_{(aq)} + OH^-_{(aq)} \rightarrow H_2O_{(l)}$$

## Practice Questions — Application

Q1 When calcium reacts with water, calcium hydroxide is produced.
  a) Write an equation for this reaction.
  b) How does the oxidation state of calcium change during this reaction?
  c) State what you would see when this reaction takes place.
  d) How would the reaction be different if strontium was used instead of calcium?

Q2 Strontium burns in air to form strontium oxide.

    a) Write an equation for this reaction.

    b) Describe the appearance of strontium oxide.

    c) Write an equation to show what would happen if water was added to strontium oxide.

    d) Give an approximate pH of the solution formed when water and strontium oxide are mixed.

Q3 a) Write an equation for the thermal decomposition of magnesium carbonate.

    b) Would you expect the temperature required for the thermal decomposition of strontium carbonate to be higher or lower than the temperature required for the thermal decomposition of magnesium carbonate?

**Tip:** When writing equations for reactions don't forget to make sure they're balanced.

## Practice Questions — Fact Recall

Q1 Explain why reactivity increases down Group 2.

Q2 a) What charge do Group 2 ions usually have?

    b) Explain why Group 2 ions normally have this charge.

Q3 What change in oxidation state do Group 2 metals usually undergo when they react?

Q4 What pH would you expect a Group 2 metal hydroxide solution to have?

Q5 Describe the trend in the thermal stability of the Group 2 carbonates as you go down the group.

Q6 Give two uses of Group 2 hydroxides.

**Exam Tip**
You're often asked to apply your knowledge of trends to say how or why one reaction would be different from another. Start by finding the elements involved on the periodic table and seeing whether they are in the same group or the same period. The trends across groups and periods are different.

**Learning Objectives:**

- Be able to explain, in terms of van der Waals' forces, the trend in boiling points of $Cl_2$, $Br_2$ and $I_2$.
- Be able to explain the trend in reactivity of Group 7 elements down the group from the decreasing ease of forming negative ions, in terms of atomic size, shielding and nuclear attraction.
- Be able to describe the redox reactions, including ionic equations, of the Group 7 elements $Cl_2$, $Br_2$ and $I_2$ with other halide ions, in the presence of an organic solvent.
- Be able to interpret and make predictions from the chemical and physical properties of the Group 7 elements and their compounds.
- Be able to describe the precipitation reactions, including ionic equations, of the aqueous anions $Cl^-$, $Br^-$ and $I^-$ with aqueous silver ions, followed by aqueous ammonia.
- Be able to describe the use of these precipitation reactions as a test for different halide ions.

**Specification Reference 1.3.2, 1.3.3**

**Tip:** The word <u>halogen</u> should be used when describing the atom (X) or molecule ($X_2$), but the word <u>halide</u> is used to describe the negative ion ($X^-$).

# 4. Group 7 — The Halogens

*The halogens are highly-reactive non-metals found in Group 7 of the periodic table. You need to know about their properties, trends and reactions.*

## Properties of halogens

The table below gives some of the main properties of the first four halogens, at room temperature.

| halogen | formula | colour | physical state | electronic structure |
|---------|---------|--------|----------------|----------------------|
| fluorine | $F_2$ | pale yellow | gas | $1s^2\ 2s^2\ 2p^5$ |
| chlorine | $Cl_2$ | green | gas | $1s^2\ 2s^2\ 2p^6\ 3s^2\ 3p^5$ |
| bromine | $Br_2$ | red-brown | liquid | $1s^2\ 2s^2\ 2p^6\ 3s^2\ 3p^6\ 3d^{10}\ 4s^2\ 4p^5$ |
| iodine | $I_2$ | grey | solid | $1s^2\ 2s^2\ 2p^6\ 3s^2\ 3p^6\ 3d^{10}\ 4s^2\ 4p^6\ 4d^{10}\ 5s^2\ 5p^5$ |

## Trend in boiling points

The boiling and melting points of the halogens increase down the group. This is due to the increasing strength of the **van der Waals forces** as the number of electrons increases when the size and relative mass of the atoms increases. This trend is shown in the changes of physical state from fluorine to iodine (see Figure 1). A substance is said to be **volatile** if it has a low boiling point. So you could also say that volatility decreases down the group.

**Figure 1:** *Chlorine (left) is a gas at r.t.p. (room temperature and pressure), bromine (centre) is a liquid at r.t.p. and iodine (right) is a solid at r.t.p.*

## Trend in reactivity

Halogen atoms react by gaining an electron in their outer shell. This means they're reduced. When halogens are reduced, **halide** ions are formed. The general equation for the reduction of a halogen (X) to a halide ion ($X^-$) is shown below:

$$X + e^- \rightarrow X^-$$

*oxidation number:* $\qquad 0 \qquad\qquad -1$

As the halogens are reduced, they oxidise another substance (it's a redox reaction — see page 44) — so they're **oxidising agents**.

As you go down the group, the atoms become larger so the outer electrons are further from the nucleus. The outer electrons are also shielded more from the attraction of the positive nucleus, because there are more inner electrons. This makes it harder for larger atoms to attract the electron needed to form an ion (despite the increased charge on the nucleus), so larger atoms are less reactive. Another way of saying that the halogens get less reactive down the group is to say that they become less oxidising.

# Displacement reactions

The halogens' relative oxidising strengths can be seen in their **displacement reactions** with halide ions. More reactive halogens will oxidise and displace the halide ions of less reactive halogens. Reactivity decreases down the group so a halogen will displace a halide from solution if the halide is below it in the periodic table. You need to know which halogens displace what and the **ionic equations** for these displacement reactions.

**Tip:** The displacement reactions of the halogens can be used to identify them in solution. See page 94 for more.

| Halogen | Displacement reactions | Ionic equations |
|---------|------------------------|-----------------|
| Cl | chlorine ($Cl_2$) will displace bromide ($Br^-$) and iodide ($I^-$) | $Cl_{2(aq)} + 2Br^-_{(aq)} \rightarrow 2Cl^-_{(aq)} + Br_{2(aq)}$ <br> $Cl_{2(aq)} + 2I^-_{(aq)} \rightarrow 2Cl^-_{(aq)} + I_{2(aq)}$ |
| Br | bromine ($Br_2$) will displace iodide ($I^-$) | $Br_{2(aq)} + 2I^-_{(aq)} \rightarrow 2Br^-_{(aq)} + I_{2(aq)}$ |
| I | no reaction with $F^-$, $Cl^-$, $Br^-$ | |

**Tip:** This is an ionic equation — it only shows the reacting particles. See pages 26-27 for more on ionic equations.

When these displacement reactions happen, there are colour changes — you can see what happens by following them.

---

**Examples**

### Bromine water and potassium iodide

If you mix bromine water, $Br_{2\,(aq)}$, with potassium iodide solution, the bromine displaces the iodide ions (it oxidises them), giving iodine ($I_2$) and potassium bromide solution, $KBr_{(aq)}$. The equation for this reaction is:

$$Br_{2(aq)} + 2I^-_{(aq)} \rightarrow 2Br^-_{(aq)} + I_{2(aq)}$$

*Oxidation number of Br:* $\quad 0 \qquad\qquad \rightarrow \quad -1$

*Oxidation number of I:* $\qquad\qquad -1 \quad \rightarrow \qquad\qquad 0$

Iodine water ($I_{2\,(aq)}$) is brown and bromine water ($Br_{2\,(aq)}$) is orange. So when bromine displaces the iodide ions in potassium iodide, the solution changes colour from orange to brown.

### Chlorine water and potassium bromide

If you mix chlorine water, $Cl_{2\,(aq)}$, with potassium bromide, $KBr_{(aq)}$, the solution changes from colourless to orange. The chlorine displaces the bromide ions, forming bromine water ($Br_{2\,(aq)}$), which is orange.

$$Cl_{2(aq)} + 2Br^-_{(aq)} \rightarrow 2Cl^-_{(aq)} + Br_{2(aq)}$$

*Oxidation number of Cl:* $\quad 0 \qquad\qquad \rightarrow \quad -1$

*Oxidation number of Br:* $\qquad\qquad -1 \quad \rightarrow \qquad\qquad 0$

---

Brown and orange can sometimes look a bit similar. You can make the changes easier to see by shaking the reaction mixture with an **organic solvent** like hexane. The halogen that's present will dissolve readily in the organic solvent, which settles out as a distinct layer (called the **solvent layer**) above the aqueous solution. The different halogens are very different colours when they are dissolved in organic solvent so you can easily see which halogen has been produced.

- A violet/pink colour shows the presence of iodine (see Figure 2).
- An orange/red colour shows bromine.
- A very pale yellow/green shows chlorine.

The table on the next page summarises the colour changes you'll see when different displacement reactions take place.

**Figure 2:** *Iodine mixed with hexane (an organic solvent). The top layer shows the violet colour of the solution formed when iodine dissolves in an organic solvent. The bottom layer is an aqueous solution of $I_2$.*

**Tip:** Make sure you learn all of these colour changes. You'll need them for the exam.

**Figure 3:** *The initial (left) and final (right) appearance of the test tube when an organic solvent is added to bromine water. Notice the red/orange colour of the solvent layer which settles at the top of the test tube.*

|  | Potassium chloride solution ($KCl_{(aq)}$) | Potassium bromide solution ($KBr_{(aq)}$) | Potassium iodide solution ($KI_{(aq)}$) |
| --- | --- | --- | --- |
| Chlorine water ($Cl_{2(aq)}$) – Colourless | No reaction | orange/red solution ($Br_2$) formed with organic solvent | violet/pink solution ($I_2$) formed with organic solvent |
| Bromine water ($Br_{2(aq)}$) – Orange | No reaction | No reaction | violet/pink solution ($I_2$) formed with organic solvent |
| Iodine solution ($I_{2(aq)}$) – Brown | No reaction | No reaction | No reaction |

# Identifying halogens in solution

The halogen displacement reactions can be used to help identify which halogen or halide is present in a solution. All you have to do is mix your unknown solution with some known halogen solutions and watch to see what colour changes take place.

┌ **Examples** ─────────────────────────

**Chlorine water is added to a solution of an unknown potassium halide. When hexane is added, a solvent layer forms which is violet in colour. Identify the halide ions present in the unknown solution.**

Because the solvent layer turns violet, you know that $I_2$ must have been formed. So, $I^-$ ions must have been present in the unknown solution. When the chlorine water is added the following reaction occurs:

$$Cl_{2(aq)} + 2I^-_{(aq)} \rightarrow 2Cl^-_{(aq)} + I_{2(aq)}$$

**An unknown halogen solution is added to solutions of KBr and KCl. A colour change occurs with KBr but not with KCl. Identify the halogen present in the unknown solution.**

Because there is a colour change when the halogen solution is added to KBr, you know that a displacement reaction has occurred and $Br_2$ has been formed. So the halogen can't be $I_2$ or $Br_2$ because neither of these can displace $Br^-$ ions. Because no colour change happens when the unknown halogen solution is added to KCl you know the halogen can't be $F_2$ (because this would displace the $Cl^-$ ions). So the unknown halogen must be $Cl_2$.

# Testing for halides

The halogens are pretty distinctive to look at. Unfortunately, the same can't be said of halide solutions, which are colourless. You can test for halides using the **silver nitrate test** — it's dead easy. First you add dilute nitric acid to remove ions which might interfere with the test. Then you just add silver nitrate solution ($AgNO_{3\ (aq)}$). A precipitate is formed (of the silver halide).

$$Ag^+_{(aq)} + X^-_{(aq)} \rightarrow AgX_{(s)} \qquad ...where\ X\ is\ F,\ Cl,\ Br\ or\ I$$

The colour of the precipitate identifies the halide (see Figures 4 and 5).

**Exam Tip**
You could be asked to identify any halogen or halide solution in your exam so make sure you learn which reactions happen and what the colour changes are.

**Tip:** When identifying halogen or halide solutions, looking at which reactions don't happen is as important as looking at the reactions that do happen.

**Tip:** You can't use hydrochloric acid instead of nitric acid because the silver nitrate would just react with the chloride ions from the HCl — and that would mess up your results completely.

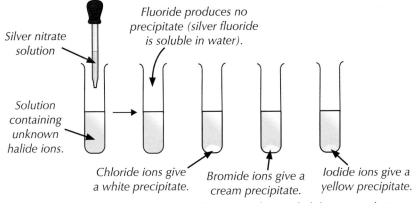

Silver nitrate solution

Fluoride produces no precipitate (silver fluoride is soluble in water).

Solution containing unknown halide ions.

Chloride ions give a white precipitate.

Bromide ions give a cream precipitate.

Iodide ions give a yellow precipitate.

**Figure 4:** *The silver nitrate test for identifying an unknown halide ion in solution.*

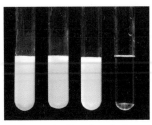

**Figure 5:** *Results of silver nitrate tests for solutions containing (L-R) fluoride, chloride, bromide and iodide ions.*

Then to be extra sure, you can test your results by adding ammonia solution. Each silver halide has a different solubility in ammonia (see Figures 6 and 7).

| Halide | Result |
|--------|--------|
| Chloride $Cl^-$ | precipitate dissolves in dilute $NH_{3(aq)}$ |
| Bromide $Br^-$ | precipitate dissolves in conc. $NH_{3(aq)}$ |
| Iodide $I^-$ | precipitate insoluble in conc. $NH_{3(aq)}$ |

**Figure 6:** *Solubility of silver halide precipitates in ammonia.*

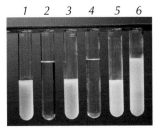

1  2  3  4  5  6

**Figure 7:** *The chloride, bromide and iodide test tubes from Figure 4 (1, 3 and 5), and the same tubes with $NH_{3(aq)}$ added (2, 4 and 6).*

## Practice Questions — Application

Q1  Explain why the boiling point of bromine is lower than that of iodine.

Q2  Fluorine is the most reactive of the halogens. Explain why the other halogens are less reactive than fluorine.

Q3  When bromine is added to an unknown solution of halide ions and an organic solvent is added, the solvent layer turns violet.

a)  Identify the halide ions present in the solution.

b)  Write an equation for the displacement reaction that occurs.

Q4  An experiment is carried out to identify the halide ions in three different solutions. The results are shown in the table below.

| Sample | Colour of precipitate following addition of silver nitrate | Effect of adding concentrated $NH_3$ solution to the precipitate |
|--------|--------|--------|
| A | yellow | no change |
| B | no precipitate | no change |
| C | cream | precipitate dissolves |

Identify the halide ion in each sample.

## Practice Questions — Fact Recall

Q1  Describe and explain the trend in the boiling points of the halogens.

Q2  Explain why the halogens get less reactive as you go down the group.

Q3  Which halide ions are displaced by reaction with chlorine water?

Q4  What colour is the solvent layer when an organic solvent is added to:

a)  chlorine water     b)  bromine water     c)  iodine water

Q5  Describe a test for distinguishing between different halide solutions.

**Learning Objectives:**

- Be able to describe the term disproportionation as a reaction in which an element is simultaneously oxidised and reduced.

- Know that the reaction of chlorine with cold, dilute aqueous sodium hydroxide is a disproportionation reaction and is used to form bleach.

- Know that the reaction of chlorine with water is a disproportionation reaction and is used in water purification.

- Be able to contrast the benefits of chlorine use in water treatment with associated risks.

- Understand the health benefits of chlorine use in water and the ethical implications of adding chlorine and fluorine to public water supplies.

**Specification Reference 1.3.3**

# 5. Disproportionation and Water Treatment

*Disproportionation doesn't have a snappy name and it's got far more letters than you expect, but it is quite handy — and you have to know all about it for your exam.*

## What is disproportionation?

**Disproportionation** is when a single element is simultaneously oxidised and reduced. The halogens undergo disproportionation when they react with cold dilute alkali solutions (e.g. NaOH or KOH). The general equation for the reaction of a halogen (X) with sodium hydroxide (NaOH) is shown below:

| | |
|---|---|
| *Full equation:* | $X_2 + 2NaOH \rightarrow NaXO + NaX + H_2O$ |
| *Ionic equation:* | $X_2 + 2OH^- \rightarrow XO^- + X^- + H_2O$ |
| *Oxidation number of X:* | $0 \qquad\qquad +1 \quad -1$ |

All of the halogens, except fluorine, can exist in a wide range of oxidation states. For example chlorine can exist as:

| -1 | 0 | +1 |
|---|---|---|
| $Cl^-$ | $Cl_2$ | $ClO^-$ |
| chloride | chlorine | chlorate(I) |

---

**Example**

Bromine reacts with NaOH to give sodium bromate(I), sodium bromide and water:

$$Br_2 + 2NaOH \rightarrow NaBrO + NaBr + H_2O$$

As $Br_2$, bromine has an oxidation state of 0. In NaBrO the oxidation state of bromine is +1, so when bromine forms NaBrO it is oxidised. In NaBr the oxidation state of bromine is –1, so when bromine forms NaBr it is reduced. So in the reaction above, the bromine is simultaneously oxidised and reduced and it is a disproportionation reaction.

---

## Making bleach

If you mix chlorine gas with dilute sodium hydroxide at room temperature, you get sodium chlorate(I) solution, $NaClO_{(aq)}$, which just happens to be common household bleach. In this reaction some of the chlorine is oxidised and some of it is reduced so it's a disproportionation reaction.

$$2NaOH_{(aq)} + Cl_{2\,(g)} \rightarrow NaClO_{(aq)} + NaCl_{(aq)} + H_2O_{(l)}$$

*Chlorine is bonded to chlorine so its oxidation state is 0.*

*$ClO^-$ is the chlorate(I) ion. Chlorine's oxidation state is +1 in this ion.*

*Here, chlorine's oxidation state is –1.*

The sodium chlorate(I) solution (bleach) has loads of uses — it's used in water treatment, to bleach paper and textiles... and it's good for cleaning toilets, too. Handy...

**Tip:** Don't get disproportionation and displacement reactions mixed up. See page 93 for more on displacement reactions.

**Tip:** Take a look at pages 40-43 for more on oxidation states and how to work them out.

# Chlorine and water

When you mix chlorine with water, it undergoes disproportionation. You end up with a mixture of hydrochloric acid and chloric(I) acid (also called hypochlorous acid).

$$Cl_{2(g)} + H_2O_{(l)} \rightleftharpoons HCl_{(aq)} + HClO_{(aq)}$$

*Chlorine's oxidation state is 0.*     *In hydrochloric acid chlorine's oxidation state is −1.*    *In chloric(I) acid chlorine's oxidation state is +1.*

Aqueous chloric(I) acid ionises to make chlorate(I) ions (also called hypochlorite ions):

$$HClO_{(aq)} + H_2O_{(l)} \rightleftharpoons ClO^-_{(aq)} + H_3O^+_{(aq)}$$

**Figure 1:** *Chlorine is used to treat tap water in the UK.*

# Water treatment

Chlorate(I) ions kill bacteria. So, adding chlorine (or a compound containing chlorate(I) ions) to water can make it safe to drink or swim in. In the UK our drinking water is treated to make it safe.

Chlorine is an important part of water treatment. It kills disease-causing microorganisms (and some chlorine persists in the water and prevents reinfection further down the supply). It also prevents the growth of algae, eliminating bad tastes and smells, and removes discolouration caused by organic compounds.

However, there are risks from using chlorine to treat water. Chlorine gas is toxic. It's very harmful if it's breathed in — it irritates the respiratory system. Liquid chlorine on the skin or eyes causes severe chemical burns. Accidents involving chlorine could be really serious, or fatal. Water contains a variety of organic compounds, e.g. from the decomposition of plants. Chlorine reacts with these compounds to form chlorinated hydrocarbons, e.g. chloromethane ($CH_3Cl$), and many of these chlorinated hydrocarbons are carcinogenic (cancer-causing). However, this increased cancer risk is small compared to the risks from untreated water — a cholera epidemic, say, could kill thousands of people. There are ethical considerations too. We don't get a choice about having our water chlorinated — some people object to this as forced 'mass medication'.

**Tip:** See page 4 for more about weighing up the benefits and risks of scientific techniques (like using chlorine to treat drinking water).

**Figure 2:** *The distinctive 'swimming pool smell' is due to the chlorine in the water.*

# Fluoridated water

It's not just chlorine that is added to water. In some areas of the UK fluoride ions are also added to drinking water. Health officials recommend this because it helps to prevent tooth decay — there's loads of good evidence for this. But, there's also a small amount of evidence linking fluoridated water to a slightly increased risk of some bone cancers. Most toothpaste is fluoridated, so some people think extra fluoride ions in water is unnecessary.

**Figure 3:** *Most toothpastes contain fluoride.*

Q1  When iodine is mixed with potassium hydroxide (KOH) a disproportionation reaction occurs.

    a)  Write an equation to show the reaction of iodine with KOH.

    b)  Using oxidation states, explain why this reaction is a disproportionation reaction.

Q2  The equation below shows the decomposition of hydrogen peroxide ($H_2O_2$) to water and oxygen:

$$2H_2O_2 \rightarrow 2H_2O + O_2$$

Is this a disproportionation reaction?  Explain your answer.

Q3  The equation below shows the reaction of chlorine gas with water:

$$Cl_{2(g)} + H_2O_{(l)} \rightleftharpoons HCl_{(aq)} + HClO_{(aq)}$$

    a)  Write an equation to show how chlorate(I) ions can be produced from the products of this reaction.

    b)  Explain why chlorate(I) ions are added to water.

**Tip:** The oxidation state of oxygen in $H_2O_2$ is –1, the oxidation state of oxygen in $H_2O$ is –2 and the oxidation state of oxygen in $O_2$ is 0.

Q1  What is disproportionation?

Q2  a)  Name three products of the reaction between sodium hydroxide and chlorine.

    b)  Give the balanced equation for this reaction.

Q3  Describe the reactions that occur when chlorine is mixed with water.

Q4  a)  Explain why chlorine is used to treat water.

    b)  Describe the disadvantages of using chlorine to treat water.

Q5  a)  Name a halogen, other than chlorine, that is often added to water supplies.

    b)  Explain why this halogen is added to water supplies in some areas of the UK.

    c)  Explain why this type of water treatment isn't used in all areas of the UK.

# Section Summary

Make sure you know...

- How Döbereiner, Newlands, Mendeleev, Moseley and Seaborg contributed to the development of the periodic table.
- That in the modern periodic table the elements are arranged in order of increasing atomic number.
- That the modern periodic table is organised into periods (rows), groups (columns) and blocks (the s-block, p-block, d-block and f-block).
- That the elements within a period all have the same number of electron shells.
- That the elements within a group all have the same number of electrons in their outer shell and as a result have similar physical and chemical properties.
- How the periodic table can be used to work out the electronic configuration of an element.
- That periods show repeating trends in physical and chemical properties and that this is known as periodicity.
- The trend in melting and boiling points as you move across Periods 2 and 3.
- How to explain the trend in melting and boiling points across Periods 2 and 3 in terms of structure and bonding.
- Why atomic radius generally decreases across a period.
- Why first ionisation energy generally increases across a period and decreases down a group.
- Why the Group 2 elements get more reactive as you move down the group.
- That the Group 2 elements generally form $M^{2+}$ ions when they react because this gives them a stable electronic configuration (that of a noble gas).
- That the Group 2 elements undergo redox reactions with water to form metal hydroxides and hydrogen gas.
- That the Group 2 elements burn in air to form metal oxides.
- That the Group 2 oxides are solid white powders which react with water to form hydroxide solutions with a pH of 12–13.
- That Group 2 carbonates decompose when heated to form a metal oxide and carbon dioxide.
- That the thermal stability of the Group 2 carbonates increases as you move down the group.
- That calcium hydroxide ($Ca(OH)_2$) is used in agriculture to neutralise acid soils.
- That magnesium hydroxide ($Mg(OH)_2$) is used in some indigestion tablets as an antacid.
- Why the boiling and melting points of the halogens increase as you move down Group 7.
- Why the halogens get less reactive as you move down Group 7.
- How to write ionic equations for displacement reactions involving two Group 7 elements.
- How halogen and halide ion solutions can be identified using displacement reactions.
- How the silver nitrate test can be used to test for halide ions.
- How the addition of ammonia can confirm the results of a silver nitrate test.
- That a disproportionation reaction is a reaction where a single element is simultaneously oxidised and reduced.
- How bleach is formed using chlorine and sodium hydroxide, and its uses.
- The equations for the reactions of chlorine with water.
- The benefits and risks of using chlorine in water treatment.
- The benefits and risks of adding fluoride ions to drinking water.

**1** The periodic table is a table of elements arranged into periods and groups.

**(a) (i)** Identify the fifteenth element in Period 4 of the periodic table.
State which block of the periodic table this element is in.

*(1 mark)*

**(ii)** Use your knowledge of the periodic table to write the electronic configuration for this element.

*(1 mark)*

**(b)** Strontium and barium are both in Group 2 of the periodic table.
Both react with oxygen forming solid white oxides.

**(i)** Write equations (including state symbols) for the reactions of strontium and barium with oxygen.

*(2 marks)*

**(ii)** Use your knowledge of the periodic table to explain why strontium and barium react with oxygen in similar ways.

*(2 marks)*

**2** This question is about trends in the periodic table.

**(a)** The graph below shows the trend in boiling point as you move across Period 3:

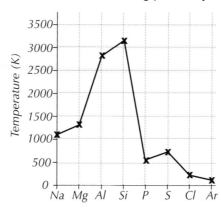

**(i)** Explain why the boiling point generally increases from Na to Al.

*(3 marks)*

**(ii)** Explain why Si has the highest boiling point of all the Period 3 elements.

*(3 marks)*

**(iii)** Explain why the boiling point of sulfur ($S_8$) is higher than that of chlorine ($Cl_2$).

*(3 marks)*

**(b)** Magnesium and aluminium are in Period 2 of the periodic table.
The atomic radii of magnesium and aluminium are shown below.

| Element | Atomic Radius (pm) |
|---------|--------------------|
| Magnesium | 150 |
| Aluminium | 125 |

**(i)** Explain why the radius of aluminium is smaller than that of magnesium.

*(3 marks)*

**(ii)** Suggest an element in Period 2 with a smaller atomic radius than aluminium.

*(1 mark)*

**(c)** State and explain the general trend in first ionisation energy as you move across Period 2.

*(5 marks)*

 In your answer, you should use appropriate technical terms, spelled correctly.

**3** The elements in Group 2 of the periodic table are commonly known as the alkaline earth metals. The alkaline earth metals react with water to form metal hydroxides.

**(a) (i)** Write a balanced equation for the reaction of calcium with water.

*(1 mark)*

**(ii)** Describe what you would see when this reaction takes place.

*(2 marks)*

**(iii)** State the approximate pH of the resulting calcium hydroxide solution.

*(1 mark)*

**(b) (i)** Give one use of calcium hydroxide.

*(1 mark)*

**(ii)** Write an ionic equation for the reaction that takes place when calcium hydroxide is used in this way.

*(1 mark)*

**(c)** Magnesium hydroxide can be produced in a similar way to calcium hydroxide, by reacting magnesium with water. The reaction of magnesium with water is much slower and less vigorous than the reaction of calcium with water.

**(i)** State and explain the trend in first ionisation energy as you move down Group 2.

*(6 marks)*

**(ii)** Use your answer to part (i) to explain why the reaction of magnesium with water is less vigorous than the reaction of calcium with water.

*(2 marks)*

**(iii)** Give one use for magnesium hydroxide.

*(1 mark)*

**4**      A student was demonstrating that an unknown potassium halide solution was potassium bromide. To do this he used the knowledge that chlorine is a stronger oxidising agent than bromine.

    **(a)**      Explain why chlorine is a stronger oxidising agent than bromine.

                                                                            *(3 marks)*

    **(b)**      He mixed some of the solution with chlorine water ($Cl_{2(aq)}$) and added hexane. Then he observed the results.

        **(i)**      Write an ionic equation for the displacement reaction that would occur if the solution was potassium bromide.

                                                                            *(1 mark)*

        **(ii)**      State how the colour of the solvent layer could be used to distinguish between a solution of potassium bromide and potassium iodide.

                                                                      *(2 marks)*

    **(c)**      The student's results confirmed that the solution was potassium bromide. The student further confirmed his results using the silver nitrate test.

        **(i)**      Describe how the student would perform a silver nitrate test to confirm that bromide ions were present in the unknown solution.

                                                                      *(3 marks)*

        **(ii)**      Write an ionic equation, including state symbols, for the reaction that occurs when a silver nitrate test is used to detect bromide ions.

                                                                      *(2 marks)*

        **(iii)** Explain how the student could double-check his results.

                                                                      *(2 marks)*

**5**      This question is about the uses of chlorine.

    **(a)**      Bleach can be made by reacting chlorine with sodium hydroxide (NaOH).
- Write a balanced equation to show the reaction of chlorine with sodium hydroxide.
- Indicate which of the products of this reaction is used as bleach and give two common uses of bleach.
- Use your knowledge of oxidation states to explain why this is a disproportionation reaction

                                                                      *(6 marks)*

    **(b)**      Chlorine is often added to water supplies.
- Write equations for the reactions that occur when chlorine is added to water.
- Discuss the advantages and disadvantages of adding chlorine to water supplies.

                                                                      *(6 marks)*

# 1. Organic Chemistry

*Organic chemistry is the study of carbon-containing compounds.*
*Here's a brief introduction to some of the basic concepts you'll need to get your head around before you can study organic chemistry in more detail.*

**Learning Objective:**

- Know that a functional group is a group of atoms responsible for the characteristic reactions of a compound.

**Specification Reference 2.1.1**

## The basics

There are a few basic concepts in organic chemistry which you need to understand to really get on with this module.

### Nomenclature

There are thousands, if not millions, of known organic compounds and it would be pretty silly if we didn't have an easy way to describe them. That's where **nomenclature** comes in. Don't be put off by the long name, all it means is naming molecules using specific rules. These rules (known as the IUPAC system for naming organic compounds) allow scientists to discuss organic chemistry safe in the knowledge that they're all talking about the same molecules. It means that some molecules end up with really long and complicated looking names (e.g. 1,2-dichloro-3-methylbutane) but once you know the rules it's easy to work out what they all mean. There's more about nomenclature on pages 118-120.

### Formulas

Picturing molecules can be pretty difficult when you can't see them all around you. We can use the elemental symbols from the periodic table to help visualise molecules. For example, a molecule of methane is one carbon atom attached to four hydrogen atoms. You could show this by giving its molecular formula, $CH_4$, or you could draw its displayed formula like this:

$$H-\overset{\displaystyle H}{\underset{\displaystyle H}{C}}-H$$

There's more on formulas on page 104. This isn't exactly what methane looks like, but visualising it like this lets us compare it to other molecules and means we can predict its properties and how it might react with other molecules. Molecular models can also be used to represent molecules (see Figure 1).

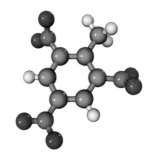

*Figure 1: A molecular model of a TNT molecule. Each grey sphere represents a carbon atom, each white sphere represents a hydrogen atom, the purple ones represent nitrogen atoms and the red ones oxygen atoms.*

### Functional groups

The functional group of a molecule is the group of atoms that's responsible for its characteristic reactions — it's where all the interesting stuff happens. They're usually pretty easy to spot because they're the bits which aren't just hydrogen and carbon atoms (e.g. bromine atoms, oxygen atoms, etc.). You'll come across a few different functional groups in AS chemistry — here are a few examples...

Functional groups of...   −OH        $-\overset{\displaystyle O}{\underset{}{\underset{\displaystyle \|}{C}}}-OH$        $\diagdown C = C \diagup$
                          *alcohols*    *carboxylic acids*    *alkenes*

For now, remember that carbon atoms have four bonds, hydrogen atoms have one bond and oxygen atoms have two bonds joining them to other atoms.

So there you go. That's pretty much all you need to know to get started. You'd better get on — next up is formulas...

**Tip:** That stuff about carbon atoms making four bonds, hydrogen making one bond and oxygen making two is right <u>most</u> of the time, but isn't always the case. The good news is that you don't need to worry about that right now.

## Learning Objectives:

- Know that a molecular formula gives the actual number of atoms of each element in a molecule.

- Know that a structural formula gives the minimal detail that shows the arrangement of atoms in a molecule.

- Know that a displayed formula shows the relative positioning of atoms and the bonds between them.

- Know that an empirical formula is the simplest whole number ratio of atoms of each element present in a compound.

- Know that a general formula is the simplest algebraic formula of a member of a homologous series.

- Know that a homologous series is a series of organic compounds having the same functional group but with each successive member differing by $CH_2$.

- Be able to use the general formula of a homologous series to predict the formula of any member of the series.

- Know that a skeletal formula is a simplified organic formula, shown by removing hydrogen atoms from alkyl chains, leaving just a carbon skeleton and associated functional groups.

**Specification Reference 2.1.1**

# 2. Formulas

*Organic compounds can be represented in lots of different ways, using different types of formulas. You need to be familiar with what these formulas show and how to switch between them.*

## Types of formulas

### Molecular formulas

A molecular formula gives the actual number of atoms of each element in a molecule.

---Examples---

Ethane has the molecular formula $C_2H_6$ — each molecule is made up of 2 carbon atoms and 6 hydrogen atoms.

Pentene has the molecular formula $C_5H_{10}$ — each molecule is made up of 5 carbon atoms and 10 hydrogen atoms.

1,4-dibromobutane has the molecular formula $C_4H_8Br_2$ — each molecule is made up of 4 carbon atoms, 8 hydrogen atoms and 2 bromine atoms.

1,3-dichloropropane has the molecular formula $C_3H_6Cl_2$ — each molecule is made up of 3 carbon atoms, 6 hydrogen atoms and 2 chlorine atoms.

### Structural formulas

A structural formula shows the atoms carbon by carbon, with the attached hydrogens and functional groups.

---Examples---

Ethane has the structural formula $CH_3CH_3$.

Pentene has the structural formula $CH_3CH_2CH_2CHCH_2$.

1,4-dibromobutane has the structural formula $BrCH_2CH_2CH_2CH_2Br$.

1,3-dichloropropane has the structural formula $ClCH_2CH_2CH_2Cl$.

### Displayed formulas

A displayed formula shows how all the atoms are arranged, and all the bonds between them.

---Examples---

Displayed formula of ethane:

Displayed formula of pentene:

Displayed formula of 1,4-dibromobutane:

Displayed formula of 1,3-dichloropropane:

## Empirical formulas

An empirical formula gives the simplest whole number ratio of atoms of each element in a compound. To find the empirical formula you have to divide the molecular formula by the smallest number of atoms for a given element in the molecule. For example, if the molecular formula is $C_2H_4Cl_2$, the smallest number of atoms is 2 (for both C and Cl). So you divide the molecular formula by 2 and get the empirical formula $CH_2Cl$. Sometimes the empirical formula will be the same as the molecular formula. This happens when you can't divide the molecular formula by the smallest number of atoms and still end up with whole numbers of atoms.

**Tip:** If there's just one atom of something in a formula then you know you've got an empirical formula — it can't be simplified any further.

$C_4H_{10}O$ is an empirical formula — there's only 1 oxygen atom.

┌─ Examples ─────────────────

| Name | Molecular Formula | Divide by... | Empirical Formula |
|---|---|---|---|
| Ethane | $C_2H_6$ | 2 | $CH_3$ |
| Pentene | $C_5H_{10}$ | 5 | $CH_2$ |
| 1,4-dibromobutane | $C_4H_8Cl_2$ | 2 | $C_2H_4Cl$ |
| 1,3-dichloropropane | $C_3H_6Cl_2$ | | $C_3H_6Cl_2$ |
| 1,2,3-trichloroheptane | $C_7H_{13}Cl_3$ | | $C_7H_{13}Cl_3$ |

In the last two examples in the table, the molecular formula is the same as the empirical formula — you can't divide by the smallest number of atoms for a given element and still get whole numbers.

**Exam Tip**
You need to make sure you know which type of formula is which. You won't get any marks for writing a structural formula when the examiner wants a molecular one.

## General formulas and homologous series

A **general formula** is an algebraic formula that can describe any member of a family of compounds. Organic chemistry is more about groups of similar chemicals than individual compounds. These groups are called **homologous series**. A homologous series is a family of compounds that have the same functional group and general formula. Consecutive members of a homologous series differ by $-CH_2-$.

┌─ Example ─────────────────

The simplest homologous series is the alkanes. They're straight chain molecules that contain only carbon and hydrogen atoms. There are always twice as many hydrogen atoms as carbon atoms, plus two more. So the general formula for alkanes is $C_nH_{2n+2}$. You can use this formula to work out how many hydrogen atoms there are in any alkane if you know the number of carbon atoms. For example...

If an alkane has 1 carbon atom, n = 1.
This means the alkane will have $(2 \times 1) + 2 = 4$ hydrogen atoms.
So the molecular formula of this alkane would be $CH_4$ (you don't need to write the 1 in $C_1$).

If an alkane has 5 carbon atoms, n = 5.
This means the alkane will have $(2 \times 5) + 2 = 12$ hydrogen atoms.
So its molecular formula would be $C_5H_{12}$.

If an alkane has 15 carbon atoms, n = 15.
This means the alkane will have $(2 \times 15) + 2 = 32$ hydrogen atoms.
So its molecular formula is $C_{15}H_{32}$.

**Tip:** There's a lot more about the alkanes on page 118.

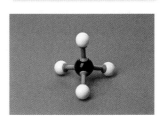

***Figure 1:*** *Molecular model of methane — the alkane where n = 1.*

## Skeletal formulas

A skeletal formula shows the bonds of the carbon skeleton only, with any functional groups. The hydrogen and carbon atoms that are part of the main carbon chain aren't shown. This is handy for drawing large complicated structures, like cyclic hydrocarbons. The carbon atoms are found at each junction between bonds and at the end of bonds (unless there's already a functional group there). Each carbon atom has enough hydrogen atoms attached to make the total number of bonds from the carbon up to four.

**Exam Tip**
Skeletal formulas are notoriously difficult to draw in an exam without making any mistakes... If you're not 100% happy with them stick to displayed formulas — you don't want to introduce silly errors into your answers. Of course, if the exam question asks for a skeletal formula you've got no choice — just give it your best shot.

─ Examples ─

Displayed and skeletal formulas of 1,5-difluoropentane:

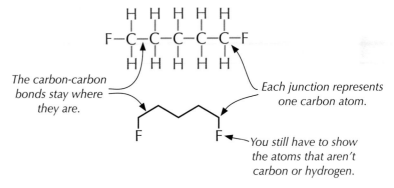

The carbon-carbon bonds stay where they are.

Each junction represents one carbon atom.

You still have to show the atoms that aren't carbon or hydrogen.

**Tip:** You have to draw skeletal formulas as zig-zag lines, otherwise you can't tell where one bond ends and the next begins.

Skeletal formula of hex-1-ene:

A double line represents a carbon-carbon double bond.

This carbon atom only has one carbon-carbon bond drawn on the molecule. This means that it has three hydrogen atoms attached to make the number of bonds up to four.

This carbon atom has two carbon-carbon double bonds, so it must have two hydrogen atoms attached to make the number of bonds up to four.

## Practice Questions — Application

**Q1** 2-bromopropane has the structural formula $CH_3CHBrCH_3$. Draw the displayed formula of 2-bromopropane.

**Q2** Here is the structure of 3-ethyl-2-methylpentane.

$$H-\underset{\underset{H}{|}}{\overset{\overset{H}{|}}{\underset{5}{C}}}-\underset{\underset{H}{|}}{\overset{\overset{H}{|}}{\underset{4}{C}}}-\underset{\underset{CH_2}{|}}{\overset{\overset{H}{|}}{\underset{3}{C}}}-\underset{\underset{H}{|}}{\overset{\overset{CH_3}{|}}{\underset{2}{C}}}-\underset{\underset{H}{|}}{\overset{\overset{H}{|}}{\underset{1}{C}}}-H$$
$$CH_3$$

Write down the molecular formula for 3-ethyl-2-methylpentane.

**Q3** Write down the empirical formula of the following compounds:
a) $C_2H_4$
b) $C_8H_{14}Br_2$
c) $C_9H_{17}Cl_3$

**Tip:** Drawing a displayed formula from a structural formula is dead easy — just draw it out exactly as it's written:

$CH_3CH_2 CH_2 CH_2Cl$

$$H-\underset{\underset{H}{|}}{\overset{\overset{H}{|}}{C}}-\underset{\underset{H}{|}}{\overset{\overset{H}{|}}{C}}-\underset{\underset{H}{|}}{\overset{\overset{H}{|}}{C}}-\underset{\underset{H}{|}}{\overset{\overset{H}{|}}{C}}-Cl$$

Q4 Alkenes have the general formula $C_nH_{2n}$.

a) Butene is an alkene with 4 carbon atoms. Write the molecular formula of butene.

b) Heptene is an alkene with 7 carbon atoms. How many hydrogen atoms does it contain?

Q5 1,2-dibromopropane has the structural formula $CH_3CHBrCH_2Br$.

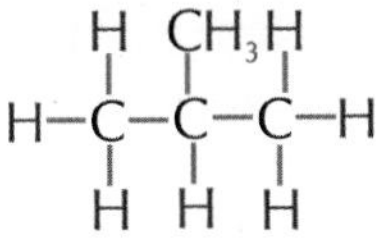

a) Write down the molecular formula of 1,2-dibromopropane.

b) Draw the displayed formula of 1,2-dibromopropane.

c) Write the empirical formula of 1,2-dibromopropane.

Q6 Here is the displayed formula of pent-1-ene.

a) Write down the molecular formula of pent-1-ene.

b) Write down the structural formula of pent-1-ene.

c) What is the empirical formula of pent-1-ene?

Q7 Draw skeletal formulas of the molecules below:

a)

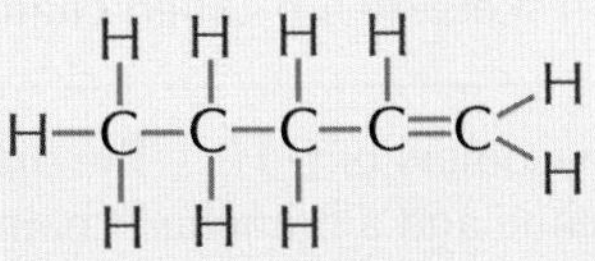

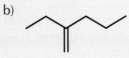

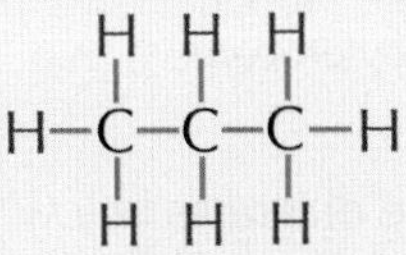

b)

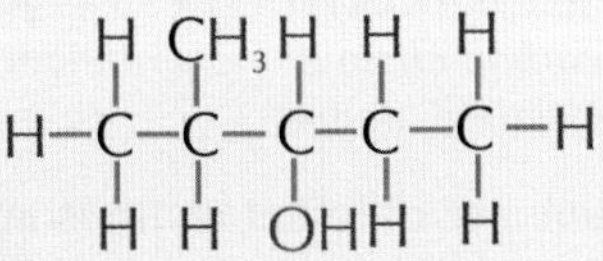

c)

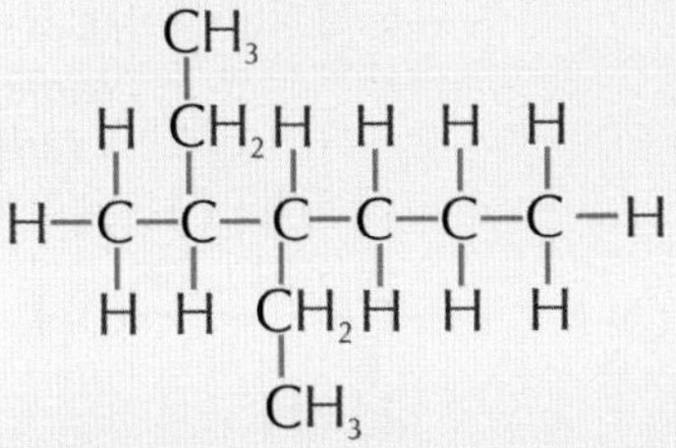

d)

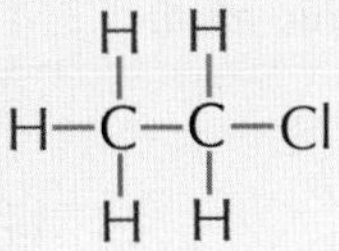

Q8 Give structural formulas for the molecules below:

a)

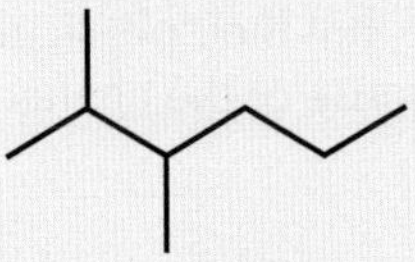

b)

c)

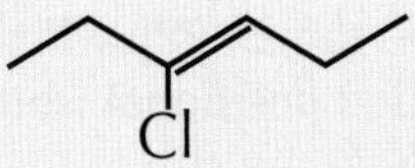

d)

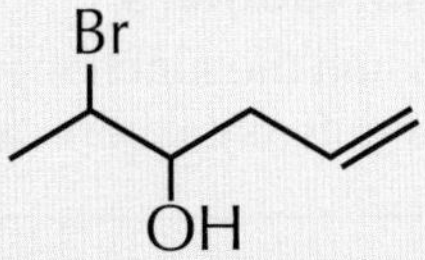

## Practice Questions — Fact Recall

Q1 What is a molecular formula?

Q2 What does a displayed formula show?

Q3 How do you work out the empirical formula of a compound?

Q4 What is a homologous series?

**Exam Tip**
It's really important to double-check your answers for questions like these. It's so easy to miscount and you need to make sure you collect all the easy marks in the exam.

**Tip:** It doesn't matter whether you show atoms bonding above, below or to the side of a carbon atom, they all mean the same thing — it's which atoms they're bonding to that's the important thing.

**Tip:** When you're writing the molecular formulas of branched molecules, you put the branch in brackets. E.g. methylpropane...

... has the structural formula:

$CH_3CH(CH_3)CH_3$

- Know that structural isomers are compounds with the same molecular formula but different structural formulas.

**Specification Reference 2.1.1**

# 3. Structural Isomers

*You can put the same atoms together in different ways to make completely different molecules. Two molecules that have the same molecular formula but are put together in a different way are isomers of each other.*

## What are structural isomers?

In structural isomers, the molecular formula is the same, but the structural formula is different. There are three different types of structural isomer:

### 1. Chain isomers

The carbon skeleton can be arranged differently — for example, as a straight chain, or branched in different ways. Molecules that have different arrangements of the carbon skeleton are called **chain isomers**.

---
**Examples**

There are different chain isomers of $C_4H_{10}$. The diagrams below show the straight chain isomer butane and a branched chain isomer methylpropane.

*Here the longest carbon chain is 3 carbon atoms.*

*Here the longest carbon chain is 4 carbon atoms.*

butane          methylpropane

There are different chain isomers of $C_4H_8O_2$. The diagrams below show the straight chain isomer butanoic acid and a branched chain isomer methylpropanoic acid.

*Here the longest carbon chain is 3 carbon atoms.*

*Here the longest carbon chain is 4 carbon atoms.*

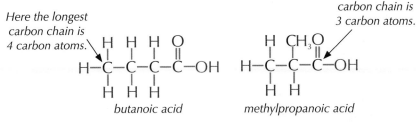

butanoic acid          methylpropanoic acid

---

Chain isomers have similar chemical properties — but their physical properties, like boiling point, will be different because of the change in shape of the molecule.

### 2. Positional isomers

The skeleton and the functional group could be the same, only with the group attached to a different carbon atom. These are called **positional isomers**.

---
**Example**

There are two positional isomers of $C_4H_9Cl$. The chlorine atom is attached to different carbon atoms in each isomer.

*The Cl is attached to the first carbon atom.*

1-chlorobutane

---

**Figure 1:** *Molecular models showing two chain isomers of $C_4H_{10}$ — butane (left) and methylpropane (right).*

**Exam Tip**
You don't always have to draw all of the bonds when you're drawing a molecule — writing $CH_3$ next to a bond is just as good as drawing out the carbon atom, three bonds and three hydrogen atoms. But if you're asked for a displayed formula you <u>must</u> draw out all of the bonds to get the marks.

**Tip:** If the chlorine atom was attached to the carbon atom on the left, it would still be the <u>same molecule</u> — just drawn the other way round. It would still be 1-chlorobutane.

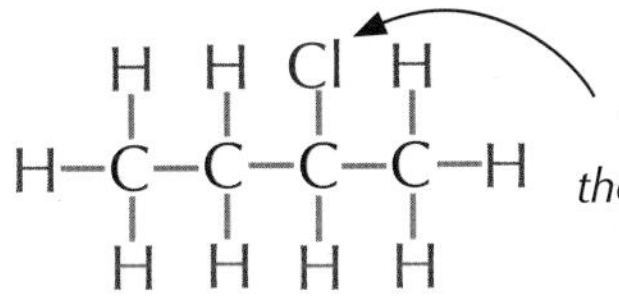

H H Cl H

H—C—C—C—C—H

H H H H

*2-chlorobutane*

*The Cl is attached to the second carbon atom.*

Positional isomers also have different physical properties, and the chemical properties might be different too.

### 3. Functional group isomers

Functional group isomers have the same atoms arranged into different functional groups.

┌─ Examples ────────────────────────────────

The formulas below show two functional group isomers of $C_6H_{12}$.

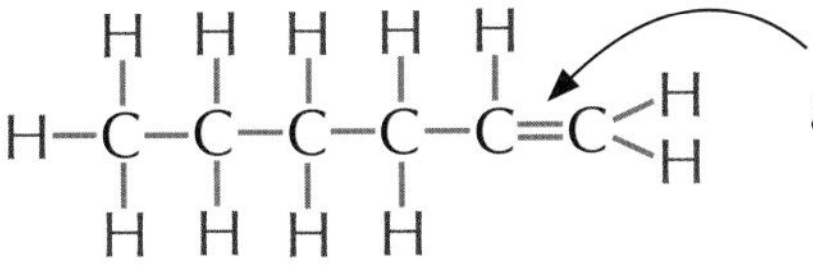

*hex-1-ene*

*The functional group is the C=C — it's an alkene.*

*This molecule is an alkane.*

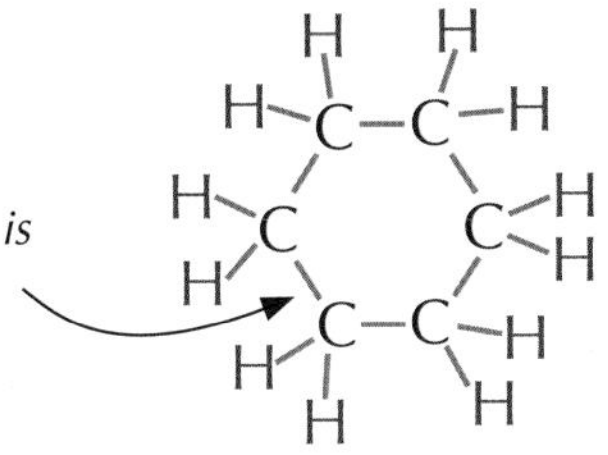

*cyclohexane*

Functional group isomers have very different physical and chemical properties.

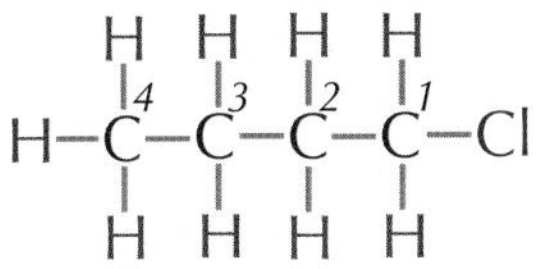

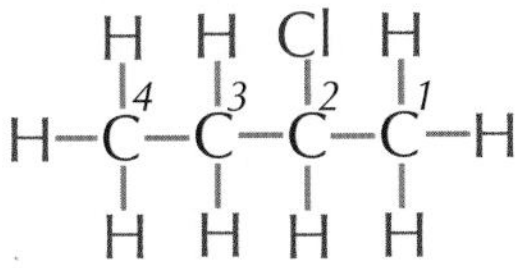

# Identifying isomers

Atoms can rotate as much as they like around single C–C bonds. Remember this when you work out structural isomers — sometimes what looks like an isomer, isn't.

┌─ Examples ────────────────────────────────

There are only two positional isomers of $C_3H_7Br$:

#### 1-bromopropane

The Br is always on the first carbon atom.

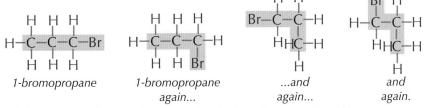

*1-bromopropane*   *1-bromopropane again...*   *...and again...*   *and again.*

All these molecules are the same, they're just drawn differently.

#### 2-bromopropane

The Br is always on the second carbon atom.

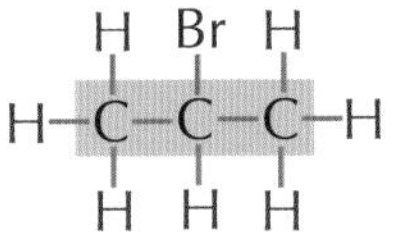

*2-bromopropane* 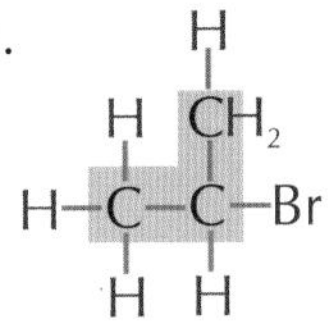   *2-bromopropane again*

**Tip:** Number the carbon atoms — it makes it easier to see what the longest carbon chain is and where side chains and atoms are attached:

H H H H

H—C—C—C—C—Cl

H H H

H H Cl H

H—C—C—C—C—H

H H H H

**Exam Tip**
To avoid mistakes when you're identifying isomers in an exam, draw the molecule so the longest carbon chain goes left to right across the page. This will make it easier to see the isomers.

**Tip:** In propane, the Br can only really go on the first or second carbon atom. If it was on the "third" it would be the same as being on the first again because you start counting from whichever end the Br is on.

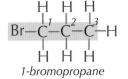

*1-bromopropane*

## Practice Questions — Application

**Exam Tip**
Be really careful when you're drawing out isomers that you do draw a different isomer and not just the same isomer again in a slightly different way — numbering the carbons and making sure the functional group's on a different one might help.

**Q1** Here is an isomer of chloro-2-methylpropane.

$$CH_3$$
$$H_3C-C-CH_3$$
$$Cl$$

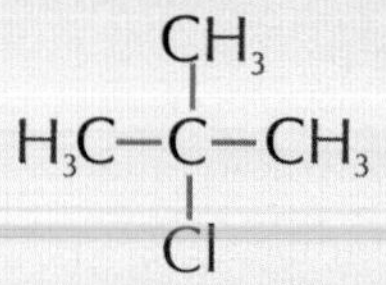

Draw the other positional isomer of chloro-2-methylpropane.

**Q2** Draw all the chain isomers of $C_5H_{12}$.

**Q3** Here is the displayed formula of propanal.

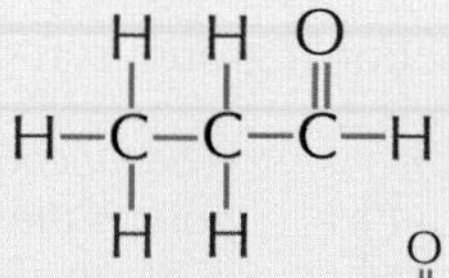

$$\begin{array}{ccc} H & H & O \\ | & | & || \\ H-C-C-C-H \\ | & | \\ H & H \end{array}$$

Propanal has the functional group $\overset{\displaystyle O}{\overset{\displaystyle ||}{C}}-H$.

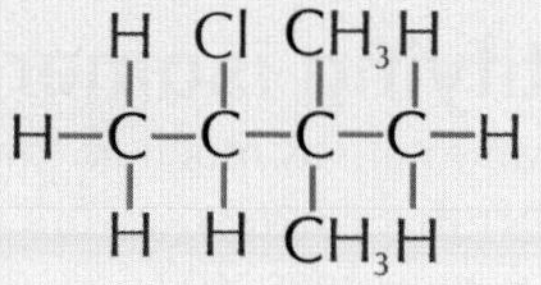

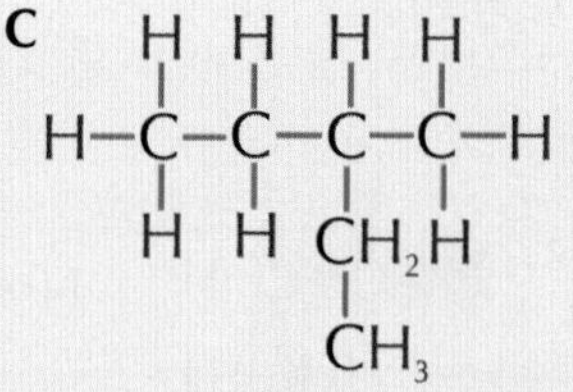

Draw an isomer of propanal with the functional group $\overset{\displaystyle O}{\overset{\displaystyle ||}{C}}$.

**Q4** Here is the displayed formula of 1-chlorohexane.

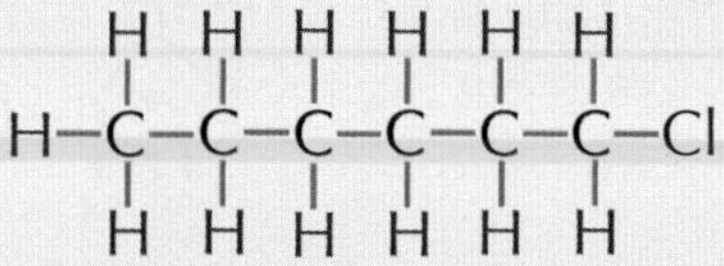

$$\begin{array}{ccccccc} H & H & H & H & H & H \\ | & | & | & | & | & | \\ H-C-C-C-C-C-C-Cl \\ | & | & | & | & | & | \\ H & H & H & H & H & H \end{array}$$

**Exam Tip**
If you get confused between different isomers of a molecule, try drawing the structure of the molecule out again in a slightly different way — everything might become clear.

a) Which of the molecules (A–D) are isomers of 1-chlorohexane?

**A**
$$\begin{array}{cccc} H & Cl & H & H \\ | & | & | & | \\ H-C-C-C-C-H \\ | & | & | & | \\ H & H & CH_2 & H \\ & & | \\ & & CH_3 \end{array}$$

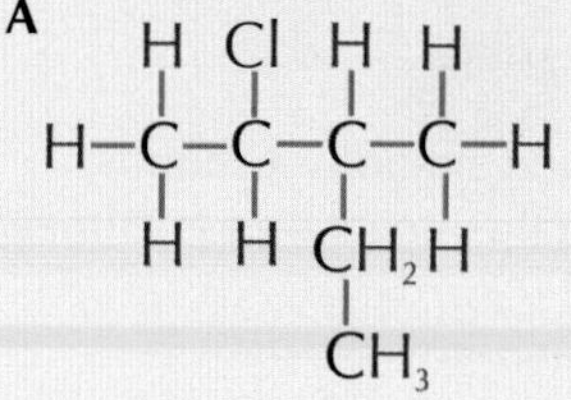

**B**
$$\begin{array}{cccc} H & Cl & CH_3 & H \\ | & | & | & | \\ H-C-C-C-C-H \\ | & | & | & | \\ H & H & CH_3 & H \end{array}$$

**C**
$$\begin{array}{cccc} H & H & H & H \\ | & | & | & | \\ H-C-C-C-C-H \\ | & | & | & | \\ H & H & CH_2 & H \\ & & | \\ & & CH_3 \end{array}$$

**D**
$$\begin{array}{ccccc} H & H & Cl & H & H \\ | & | & | & | & | \\ H-C-C-C-C-C-H \\ | & | & | & | & | \\ H & H & H & H & H \end{array}$$

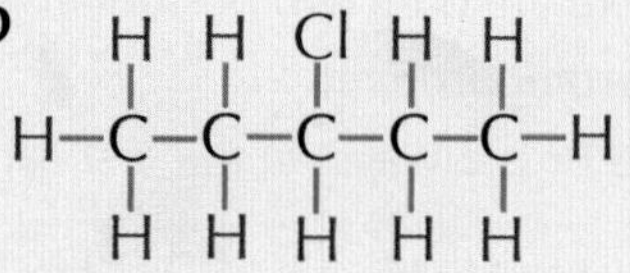

b) State the type of isomerism shown in part a).

## Practice Questions — Fact Recall

**Q1** What is a chain isomer?

**Q2** What is a positional isomer?

**Q3** What is a functional group isomer?

# 4. Stereoisomers

*Structural isomers aren't the only isomers you need to know about. You also need to know all about stereoisomers... which is what this topic is about.*

## E/Z isomerism

**Stereoisomers** have the same structural formula but a different arrangement in space. Some alkenes have stereoisomers — this is because there's a lack of rotation around the C=C double bond. When the double-bonded carbon atoms each have two different atoms or groups attached to them, you get an 'E-isomer' and a 'Z-isomer'.

Each of the groups linked to the double-bonded carbons is given a priority. If the two carbon atoms have their 'higher priority groups' on opposite sides, then it's an E isomer. If the two carbon atoms have their 'higher priority groups' on the same side, then it's a Z isomer — see Figure 1.

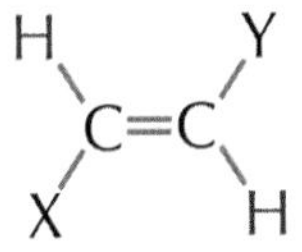

*E-isomer* 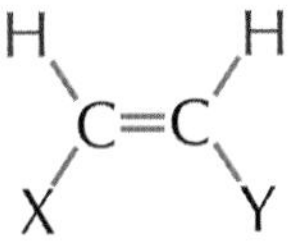          *Z-isomer*

**Figure 1:** *E-isomers and Z-isomers.*
*In these diagrams X and Y are the higher priority groups.*

### Examples

The double-bonded carbon atoms in but-2-ene ($C_4H_8$) each have an H and a $CH_3$ group attached.

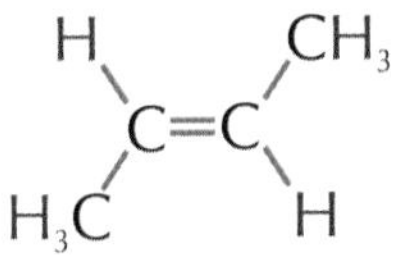

*E-isomer*

When the $CH_3$ groups are across the double bond then it's the E-isomer.
This molecule is E-but-2-ene.

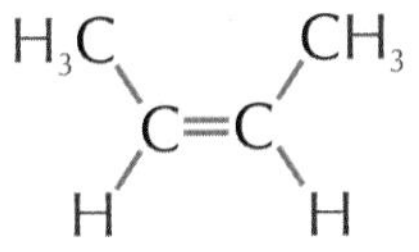

*Z-isomer*

When the $CH_3$ groups are both above or both below the double bond then it's the Z-isomer.
This molecule is Z-but-2-ene.

In pent-2-ene ($C_5H_{10}$) one of the double-bonded carbon atoms has an H and a $CH_3$ group attached to it. The other has an H and a $CH_2CH_3$ group attached.

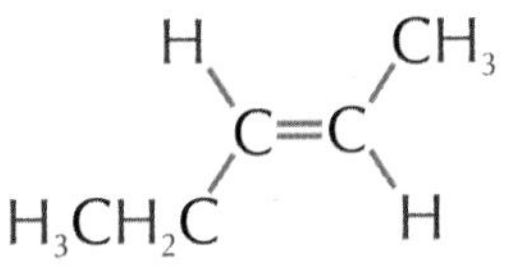

*E-isomer*

The high priority groups ($CH_3$ and $CH_2CH_3$) are across the double bond so it's the E-isomer.
This molecule is E-pent-2-ene.

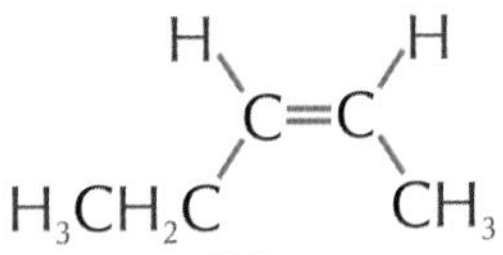

*Z-isomer*

The high priority groups are both below the double bond so it's the Z-isomer.
This molecule is Z-pent-2-ene.

**Learning Objectives:**

- Know that stereoisomers are compounds with the same structural formula but with a different arrangement in space.
- Know that E/Z isomerism is an example of stereoisomerism, which occurs due to restricted rotation about a double bond when two different groups are attached to each carbon atom of the C=C group.
- Know that cis-trans isomerism is a special case of E/Z isomerism in which two of the substituent groups are the same.
- Be able to determine the possible structural formulas and/or stereoisomers of an organic molecule, given its molecular formula.

**Specification Reference 2.1.1**

**Tip:** See page 135 for more about why double bonds can't rotate.

**Tip:** If all this isomer stuff is a bit confusing, try to get your hands on a molecular modelling kit and have a go making the isomers yourself — it should make it all a bit clearer.

# Cis-trans isomerism

**Cis-trans isomerism** is a special type of E/Z isomerism where the two carbon atoms either side of the double bond have at least one group in common. The cis-isomer is the one that has the two identical groups on the same side of the C=C double bond (equivalent to the Z-isomer). The trans-isomer is the one that has the two identical groups on opposite sides of the C=C double bond (equivalent to the E-isomer) — see Figure 2.

**Tip:** Because cis-trans isomerism is a type of E/Z isomerism, any molecule that shows cis-trans isomerism will also show E/Z isomerism.

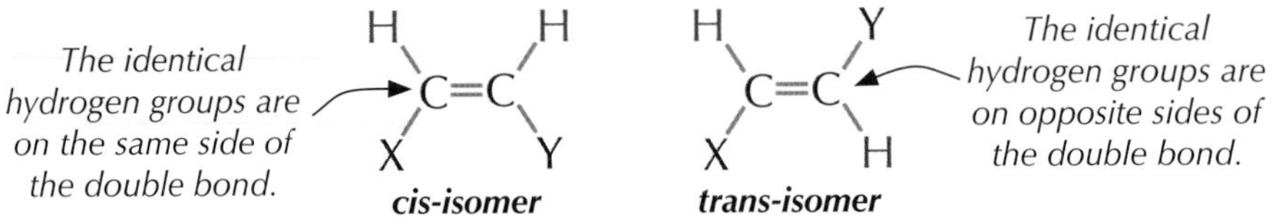

*The identical hydrogen groups are on the same side of the double bond.*

*The identical hydrogen groups are on opposite sides of the double bond.*

**cis-isomer**          **trans-isomer**

**Figure 2:** *cis-isomers and trans-isomers.*

---

**Example**

This is cis-1-fluoropropene:

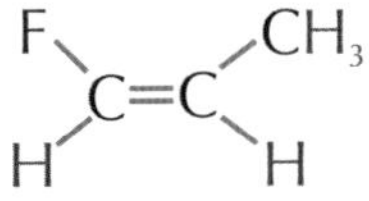

1-fluoropropene shows cis-trans isomerism because both of the carbons around the double bond have a hydrogen atom and another group (F or $CH_3$) attached to them.

---

You can't use the cis-trans system if there are more than two different groups (other than hydrogen atoms) attached around the double bond because you can't tell which isomer is which.

---

**Example**

Here is the structure of 1-bromo-1-fluoropropene:

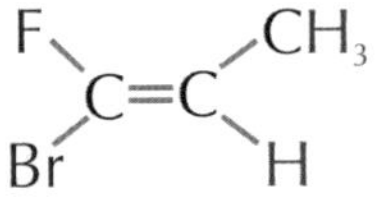

1-bromo-1-fluoropropene has more than two different groups (other than hydrogen atoms) attached around the double bond. As a result the cis–trans system doesn't work. The E/Z system keeps on working though. In the E/Z system, Br has a higher priority than F, so the names depend on where the Br atom is in relation to the $CH_3$ group (which has a higher priority than the H atom).

---

**Tip:** At A-level, you don't need to know the rules for deciding the order of the priorities of functional groups — hoorah.

## Practice Questions — Application

**Q1** For each of the molecules below, state if it is:

a) an E-isomer or a Z-isomer.

b) a cis-isomer or a trans-isomer.

i) 

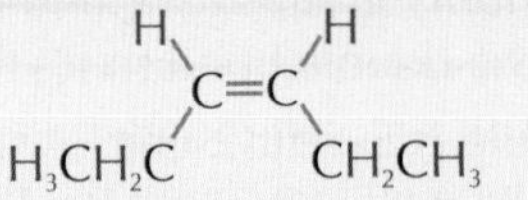

ii) 

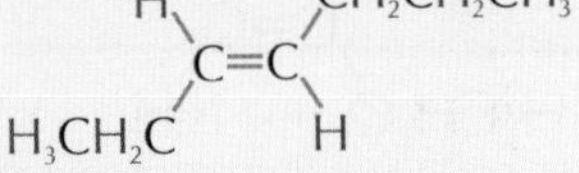

**Q2** Draw the two stereoisomers of 3,4-dimethylhex-3-ene and label which is the E-isomer and which is the Z-isomer.
The structure of 3,4-dimethylhex-3-ene is shown below.

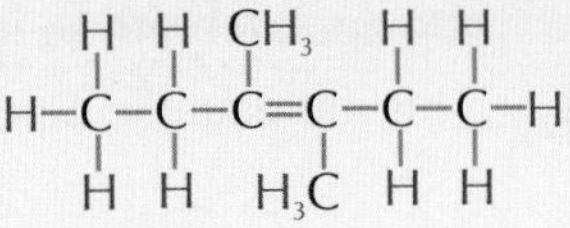

# 5. Chemical Yield

*If you're making a chemical (in a lab or a factory), it helps to know how much of it you can expect to get. In real life you'll never manage to make exactly that much — but percentage yield can give you an idea of how close you got.*

**Learning Objective:**

- Be able to carry out calculations to determine the percentage yield of a reaction.

**Specification Reference 2.1.1**

## Calculating theoretical yield

The **theoretical yield** is the mass of product that should be formed in a chemical reaction. It assumes no chemicals are 'lost' in the process. You can use the masses of reactants and a balanced equation to calculate the theoretical yield for a reaction. It's a bit like calculating reacting masses (see page 28) — here are the steps you have to go through:

1. Work out how many moles of the limiting reactant you have.

2. Use the equation to work out how many moles of product you would expect that much reactant to make.

3. Calculate the mass of that many moles of product — and that's the theoretical yield.

**Tip:** The limiting reactant is the one that you have a limited amount of (i.e. the reactant that's not in excess).

**Example**

Ethanol can be oxidised to form ethanal:

$$C_2H_5OH + [O] \rightarrow CH_3CHO + H_2O$$

9.2 g of ethanol was reacted with an oxidising agent in excess. Calculate the theoretical yield of this reaction.

1. Ethanol is the limiting reactant so work out how many moles of ethanol you have:
   Molar mass of $C_2H_5OH = (2 \times 12) + (5 \times 1) + 16 + 1 = 46$ g mol$^{-1}$
   Number of moles $C_2H_5OH$ = mass ÷ molar mass
   $= 9.2 \div 46 = 0.20$ moles.

2. Work out how many moles of product you would expect to make:
   From the equation, you know that 1 mole of $C_2H_5OH$ produces 1 mole of $CH_3CHO$ so 0.20 moles of $C_2H_5OH$ should produce 0.20 moles of $CH_3CHO$.

3. Now calculate the mass of that many moles of product:
   Molar mass of $CH_3CHO = (2 \times 12) + (4 \times 1) + 16 = 44$ g mol$^{-1}$
   Theoretical yield = number of moles × molar mass
   $= 0.20 \times 44 = 8.8$ g

**Tip:** The theoretical yield is the amount of product you would <u>expect</u> to form. The actual yield is the amount of product that is <u>actually</u> obtained.

## Calculating percentage yield

For any reaction, the actual mass of product obtained (the actual yield) will always be less than the theoretical yield. There are many reasons for this. For example, sometimes not all the 'starting' chemicals react fully. And some chemicals are always 'lost', e.g. some solution gets left on filter paper, or is lost during transfers between containers. Once you've found the theoretical yield and the actual yield, you can work out the **percentage yield**.

$$\text{Percentage Yield} = \frac{\text{Actual Yield}}{\text{Theoretical Yield}} \times 100$$

***Figure 1:** A student pouring and filtering a solution. Some chemicals will be left on the glassware and some will be left on the filter paper.*

## Examples

In the ethanal example on the previous page, the theoretical yield was 8.80 g. Say you weighed the ethanal produced and found the actual yield was 2.10 g.

Then to work out the percentage yield you just have to plug the numbers into the formula:

$$\text{Percentage yield} = \frac{\text{Actual yield}}{\text{Theoretical yield}} \times 100$$

$$= (2.10 \div 8.80) \times 100 = 23.9\,\%$$

Here's another example:

5.00 g of ethanoyl chloride reacted with water to produce ethanoic acid. The theoretical yield of this reaction was 3.82 g. When the ethanoic acid was weighed it was found to have a mass of 2.46 g.

Calculate the percentage yield of this reaction.

All you need to do here is put the right numbers into the formula:

$$\text{Percentage yield} = \frac{\text{Actual yield}}{\text{Theoretical yield}} \times 100$$

$$= (2.46 \div 3.82) \times 100 = 64.4\%$$

**Exam Tip**

If you get a question in the exam on percentage yield and you've never heard of the compounds involved, don't be put off. You can just ignore the names — all you need is the theoretical and actual yields.

**Exam Tip**

This is a percentage yield, so it can never be more than 100%. If your answer is bigger than 100%, check the working for mistakes.

**Exam Tip**

Percentage yields can be calculated for organic or inorganic reactions. The method is exactly the same so don't be put off if you're asked to calculate the percentage yield of an inorganic reaction in your exam.

## Practice Questions — Application

Q1 The theoretical yield of a reaction used in an experiment was 3.24 g. The actual yield was 1.76 g. Calculate the percentage yield of the reaction.

Q2 In an experiment nitrobenzene was reduced to produce phenylamine. The theoretical yield of this reaction was 6.10 g. The phenylamine produced had a mass of 3.70 g. Calculate the percentage yield of this reaction.

Q3 3.00 g of ethanoic anhydride reacts with water to give ethanoic acid:

$$(CH_3CO)_2O + H_2O \rightarrow 2CH_3COOH$$

a) How many moles of ethanoic anhydride are there in 3.00 g?

b) Calculate the theoretical yield of ethanoic acid for this reaction.

c) Calculate the percentage yield if 2.80 g of ethanoic acid is made.

Q4 Propene reacts with HCl to produce 1-chloropropane:

$$CH_3CHCH_2 + HCl \rightarrow CH_3CH_2CH_2Cl$$

a) How much 1-chloropropane would you expect to get from 50.0 g of propene?

b) Calculate the percentage yield if only 54.0 g is made.

Q5 4.70 g of methanoic acid reacts to form 3.60 g of methanoic anhydride. The equation for this reaction is:

$$2HCOOH \rightarrow (CHO)_2O + H_2O$$

Calculate the percentage yield of this reaction.

## Practice Questions — Fact Recall

Q1 What is meant by the 'theoretical yield' of a reaction?

Q2 Write down the formula for percentage yield.

# 6. Atom Economy

*Atom economy is one way to work out how efficient a reaction is. Efficient reactions are better for the environment and save the chemical industry money.*

## What is atom economy?

The efficiency of a reaction is often measured by the percentage yield. This tells you how wasteful the process is — it's based on how much of the product is lost because of things like reactions not completing or losses during collection and purification. But percentage yield doesn't measure how wasteful the reaction itself is. A reaction that has a 100% yield could still be very wasteful if a lot of the atoms from the reactants wind up in by-products rather than the desired product. **Atom economy** is a measure of the proportion of reactant atoms that become part of the desired product (rather than by-products) in the balanced chemical equation.

## Calculating atom economy

Atom economy is calculated using this formula:

$$\% \text{ atom economy} = \frac{\text{Molecular mass of desired product}}{\text{Sum of molecular masses of all products}} \times 100$$

To calculate the atom economy for a reaction, you just need to add up the molecular masses of the products, find the molecular mass of the product you're interested in and put them both into the formula.

┌ **Example** ─────────────

**Bromomethane is reacted with sodium hydroxide to make methanol:**

$$CH_3Br + NaOH \rightarrow CH_3OH + NaBr$$

**Calculate the percentage atom economy for this reaction.**

First, calculate the total mass of the products — add up the relative molecular masses of everything on the right side of the balanced equation:

Total mass of products = $(12 + (3 \times 1) + 16 + 1) + (23 + 79.9) = 134.9$

Then find the mass of the desired product — that's the methanol:

Mass of desired product = $12 + (3 \times 1) + 16 + 1 = 32$

Now you can find the % atom economy:

$$\% \text{ atom economy} = \frac{\text{Molecular mass of desired product}}{\text{Sum of molecular masses of all products}} \times 100$$

$$= \frac{32}{134.9} \times 100 = 23.7\%$$

When you calculate the masses, you should use the number of moles of each compound that is in the balanced equation (e.g. the mass of '$2H_2$' should be $2 \times (2 \times 1) = 4$). Here's a quick example:

┌ **Example** ─────────────

**Ethanol can be produced by fermenting glucose:**

$$C_6H_{12}O_6 \rightarrow 2C_2H_5OH + 2CO_2$$

**Calculate the percentage atom economy for this reaction.**

**Learning Objectives:**

- Be able to explain that the atom economy of a reaction is the molecular mass of the desired products divided by the sum of molecular masses of all the products multiplied by 100%.

- Be able to carry out calculations to determine the atom economy of a reaction.

- Be able to explain that addition reactions have an atom economy of 100%, whereas substitution reactions are less efficient.

- Be able to explain that a reaction may have a high percentage yield but a low atom economy.

- Be able to describe the benefits of developing chemical processes with a high atom economy in terms of fewer waste materials.

**Specification Reference 2.1.1**

*Figure 1: Tablets of the painkiller ibuprofen. Ibuprofen was originally made using a reaction with a 40% atom economy. Now a new way of making it with a 77% atom economy is used. This produces much less waste.*

**Exam Tip**
If you're asked to calculate atom economy in an exam, make sure that you start from the balanced equation.

Calculate the total mass of the products:

Total mass of products = $2((2 \times 12) + (5 \times 1) + 16 + 1) + 2(12 + (16 \times 2)) = 180$

Then find the mass of the desired product (2 moles of ethanol):

Mass of desired product = $2 \times ((12 \times 2) + (5 \times 1) + 16 + 1) = 92$ So,

$$\% \text{ atom economy} = \frac{\text{Molecular mass of desired product}}{\text{Sum of molecular masses of all products}} \times 100$$

$$= \frac{92}{180} \times 100 = 51.1\%$$

## Addition and substitution reactions

In an **addition reaction**, the reactants combine to form a single product. The atom economy for addition reactions is always 100% since no atoms are wasted.

**Tip:** Any reaction where there's only one product will have a 100% atom economy because the mass of reactants has to equal the mass of product — atoms can't go anywhere else.

**Example**

Ethene ($C_2H_4$) and hydrogen react to form ethane ($C_2H_6$) in an addition reaction: $C_2H_4 + H_2 \rightarrow C_2H_6$

The only product is ethane — the desired product. So no reactant atoms are wasted — the atom economy is 100%.

A **substitution reaction** is one where some atoms from one reactant are swapped with atoms from another reactant. This type of reaction always results in at least two products — the desired product and at least one by-product. So the atom economy of substitution reactions is always less than 100%.

**Example**

The reaction of bromoethane with sodium hydroxide (on the previous page) is a substitution reaction and has a low atom economy.

## Atom economy and percentage yield

Atom economy and percentage yield measure different things — so a reaction that has a high percentage yield might have a really low atom economy.

**Tip:** See page 113 for more about calculating percentage yield.

**Example**

**0.475 g of $CH_3Br$ reacts with an excess of NaOH in this reaction:**

$$CH_3Br + NaOH \rightarrow CH_3OH + NaBr$$

**0.153 g of $CH_3OH$ is produced. What is the percentage yield?**

Number of moles = mass of substance ÷ molar mass

Moles of $CH_3Br = 0.475 \div (12 + 3 \times 1 + 80) = 0.475 \div 95 = 0.005$ moles

The reactant : product ratio is 1 : 1, so the maximum number of moles of $CH_3OH$ is 0.005.

Theoretical yield = $0.005 \times M_r(CH_3OH) = 0.005 \times (12 + (3 \times 1) + 16 + 1)$
$= 0.005 \times 32 = 0.160$ g

$$\text{percentage yield} = \frac{\text{actual yield}}{\text{theoretical yield}} \times 100\% = \frac{0.153}{0.160} \times 100\% = 95.6\%$$

So this reaction has a very high percentage yield, but, as you saw on the previous page, the atom economy is low.

# Atom economy in industry

Companies in the chemical industry will often choose to use reactions with high atom economies. High atom economy has environmental and economic benefits.

- Reactions with low atom economies are less sustainable (see page 205). Many raw materials are in limited supply, so it makes sense to use them efficiently so they last as long as possible. Also, waste has to go somewhere — it's better for the environment if less is produced.

- A low atom economy means there's lots of waste produced. It costs money to separate the desired product from the waste products and more money to dispose of the waste products safely so they don't harm the environment. Companies will usually have paid good money to buy the reactant chemicals. It's a waste of money if a high proportion of them end up as useless products.

But reactions with a low atom economy may still be used if the waste products can be sold and used for something else (waste products like gases, salts and acids can often be useful reactants for other reactions).

*Figure 2:* A container of chemical waste at a waste disposal site. Disposing of chemicals is expensive so reactions with high atom economies and less waste are better in industry.

## Practice Questions — Application

Q1 Chlorine gas can react with excess methane to make chloromethane:
$$CH_4 + Cl_2 \rightarrow CH_3Cl + HCl$$
   a) Find the total molecular mass of the products in this reaction.
   b) Find the molecular mass of the chloromethane produced.
   c) Calculate the percentage atom economy of this reaction.
   d) A company wants to use this reaction to make chloromethane, despite its low atom economy. Suggest one way that they could increase their profit and reduce the waste they produce.

Q2 Ethanol can be produced using this reaction:
$$C_2H_4 + H_2O \rightarrow C_2H_5OH$$
   What is the percentage atom economy of this reaction?

Q3 Ethene can be produced from ethanol in a dehydration reaction:
$$C_2H_5OH \rightarrow C_2H_4 + H_2O$$
   Calculate the percentage atom economy of this reaction.

Q4 In industry, ammonia ($NH_3$) is usually produced using this reaction:
   Reaction 1:  $N_2 + 3H_2 \rightarrow 2NH_3$
   It can also be made using this reaction:
   Reaction 2:  $2NH_4Cl + Ca(OH)_2 \rightarrow CaCl_2 + 2NH_3 + 2H_2O$
   a) Calculate the percentage atom economy of both reactions.
   b) Give one reason why reaction 1 is used to produce ammonia industrially rather than reaction 2.

## Practice Questions — Fact Recall

Q1 What is meant by the 'atom economy' of a reaction?

Q2 Write down the formula for calculating % atom economy.

Q3 Give two reasons why reactions with a low atom economy are not used in industry.

**Learning Objectives:**

- Know that a hydrocarbon is a compound that contains hydrogen and carbon only.
- Know that alkanes and cycloalkanes are saturated hydrocarbons.
- Be able to apply IUPAC rules for naming alkanes.
- Know the names of the first ten members of the alkanes homologous series.

**Specification Reference 2.1.1, 2.1.2**

**Figure 1:** *Molecular models of cyclohexane and hexane.*

**Tip:** There's more on the IUPAC rules for naming different organic compounds throughout Unit 2 Module 1 and Unit 2 Module 2 in this book.

**Tip:** The alkanes are an example of a homologous series. See page 105 for more on this.

*Alkanes are molecules with hydrogen atoms, carbon atoms and single bonds. Nomenclature is just a fancy word for naming organic compounds.*

## Structure of alkanes

Alkanes have the general formula $C_nH_{2n+2}$. They've only got carbon and hydrogen atoms, so they're **hydrocarbons**. Every carbon atom in an alkane has four single bonds with other atoms. It's impossible for carbon to make more than four bonds, so alkanes are **saturated**.

Here are a few examples of alkanes —

*methane*          *ethane*          *propane*

You get **cycloalkanes** too. They have a ring of carbon atoms with two hydrogens attached to each carbon. Cycloalkanes have two fewer hydrogens than other alkanes (assuming they have only one ring) so cycloalkanes have a different general formula from that of normal alkanes $(C_nH_{2n})$, but they are still saturated.

*cyclohexane, $C_6H_{12}$*

## Naming alkanes

The IUPAC system for naming organic compounds is the agreed international language of chemistry. Years ago, organic compounds were given whatever names people fancied, such as acetic acid and ethylene. But these names caused confusion between different countries.

*HOW SCIENCE WORKS*

The IUPAC system means scientific ideas can be communicated across the globe more effectively. So it's easier for scientists to get on with testing each other's work, and either confirm or dispute new theories.

You need to be able to name straight-chain and branched alkanes using the IUPAC system for naming organic compounds.

### Straight-chain alkanes

There are two parts to the name of a straight-chain alkane. The first part (the stem) states how many carbon atoms there are in the molecule. The second part is always "-ane". It's the "-ane" bit that lets people know it's an alkane.

┌ **Example** ─────────────────────────────────────

This molecule is pentane:

The stem is pent-, which tells you that the molecule has 5 carbons in it, and the -ane bit at the end tells you it's an alkane.

You need to know the names of the first ten alkanes — see Figure 2.

| Number of Carbon Atoms | Stem | Alkane |
|:---:|:---:|:---:|
| 1 | meth- | methane ($CH_4$) |
| 2 | eth- | ethane ($C_2H_6$) |
| 3 | prop- | propane ($C_3H_8$) |
| 4 | but- | butane ($C_4H_{10}$) |
| 5 | pent- | pentane ($C_5H_{12}$) |
| 6 | hex- | hexane ($C_6H_{14}$) |
| 7 | hept- | heptane ($C_7H_{16}$) |
| 8 | oct- | octane ($C_8H_{18}$) |
| 9 | non- | nonane ($C_9H_{20}$) |
| 10 | dec- | decane ($C_{10}H_{22}$) |

*Figure 2: Naming the first ten alkanes.*

**Tip:** Since the names of the alkanes are based on the same stems as all other homologous series, this will help you name every other organic chemical in the world too.

**Tip:** These stems come up again and again in chemistry so it's really important that you know all of them.

## Branched alkanes

Branched alkanes have side chains. These are the carbon atoms that aren't part of the longest continuous chain. To name branched alkanes you first need to count how many carbon atoms are in the longest chain and work out the stem (just like you would for a straight-chain alkane). Once you've done that you can name the side chains. The side chains are named according to how many carbon atoms they have (see Figure 3) and which carbon atom they are attached to. If there's more than one side chain in a molecule, you place them in alphabetical order. So but-groups come before eth- groups which come before meth- groups.

| Number of Carbon Atoms | Side Chain Prefix |
|:---:|:---:|
| 1 | methyl- |
| 2 | ethyl- |
| 3 | propyl- |
| 4 | butyl- |
| 5 | pentyl- |
| 6 | hexyl- |

*Figure 3: Names of carbon side chains.*

**Tip:** Methyl-, ethyl-, propyl-, etc. groups are collectively known as alkyl groups.

**Tip:** Always number the longest continuous carbon chain so that the name contains the lowest numbers possible. For example, you could number this chain:

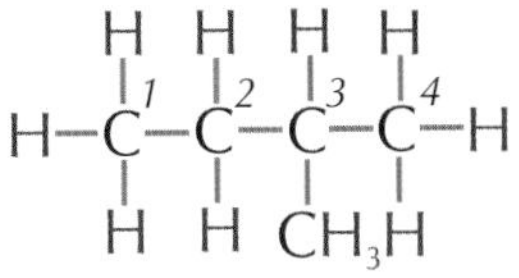

which would make it 3-methylbutane. But you should actually number it in the opposite direction to get 2-methylbutane.

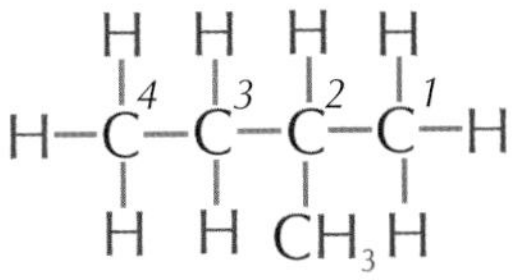

## Examples

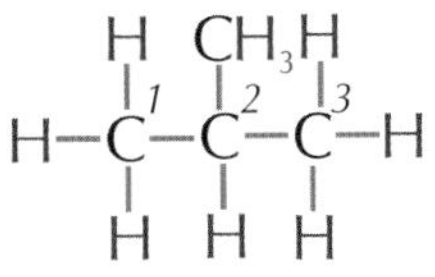

*2-methylpropane*

The longest continuous carbon chain is 3 carbon atoms, so the stem is propane.

There's one side chain, which has one carbon atom so it's a methyl group.

It's joined to the main carbon chain at the 2nd carbon atom, so it's a 2-methyl group.

The alkane is called 2-methylpropane.

The longest continuous carbon chain is 5 carbon atoms, so the stem is pentane.

There are two side chains.

One side chain is a methyl group joined to the 2nd carbon atom: 2-methyl-.

The other is an ethyl group (2 carbons) joined to the 3rd carbon atom: 3-ethyl-.

Side chains go in alphabetical order, so the alkane is 3-ethyl-2-methylpentane.

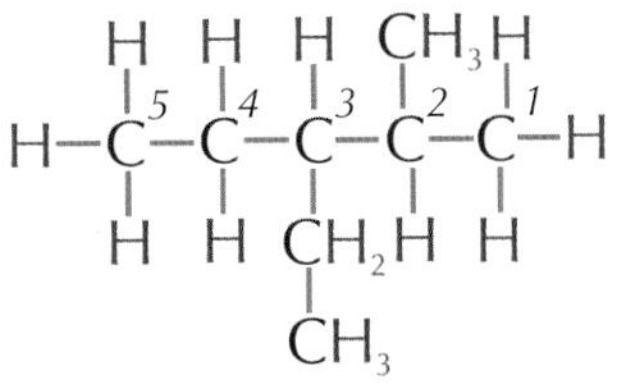

*3-ethyl-2-methylpentane*

If there are two or more side chains of the same type then you add a prefix of di- for two, tri- for three etc. (You can ignore these prefixes when you're putting the other prefixes in alphabetical order.)

**Tip:** Be careful, the longest carbon chain may not be in a straight line:

H   Cl   H   H
|₁  |₂  |₃  |
H−C−C−C−C−H
|   |   |⁴  |
H   H  CH₂ H
         |
        ⁵CH₃

---

**Example**

The longest carbon chain is 5 atoms long, so the stem is pentane.

There's an ethyl group on the 3rd carbon atom: 3-ethyl-.

There are methyl groups on the 2nd and the 4th carbon atoms: 2,4-dimethyl-.

The alkane is called 3-ethyl-2,4-dimethylpentane.

H  CH₃ H  CH₃ H
|⁵  |⁴  |³  |²  |¹
H−C−C−C−C−C−H
|   |   |   |   |
H   H  CH₂ H   H
         |
        CH₃

*3-ethyl-2,4-dimethylpentane*

---

## Practice Questions — Application

**Q1** Name the alkanes shown below.

a)
H   H   H   H
|   |   |   |
H−C−C−C−C−H
|   |   |   |
H   H   H   H

b)
H   H
|   |
H−C−C−H
|   |
H   H

c)
H
|
H−C−H
|
H

d) $C_9H_{20}$          e) $C_7H_{16}$          f) $C_{10}H_{22}$

**Q2** Name the following branched alkanes:

a)
H   H   H   H
|   |   |   |
H−C−C−C−C−H
|   |   |   |
H   H  CH₂ H
         |
        CH₃

b)
              CH₃
               |
H   H  CH₂ H
|   |   |   |
H−C−C−C−C−H
|   |   |   |
H   H  CH₂ H
         |
        CH₃

c)
          CH₃
           |
H   H  CH₂ H
|   |   |   |
H−C−C−C−C−CH₃
|   |   |   |
H   H  CH₂ H
         |
      H₃C−CH₂

d)
          CH₃
           |
H  CH₃ CH₂ H
|   |   |   |
H−C−C−C−C−CH₃
|   |   |   |
H   H  CH₂ H
         |
      H₃C−CH₂

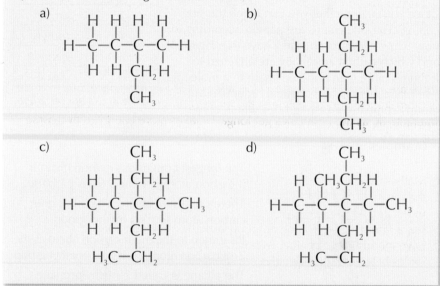

**Tip:** When you're naming molecules commas are put between numbers (for example 2,2) and dashes are put between numbers and letters (for example 2-methyl).

---

## Practice Questions — Fact Recall

**Q1** Give the general formula for an alkane.

**Q2** Describe a cycloalkane.

**Q3** What is the stem for a carbon chain containing six carbon atoms?

**Q4** What is the name for a carbon side chain containing two carbon atoms?

**Q5** If there are two methyl- side chains what prefix should you add to methyl- when naming the molecule?

# 8. Properties of Alkanes

*You need to know a little bit about the physical and chemical properties of the alkanes. Luckily for you, the next few pages happen to be about just that.*

## Shapes of alkane molecules

In an alkane molecule, each carbon atom has four pairs of bonding electrons around it. They all repel each other equally. So the molecule forms a **tetrahedral shape** around each carbon.

┌─ Examples ─────────────────────────────────────────────

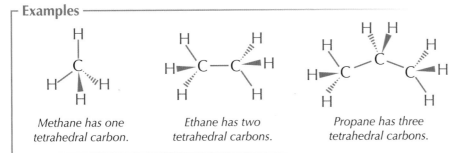

Methane has one tetrahedral carbon.

Ethane has two tetrahedral carbons.

Propane has three tetrahedral carbons.

└─────────────────────────────────────────────────────────

## Boiling points of alkanes

The boiling point of an alkane depends on its size and shape. The smallest alkanes, like methane, are gases at room temperature and pressure — they've got very low boiling points. Larger alkanes are liquids — they have higher boiling points. This is due to differences in their intermolecular forces.

Alkanes have covalent bonds inside the molecules. Between the molecules, there are **van der Waals forces** which hold them all together (see page 70). The longer the carbon chain, the more van der Waals forces there are. This is because they have a larger molecular surface area so there is more surface contact between the molecules. As a result, more electrons interact. So as the molecules get longer, it takes more energy to overcome the van der Waals forces and separate them, and the boiling point rises.

┌─ Examples ─────────────────────────────────────────────

Methane is a very small molecule so there is little surface contact between the molecules. This means that the van der Waals forces between the molecules are weak and the boiling point of methane is very low. Propane has a much higher boiling point because the molecules are much larger so have more surface contact with each other. Therefore, the van der Waals forces between the molecules are stronger.

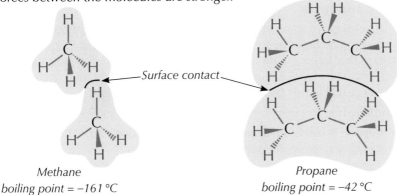

Methane
boiling point = −161 °C

Propane
boiling point = −42 °C

└─────────────────────────────────────────────────────────

**Learning Objectives:**

- Be able to explain the tetrahedral shape around each carbon atom in alkanes.
- Be able to explain, in terms of van der Waals' forces, the variations in the boiling points of alkanes with different carbon-chain length and branching.
- Be able to describe the combustion of alkanes, leading to their use as fuels in industry, in the home and in transport.
- Be able to explain using equations the incomplete combustion of alkanes in a limited supply of oxygen.
- Understand the potential dangers arising from production of CO in the home and from car use.

**Specification Reference 2.1.2**

**Tip:** If you draw lines joining up the Hs in tetrahedral molecules, the shape you get is a tetrahedron, hence the name:

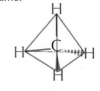

**Tip:** See pages 65-68 for lots more on the shapes of molecules.

A branched-chain alkane has a lower boiling point than its straight-chain isomer. Branched-chain alkanes can't pack closely together and they have smaller molecular surface areas — so the van der Waals forces are reduced.

**Exam Tip**
If you get a question on this in the exam, make sure you talk about the amount of surface contact and not just the surface area of the molecules — otherwise you might miss out on some marks.

─ Example ────────────

Butane and methylpropane are both isomers of $C_4H_{10}$. Butane has a higher boiling point than methylpropane because the molecules can pack closely together, therefore have more surface contact and so have more van der Waals forces holding the molecules together.

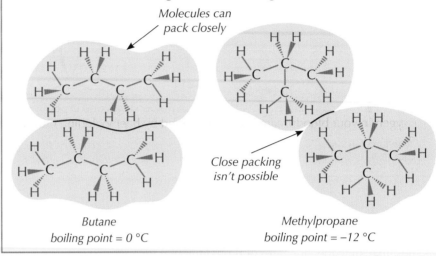

*Molecules can pack closely*

*Close packing isn't possible*

*Butane*
*boiling point = 0 °C*

*Methylpropane*
*boiling point = −12 °C*

**Tip:** You only get complete combustion when there's loads of oxygen around. If oxygen is in short supply, you'll get incomplete combustion instead. There's more on incomplete combustion on the next page.

# Complete combustion of alkanes

If you burn (oxidise) alkanes with enough oxygen, you get carbon dioxide and water — this is a **complete combustion** reaction.

─ Examples ────────────

Here's the equation for the complete combustion of propane:

$$C_3H_{8(g)} + 5O_{2(g)} \rightarrow 3CO_{2(g)} + 4H_2O_{(g)}$$

This is the equation for the complete combustion of heptane:

$$C_7H_{16(g)} + 11O_{2(g)} \rightarrow 7CO_{2(g)} + 8H_2O_{(g)}$$

Combustion reactions happen between gases, so liquid alkanes have to be vaporised first. Smaller alkanes turn into gases more easily (they're more **volatile**), so they'll burn more easily too.

### Alkanes and fuels

When alkanes burn, some energy is used to break the covalent bonds but more energy is released by forming the new product bonds in $CO_2$ and $H_2O$. This means that larger alkanes release more energy per mole than smaller alkanes, because more $CO_2$ and $H_2O$ are formed. Because they release so much energy when they burn, alkanes make excellent fuels.

─ Examples ────────────

- Propane is used as a central heating and cooking fuel.
- Butane is bottled and sold as camping gas.
- Petrol and diesel are both made up of a mixture of alkanes too (and additives) — these are used as fuels for transport.

***Figure 1:*** *A butane gas camping stove. The blue flame indicates that the combustion is complete.*

# Incomplete combustion of alkanes

If there isn't much oxygen around, an alkane will still burn, but it will produce carbon monoxide and water. This is an **incomplete combustion** reaction.

> **Examples**
>
> Here's the reaction that occurs when methane is burnt in a limited supply of oxygen:
>
> $$2CH_{4(g)} + 3O_{2(g)} \rightarrow 2CO_{(g)} + 4H_2O_{(g)}$$
>
> And here's the equation for the incomplete combustion of ethane:
>
> $$2C_2H_{6(g)} + 5O_{2(g)} \rightarrow 4CO_{(g)} + 6H_2O_{(g)}$$

**Tip:** Not all incomplete combustion reactions will only produce water and carbon monoxide. Some will produce particulate carbon or small amounts of carbon dioxide as well. Just make sure your equation <u>balances</u> and you should be fine.

## Carbon monoxide poisoning

Incomplete combustion is a problem because carbon monoxide is poisonous. The oxygen in your bloodstream is carried around by haemoglobin. Carbon monoxide is better at binding to haemoglobin than oxygen is. So if you breathe in air with a high concentration of carbon monoxide it will bind to the haemoglobin in your bloodstream before the oxygen can. This means that less oxygen will reach your cells. You will start to suffer from symptoms associated with oxygen deprivation — things like fatigue, headaches, and nausea. At very high concentrations of carbon monoxide it can even be fatal.

**Tip:** Carbon monoxide is a colourless, odourless gas. This makes it very dangerous because you don't know it's there until it's too late.

Any appliance that burns alkanes can produce carbon monoxide. This includes things like gas- or oil-fired boilers and heaters, gas stoves, and coal or wood fires. Cars also produce carbon monoxide. All appliances that use an alkane-based fuel need to be properly ventilated. They should be checked and maintained regularly, and their sources of ventilation should never be blocked. If you have any alkane burning appliances it's a good idea to have a carbon monoxide detector around.

*Figure 2:* A carbon monoxide detector.

## Practice Questions — Application

Q1 Propane ($C_3H_8$) and octane ($C_8H_{18}$) are both alkanes.
   a) Explain why octane has a higher boiling point than propane.
   b) State and explain which alkane releases more energy when burnt.
   c) Write equations for the complete and incomplete combustion of octane.

Q2 Pentane and 2,2-dimethylpropane both have the molecular formula $C_5H_{12}$. Which has the higher boiling point? Explain your answer.

## Practice Questions — Fact Recall

Q1 Describe the molecular shape around each carbon atom in an alkane.

Q2 Name two factors that affect the boiling point of an alkane.

Q3 What are the products of the complete and incomplete combustion of alkanes?

Q4 Give three examples of how alkanes are used as fuels.

Q5 Explain why carbon monoxide is poisonous.

- Be able to explain the use of crude oil as a source of hydrocarbons.
- Know that hydrocarbons are separated as fractions with different boiling points by fractional distillation.
- Know that hydrocarbons can be used as fuels or be processed into petrochemicals.
- Be able to describe the use of catalytic cracking to obtain more useful alkanes and alkenes.
- Be able to explain that the petroleum industry processes straight-chain hydrocarbons into branched alkanes and cyclic hydrocarbons to promote efficient combustion.

**Specification Reference 2.1.2**

# 9. Petroleum

*Petroleum is just a poncy word for crude oil — the black, yukky stuff they get out of the ground with huge oil wells. It's mostly alkanes. They range from smallish alkanes, like pentane, to massive alkanes with more than 50 carbons.*

## Fractional distillation

**Crude oil** isn't very useful as it is, but you can separate it into more useful bits (or fractions) by **fractional distillation**. Here's how fractional distillation works — don't try this at home.

- First, the crude oil is vaporised at about 350 °C.
- The vaporised crude oil goes into the bottom of the fractionating column and rises up through the trays.
- The largest hydrocarbons don't vaporise at all, because their boiling points are too high — they just run to the bottom and form a gooey residue.
- As the crude oil vapour goes up the fractionating column, it gets cooler, creating a temperature gradient.
- Because boiling points of alkanes increase as the molecules get bigger, each fraction condenses at a different temperature. The fractions are drawn off at different levels in the column.
- The hydrocarbons with the lowest boiling points don't condense. They're drawn off as gases at the top of the column.

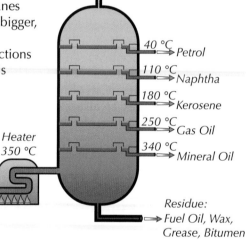

**Figure 1:** A fractionating column.

**Figure 2:** Laboratory fractional distillation apparatus.

## Uses of crude oil fractions

Most of the fractions are either used as fuels or processed to make petrochemicals. A **petrochemical** is any compound that is made from crude oil or any of its fractions and is not a fuel. Here's what each fraction is used for:

| Fraction | Carbon Chain | Uses |
|---|---|---|
| Gases | $C_1 - C_4$ | Liquefied Petroleum Gas (LPG), camping gas |
| Petrol (gasoline) | $C_5 - C_{12}$ | petrol |
| Naptha | $C_7 - C_{14}$ | processed to make petrochemicals |
| Kerosene (paraffin) | $C_{11} - C_{15}$ | jet fuel, petrochemicals, central heating fuel |
| Gas Oil (diesel) | $C_{15} - C_{19}$ | diesel fuel, central heating fuel |
| Mineral Oil (lubricating) | $C_{20} - C_{30}$ | lubricating oil |
| Fuel Oil | $C_{30} - C_{40}$ | ships, power stations |
| Wax, grease | $C_{40} - C_{50}$ | candles, lubrication |
| Bitumen | $C_{50+}$ | roofing, road surfacing |

# Cracking hydrocarbons

People want loads of the light fractions, like petrol and naphtha. They don't want so much of the heavier stuff like bitumen though. To meet this demand, the less popular heavier fractions are cracked. **Cracking** is breaking long-chain alkanes into smaller hydrocarbons. It involves breaking the C–C bonds and you end up with a mixture of alkanes and alkenes.

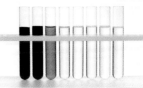

*Figure 2: Fractions produced from fractional distillation of crude oil. The fractions are arranged in order of boiling point, with higher boiling points towards the left.*

## Example

Decane could be cracked into smaller hydrocarbons like this:

$$\text{decane} \longrightarrow \text{ethene} + \text{octane}$$

But, because the bond breaking in cracking is random, this isn't the only way that decane could be cracked — it could be cracked to produce different short chain hydrocarbons. For example...

$$\text{decane} \longrightarrow \text{ethane} + \text{pent-2-ene}$$

$$+ \text{propene}$$

The main way of doing this is catalytic cracking. The heavier fractions are passed over a catalyst at a high temperature and a moderate pressure. This breaks them up into smaller molecules. Using a catalyst cuts costs, because the reaction can be done at a lower temperature and pressure. The catalyst also speeds up the reaction, and time is money and all that. This method of cracking gives a high percentage of branched hydrocarbons and aromatic hydrocarbons — these are particularly useful for making petrol.

**Exam Tip**
In the exam you might have to write equations for cracking. The marks are pretty simple to pick up, as long as you check that you have the same number of carbons and hydrogens on each side of the equation.

**Tip:** See page 133 for more on alkenes.

# Octane ratings

To understand why octane ratings are useful you need to know a bit about petrol engines, so here's a quick whizz through how a petrol engine works:

- The fuel/air mixture is squashed by a piston and ignited with a spark, creating an explosion.

- This drives the piston up again, turning the crankshaft.

- Multiple pistons (often four) work one after the other, so that the engine runs smoothly.

The problem is, straight-chain alkanes in petrol tend to auto-ignite (ignite by themselves) — when the fuel/air mixture is compressed they explode without being ignited by the spark. This extra explosion causes 'knocking' in the engine and can damage the pistons.

The **octane rating** of a petrol tells you how likely it is to auto-ignite. The higher the number, the less likely it is to auto-ignite. It's based on a scale where 100% heptane has a rating of 0, and 100% 2,2,4-trimethylpentane has a rating of 100 — see Figure 4.

**Tip:** Aromatic compounds contain benzene rings. Benzene has the molecular formula $C_6H_6$, but don't worry — you don't need to know anything about benzene until A2.

**Figure 3:** *Unleaded and super unleaded petrol pumps. Super unleaded petrol is more expensive but it has a higher octane rating (around 97 compared to 95 for normal unleaded petrol). This means it is less likely to auto-ignite and can be burnt more efficiently.*

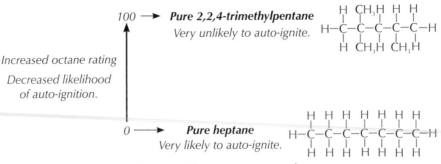

$100 \rightarrow$ **Pure 2,2,4-trimethylpentane**
*Very unlikely to auto-ignite.*

Increased octane rating
Decreased likelihood of auto-ignition.

$0 \rightarrow$ **Pure heptane**
*Very likely to auto-ignite.*

**Figure 4:** *The octane rating scale.*

To get rid of knocking and make combustion more efficient, shorter branched-chain alkanes, cycloalkanes and arenes are included in petrols, creating a high octane rating.

# Making branched or cyclic hydrocarbons

Branched or cyclic hydrocarbons have higher octane ratings than straight-chain hydrocarbons, so they can be burnt more efficiently. So, fuel manufacturers convert some of the straight-chain alkanes into branched-chain alkanes and cyclic hydrocarbons using isomerisation and reforming.

### Isomerisation

Isomerisation is used to convert straight-chain hydrocarbons into branched hydrocarbons. It occurs when you heat straight-chain alkanes with a catalyst stuck on inert aluminium oxide. The alkanes break up and join back together as branched isomers.

--- Example ---

Isomerisation can be used to convert butane into 2-methylpropane.

butane $\xrightarrow{Pt}$ methylpropane

The Pt above the arrow in this equation shows that a platinum catalyst is being used.

A molecular sieve (**zeolite** — see Figure 5) is used to separate the isomers. Straight-chain molecules go through the sieve and are recycled.

### Reforming

Reforming converts alkanes into cyclic hydrocarbons. It uses a catalyst made of platinum and another metal. Again, you need to stick the catalyst on inert aluminium oxide.

**Tip:** Zeolites are minerals that can be used as molecular sieves because they have tiny pores in their structure.

--- Example ---

Reforming can be used to convert hexane into cyclohexane:

hexane $\xrightarrow{\text{Pt and metal}}$ cyclohexane $+ H_2$

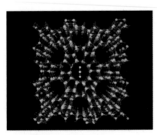

**Figure 5:** *Computer generated model of the structure of a zeolite.*

In some cases, the cyclohexane will then be converted to benzene during the reforming reaction.

Cyclohexane    Pt and metal →    Benzene    + 3H$_2$

**Tip:** The circle in the middle of the benzene molecule represents delocalised electrons. Don't worry about that now though — you'll learn lots more about aromatic hydrocarbons at A2-level.

## Practice Questions — Application

Q1 Pentane has the molecular formula C$_5$H$_{12}$. Suggest three alkanes that could be produced by the cracking of this molecule.

Q2 Hexane has a very low octane rating.
a) What does this tell you about hexane?
b) How could the octane rating of a fuel containing hexane be increased?

Q3 The fuel used in F1 racing cars has a very high octane rating.
a) Why is a high octane rating beneficial?
b) What types of alkane would you expect to find in this fuel?

Q4 a) Write an equation for the conversion of pentane to methyl butane.
b) How could the pentane and methyl butane molecules be separated following the reaction?

Q5 a) Write an equation for the conversion of pentane to cyclopentane.
b) What conditions are used for this reaction?

## Practice Questions — Fact Recall

Q1 What is petroleum?

Q2 Fractional distillation separates hydrocarbons. What property are they separated by?

Q3 a) What is cracking?
b) What conditions are required for catalytic cracking?

Q4 Why do we crack heavier petroleum fractions?

Q5 Why does using a catalyst for catalytic cracking cut costs?

Q6 a) What does the octane rating tell you about a petrol?
b) Why are petrols with high octane ratings better?

Q7 Describe how a straight-chain alkane can be converted into a branched-chain alkane.

Q8 Describe how a straight-chain alkane can be converted into a cyclic alkane.

*Figure 6: An F1 racing car being refuelled with a special high octane mixture.*

*We hear a lot about fossil fuels every day in the media, but what are they and what's everyone's beef with them — read on to find out more...*

## Uses of fossil fuels

The three **fossil fuels** — coal, oil and natural gas — are major fuels. We use them to provide energy as well as raw materials.

### Energy

The combustion of fossil fuels is very exothermic — they give out large amounts of energy when they burn, which is why they make great fuels. Different alkanes are used as fuels for various forms of transport (see page 124). Fossil fuels are burned to generate electricity in most of the world's power stations.

### Raw materials

Coal, oil and gas aren't just used as fuels, though. They're also important raw materials in the chemical industry. Hydrocarbons obtained from fossil fuels (especially oil) are used, either on their own or with other chemicals, for a whole range of purposes. For example, almost all modern plastics are polymers (see pages 137-138) made with organic chemicals from fossil fuels. Other products of the petrochemical industry include solvents, detergents, adhesives and lubricants.

## Problems with using fossil fuels

Fossil fuels are really useful — but there are a couple of major problems with them...

### The greenhouse effect

Right now we're burning more carbon-based fossil fuels (e.g. in transport, power stations etc.) than ever before. This is one factor that's helping to cause an increase in the amount of carbon dioxide in the atmosphere. Carbon dioxide is a greenhouse gas. The extra carbon dioxide we're producing is contributing to global warming and climate change by enhancing the greenhouse effect (see page 208).

### Fossil fuels are non-renewable

There's a finite amount of fossil fuels — and they're running out. Oil will be the first to go and as it gets really scarce, it'll become more expensive. It's not sustainable to keep using fossil fuels willy-nilly.

The developed world relies heavily on fossil fuels to produce energy for transport, heating and electricity generation, and to make chemicals like plastics and fibres. Some estimates suggest that if we keep using them up at the rate we are doing, there could be just 45 years' worth of oil, 70 years' worth of gas and 250 years' worth of coal left in the ground. And we could run out even sooner, because countries like China and India are developing rapidly and increasing their energy needs.

New supplies may be found, but eventually they'll run out too. There are alternative sources of energy that can be used (see the next page), and most of the chemicals currently made from crude oil can be made from coal or plants. But while there are still reserves of fossil fuels most businesses aren't keen to spend money developing these alternatives.

*Figure 1:* A research centre in Antarctica where the effects of global warming are being studied.

**Tip:** See page 205 for more on sustainability.

*Figure 2:* A coal-burning power station.

# Alternatives to fossil fuels

So we need to do something about the fuel situation — and there are various options. Plants could be an important source of fuels for the future. They're great, because they're renewable — you can grow more if you need to.

### Bioethanol

Ethanol can be used to fuel cars, either on its own or added to petrol. Bioethanol is ethanol that's produced from plants — it's made by the fermentation of sugar from crops such as maize. Bioethanol's thought of as being carbon-neutral — in other words, it has no overall carbon emission into the atmosphere. That's because all the $CO_2$ released when the fuel is burned was removed by the crop as it grew. But, there are still carbon emissions if you consider the whole process. Making the fertilisers and powering agricultural machinery will probably involve burning fossil fuels. It's still better than petrol though, and it does conserve crude oil supplies.

### Biodiesel

Biodiesel is another fuel that can come from plants. As the name suggests, it can be used in diesel engines — you can use 100% biodiesel or a mixture of biodiesel and conventional diesel. It's made by refining renewable fats and oils, such as vegetable oils (biodiesel can even be made from used restaurant fryer oil). Like bioethanol, biodiesel can be a carbon-neutral fuel (but the same big but from above applies here, too).

***Figure 3:*** *A field of oilseed rape — a crop used to make biodiesel.*

So there are quite a few advantages to using plants as alternatives to fossil fuels, for example:

- Plants are a renewable energy source — they'll never run out like fossil fuels will.
- Using plants as fuels decreases the need to use fossil fuels which contribute to global warming.
- Using plants is nearly carbon-neutral (if not quite).

# Problems with using crops to make fuels

There are some potential problems with using crops to make fuels.

It's possible that developed countries (like the UK) will create a huge demand as they try and find fossil fuel alternatives. Poorer developing countries (in South America, say) will use this as a way of earning money and rush to convert their farming land to produce these 'crops for fuels', which may mean they won't grow enough food to eat.

There are also worries that in some places forests are being cleared to make room for biofuel crops. The crops usually absorb far less $CO_2$ than the forest did — so this defeats one of the main objects of growing biofuels. Growing too many crops for fuels could reduce soil fertility too.

**Exam Tip**
Make sure you know why bioethanol and biodiesel aren't really 100% carbon-neutral. You get asked about this a lot in exams.

**Tip:** There is no ideal solution to ending our dependency on fossil fuels but using plants as fuels is one of the best options we have at the moment.

## Practice Questions — Fact Recall

Q1 Give two uses of fossil fuels.

Q2 Give two disadvantages of using fossil fuels.

Q3 a) How is bioethanol made?

b) How is biodiesel made?

Q4 Explain why biodiesel and bioethanol are thought of as carbon-neutral.

Q5 Explain why biodiesel and bioethanol aren't 100% carbon-neutral.

Q6 Discuss the advantages and disadvantages of using plant-based fuels.

# 11. Bond Fission

**Learning Objectives:**

- Be able to describe the different types of covalent bond fission.
- Know that heterolytic fission forms a cation and an anion.
- Know that homolytic fission forms two radicals.
- Be able to define the term radical as a species with an unpaired electron.
- Be able to describe a 'curly arrow' as the movement of an electron pair, showing either breaking or formation of a covalent bond.
- Be able to outline reaction mechanisms, using diagrams, to show clearly the movement of an electron pair with 'curly arrows'.

**Specification Reference 2.1.1**

*At AS-level, you need to know a bit about the different types of bond fission and how the breaking and forming of bonds can be shown using reaction mechanisms. Here's a quick summary...*

## Homolytic and heterolytic bond fission

Breaking a covalent bond is called **bond fission**. A single covalent bond is a shared pair of electrons between two atoms. It can break in two ways:

### Heterolytic fission

In heterolytic fission two different substances are formed — a positively charged cation ($X^+$), and a negatively charged anion ($Y^-$). The general equation for heterolytic fission is:

$$XY \rightarrow X^+ + Y^-$$

### Homolytic fission

In homolytic fission two electrically uncharged 'radicals' are formed. Radicals are particles that have an unpaired electron. The unpaired electron is shown by a dot after the radical. The general equation for homolytic fission is:

$$XY \rightarrow X\cdot + Y\cdot$$

Because of the unpaired electron, these radicals are very reactive.

## Reaction mechanisms

Reactions occur via a series of different processes. These processes can be shown step by step using a reaction mechanism. Reaction mechanisms use curly arrows to show the movement of electrons during a reaction. A curly arrow shows the movement of a pair of electrons and a half curly arrow shows the movement of a single electron. You can use curly arrows to show how covalent bonds are broken.

**Examples**

During heterolytic fission a pair of electrons shared in a covalent bond moves onto one of the species, giving it a negative charge. This leaves the other species with a positive charge.

$$X \dot{-} Y \rightarrow X^+ + Y^-$$

*Curly arrows show the movement of a pair of electrons.*

During homolytic fission, a pair of electrons shared in a covalent bond splits up and one electron moves onto each species, forming two free radicals.

$$X \dot{-} Y \rightarrow X\cdot + Y\cdot$$

*Half curly arrows show the movement of one electron.*

Reaction mechanisms come up a lot in chemistry — it's much easier to explain what's happening in a reaction by drawing diagrams than by using words.

**Tip:** You can use filled in arrows (like this: ➡) or line arrows (like this: →) to show the movement of an electron pair. It means the same thing as long as it's a full arrow and not a half arrow.

**Tip:** There are lots of reaction mechanisms using curly arrows on pages 142-144.

### Practice Questions — Fact Recall

Q1 What is bond fission?
Q2 a) Name the two different types of bond fission.
   b) Describe how the two different types of bond fission are different.
Q3 What is a free radical?
Q4 a) What do curly arrows show?
   b) What do half curly arrows show?

# 12. Substitution Reactions

**Learning Objectives:**

- Be able to describe the substitution of alkanes using ultraviolet radiation, by $Cl_2$ and by $Br_2$, to form halogenoalkanes.

- Be able to describe how homolytic fission leads to the mechanism of radical substitution in alkanes in terms of initiation, propagation and termination reactions.

- Be able to explain the limitations of radical substitution in synthesis, arising from further substitution with formation of a mixture of products.

**Specification Reference 2.1.2**

*A substitution reaction is a reaction where an atom in a compound gets swapped with another atom. This section is all about how halogenoalkanes can be formed by substituting a hydrogen in an alkane with a halogen.*

## Formation of halogenoalkanes

Halogenoalkanes are formed when halogens react with alkanes in photochemical reactions. **Photochemical reactions** are reactions that are started by light. During the formation of halogenoalkanes a hydrogen atom is substituted (replaced) by a halogen such as chlorine or bromine in a **free radical** substitution reaction.

Any halogen can react with any alkane in the presence of UV light to form a halogenoalkane, but one of the most industrially important free radical substitution reactions is the synthesis of chloromethane.

## Synthesis of chloromethane

A mixture of methane and chlorine will not react on its own but when exposed to UV light it reacts with a bit of a bang to form chloromethane. The overall equation for this reaction is shown below.

$$CH_4 + Cl_2 \xrightarrow{UV} CH_3Cl + HCl$$

The reaction mechanism for the synthesis of chloromethane by a photochemical reaction has three stages — initiation, propagation and termination.

### Initiation

In the initiation step, free radicals are produced. Sunlight provides enough energy to break some of the Cl–Cl bonds — this is **photodissociation**.

$$Cl_2 \xrightarrow{UV} 2Cl\bullet$$

The bond splits equally and each atom gets to keep one electron (homolytic fission). The atom becomes a highly reactive free radical, $Cl\bullet$, because of its unpaired electron.

### Propagation

During propagation, free radicals are used up and created in a chain reaction. First, $Cl\bullet$ attacks a methane molecule:

$$Cl\bullet + CH_4 \rightarrow CH_3\bullet + HCl$$

The new methyl free radical, $CH_3\bullet$, can then attack another $Cl_2$ molecule:

$$CH_3\bullet + Cl_2 \rightarrow CH_3Cl + Cl\bullet$$

The new $Cl\bullet$ can attack another $CH_4$ molecule, and so on, until all the $Cl_2$ or $CH_4$ molecules are used up.

### Termination

In the termination step, free radicals are mopped up. If two free radicals join together, they make a stable molecule — this terminates the chain reaction. There are heaps of possible termination reactions. Here's a couple of them to give you the idea:

$$CH_3\bullet + Cl\bullet \rightarrow CH_3Cl$$
$$CH_3\bullet + CH_3\bullet \rightarrow C_2H_6$$

**Tip:** The reaction between bromine and methane works in the same way as the reaction between chlorine and methane — you just swap Cl for Br. The overall equation is then:

$CH_4 + Br_2 \xrightarrow{UV} CH_3Br + HBr$

The mechanism is exactly the same too.

**Exam Tip**
When you write radical equations, make sure that there are the same number of radicals on each side (or that two radicals are combining to create a non-radical).

**Exam Tip**
Don't give:
$Cl\bullet + Cl\bullet \rightarrow Cl_2$
as a termination step. You won't get a mark for it because it's just the initiation step in reverse.

# Problems with free radical substitution

The big problem with free radical substitution is that you don't only get chloromethane, but a mixture of products. If there's too much chlorine in the reaction mixture, some of the remaining hydrogen atoms on the chloromethane molecule will be swapped for chlorine atoms. The propagation reactions happen again, this time to make dichloromethane ($CH_2Cl_2$):

$$Cl\bullet + CH_3Cl \rightarrow CH_2Cl\bullet + HCl$$

$$CH_2Cl\bullet + Cl_2 \rightarrow CH_2Cl_2 + Cl\bullet$$

It doesn't stop there. Another substitution reaction can take place to form trichloromethane ($CHCl_3$):

$$Cl\bullet + CH_2Cl_2 \rightarrow CHCl_2\bullet + HCl$$

$$CHCl_2\bullet + Cl_2 \rightarrow CHCl_3 + Cl\bullet$$

Tetrachloromethane ($CCl_4$) is formed in the last possible substitution. There are no more hydrogens attached to the carbon atom, so the substitution process has to stop. So the end product is a mixture of $CH_3Cl$, $CH_2Cl_2$, $CHCl_3$ and $CCl_4$. This is a nuisance, because you have to separate the chloromethane from the other three unwanted by-products.

The best way of reducing the chance of these by-products forming is to have an excess of methane. This means there's a greater chance of a chlorine radical colliding only with a methane molecule and not a chloromethane molecule.

**Tip:** Some of the products formed in the termination step will be trace impurities in the final sample.

**Tip:** You get exactly the same problem with any free radical substitution reaction — there's always a mixture of products, which is really annoying if you're trying to make a particular halogenoalkane.

**Exam Tip**
If you're asked to describe a mechanism, you don't have to write out a really long wordy answer — you can use equations to help you describe a particular step in the reaction.

## Practice Questions — Application

Q1 Bromine reacts with methane to form bromomethane in a three-stage reaction mechanism.

a) Give the names of the three stages of this reaction mechanism.

b) Write equations to show what happens at each of these stages.

c) What other products besides bromomethane are likely to be in the reaction mixture?

Q2 Ethane ($C_2H_6$) reacts with chlorine to form chloroethane ($C_2H_5Cl$).

a) What name is given to the mechanism for this reaction?

b) Describe this reaction mechanism.

c) This reaction gives rise to a mixture of products. Suggest how the concentration of chloroethane in the final reaction mixture could be increased.

## Practice Questions — Fact Recall

Q1 Write an equation for the production of chloromethane from chlorine and methane.

Q2 What type of light is needed to start a reaction between methane and chlorine?

Q3 What type of fission occurs in the initiation step of a free radical substitution reaction?

Q4 Explain why a mixture of products is formed during free radical substitution reactions.

**Tip:** Photochemical reactions will take place in sunlight, so if you leave a mixture of an alkane and a halogen out in the sun, free radical substitution will occur.

# 13. Alkenes and Their Properties

*The alkenes are another group of hydrocarbons. They're really similar to alkanes but they contain a carbon-carbon double bond. This topic is all about alkenes and how to name them.*

## What are alkenes?

**Alkenes** have the general formula $C_nH_{2n}$. They're just made of carbon and hydrogen atoms, so they're hydrocarbons. Alkene molecules all have at least one C=C double covalent bond. Molecules with C=C double bonds are **unsaturated** because they can make more bonds with extra atoms in addition reactions.

┌─ Examples ─────────────────────────

Here are a few pretty diagrams of alkenes:

*propene*

*penta-1,3-diene*

*cyclopentene*

A cyclic alkene has two fewer hydrogen atoms than an open-chain alkene. Carbons can only have four bonds — a double bond means that the carbons can make one less bond with a hydrogen.

## Naming alkenes

Alkenes are named in the same way as alkanes (see page 118), but the -ane ending is changed to an -ene ending — see Figure 2.

| No. of Carbon Atoms | Stem | Alkene |
|---|---|---|
| 2 | eth- | ethene $(C_2H_4)$ |
| 3 | prop- | propene $(C_3H_6)$ |
| 4 | but- | butene $(C_4H_8)$ |
| 5 | pent- | pentene $(C_5H_{10})$ |
| 6 | hex- | hexene $(C_6H_{12})$ |

**Figure 2:** *Naming some alkenes.*

For alkenes with more than three carbons, you need to say which carbon the double bond starts from.

┌─ Example ─────────────────────────

The longest chain is 5 carbons, so the stem of the name is pent-.

The functional group is C=C, so it's pentene. Number the carbons from right to left (so the double bond starts on the lowest possible number). The first carbon in the double bond is carbon 2. So this molecule is pent-2-ene.

*pent-2-ene*

**Learning Objectives:**

- Know that alkenes and cycloalkenes are unsaturated hydrocarbons.
- Be able to apply IUPAC rules for naming alkenes.
- Be able to describe the overlap of adjacent p-orbitals to form a π-bond.
- Be able to state and explain the trigonal planar shape around each carbon in the C=C of alkenes.

**Specification Reference 2.1.1, 2.1.3**

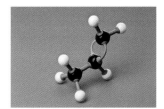

**Figure 1:** *A molecular model of propene.*

**Tip:** When you're naming alkenes the stem is based on the longest continuous carbon chain <u>containing a double bond</u> — even if there is a carbon chain that is longer.

**Tip:** If there is more than one double bond in a molecule the stem is based on the longest continuous carbon chain that contains the <u>most double bonds</u> — even if there are longer carbon chains.

If the alkene has two double bonds the suffix becomes diene. The stem of the name usually gets an extra 'a' too (e.g. buta-, penta-, not but-, pent-) when there's more than one double bond. And you might see the numbers written first.

**Exam Tip**
If you were asked to name this molecule in the exam, you could give either name and it would be correct.

**Example**

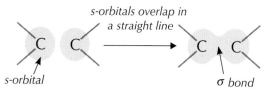

This molecule can be named as buta-1,3-diene or 1,3-butadiene.

## Structure of a double bond

**Tip:** Have a look at page 51 if you've forgotten what an s-orbital is.

A double bond is made up of a **sigma (σ) bond** and a **pi (π) bond**. A σ bond is formed when two s orbitals overlap. The two s orbitals overlap in a straight line — this gives the highest possible electron density between the two nuclei (see Figure 3). This is a single covalent bond.

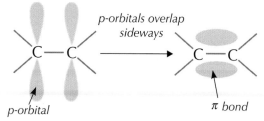

*Figure 3:* The formation of a sigma (σ) bond.

**Tip:** Don't get confused between sigma and pi bonds. Just remember, sigma bonds involve s-orbitals and are the same as covalent single bonds.

A π bond is formed when two p orbitals overlap sideways. It's got two parts to it — one 'above' and one 'below' the molecular axis. This is because the p orbitals which overlap are dumb-bell shaped — see Figure 4.

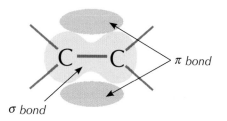

*Figure 4:* The formation of a pi (π) bond.

**Exam Tip**
If you're asked to describe a sigma or a pi bond in the exam, you can draw a diagram — just make sure you label it properly.

π bonds are weaker than σ bonds. This means that a double bond (π bond + σ bond) is not twice as strong as a single bond (just a σ bond).

## Reactivity of the alkenes

Each double bond in an alkene is a bit like a hot dog. The π bond is the bun and the σ bond is sandwiched in the middle like the sausage — see Figure 5.

**Tip:** This explains why the average bond enthalpy of a C=C double bond (+611 kJ mol⁻¹) is not twice the average bond enthalpy of a C–C single bond (+345 kJ mol⁻¹). See page 180 for more on bond enthalpies.

*Figure 5:* Structure of a double bond.

Because there are two pairs of electrons in the bond, the C=C double bond has a really high electron density. This makes alkenes pretty reactive. Another reason for the high reactivity is that the π bond sticks out above and below the rest of the molecule. So, the π bond is likely to be attacked by electrophiles. Because the double bond's so reactive, alkenes are handy starting points for making other organic compounds and for making petrochemicals.

**Tip:** See page 142 for more on electrophiles.

# Double bond rotation

Carbon atoms in a C=C double bond and the atoms bonded to these carbons all lie in the same plane (they're planar). Because of the way they're arranged, they're actually said to be trigonal planar — the atoms attached to each double-bond carbon are at the corners of an imaginary equilateral triangle — see Figure 6.

**Tip:** Because of the double bond, alkenes are much more reactive than alkanes, which don't contain a double bond.

*The bond angles in the planar unit are all 120°.*

**Figure 6:** *The trigonal planar shape around each carbon of C=C bonds in alkenes.*

Ethene, $C_2H_4$ (like in Figure 6) is completely planar, but in larger alkenes, only the >C=C< unit is planar.

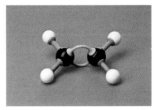

**Figure 7:** *A molecular model of ethene. All of the atoms are in the same plane.*

─ **Example** ───────

This molecule is but-1-ene. The carbon-carbon double bond section of the molecule is planar and the carbon-carbon single bond section is non-planar.

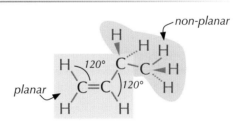

**Tip:** The C–C single bond section isn't planar because the bonding electron pairs repel each other giving a tetrahedral shape. The bond angles in a tetrahedral molecule are 109.5°.

Another important thing about C=C double bonds is that atoms can't rotate around them like they can around single bonds. This is because the p orbitals have to stay in the same position to overlap and form a π bond. Double bonds are also fairly rigid — they don't bend much. Even though atoms can't rotate about the double bond, things can still rotate about any single bonds in the molecule.

**Tip:** See pages 65-68 for loads more about the shapes of molecules.

─ **Example** ───────

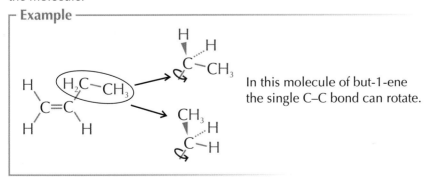

In this molecule of but-1-ene the single C–C bond can rotate.

The restricted rotation around the C=C double bond is what causes E/Z isomerism (see page 111).

**Exam Tip**
When you're naming molecules in the exam always, always, always double-check what you've written. Accidentally writing -ane instead of -ene could cost you valuable marks.

## Practice Questions — Application

Q1 Name the alkenes below:

a) 

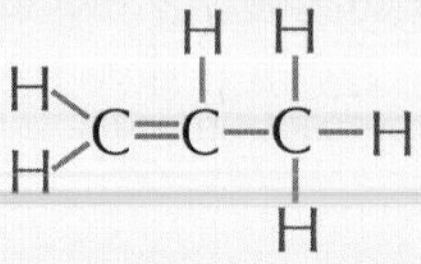

b) 

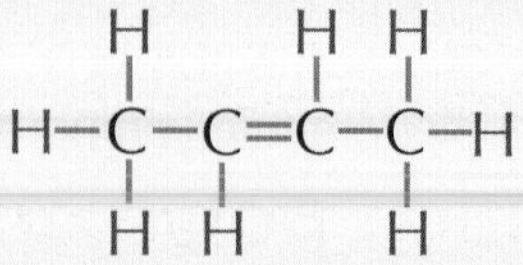

c) 

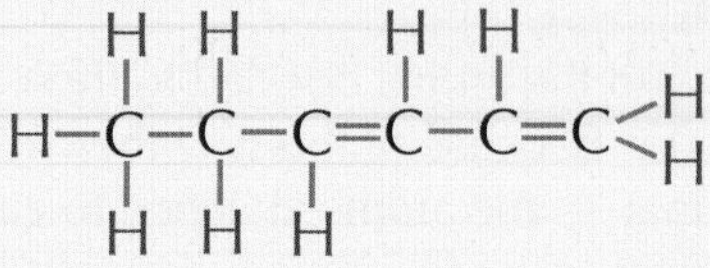

d) 

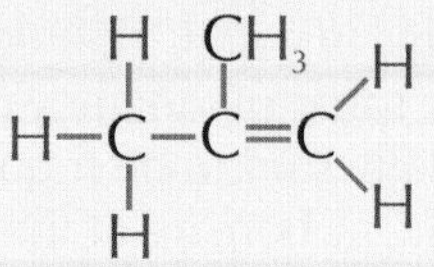

Q2 Propene is more reactive than propane. Explain why.

Q3 The table below shows the average bond enthalpies of single and double carbon-carbon bonds:

| Type of bond | Average bond enthalpy (kJ mol$^{-1}$) |
|---|---|
| C–C | +345 |
| C=C | +611 |

Using your knowledge of the structure of C=C double bonds, explain why the average bond enthalpy of a C=C double bond is not twice as large as that of a C–C single bond.

## Practice Questions — Fact Recall

Q1 What is the general formula of an alkene?

Q2 a) Draw a diagram to show how a sigma bond is formed.

b) Draw a diagram to show how a pi bond is formed.

Q3 Are C=C double bonds susceptible to attack by nucleophiles or electrophiles?

Q4 a) What does the term trigonal planar mean?

b) Which part of an alkene molecule is trigonal planar?

Q5 Explain why alkenes show E/Z isomerism.

# 14. Polymers

*Lots of small molecules (called monomers) can join together to form really long molecules (called polymers). At AS-level you need to know how alkenes come together to form addition polymers. Read on...*

## Addition polymers

The double bonds in alkenes can open up and join together to make long chains called **polymers**. It's kind of like they're holding hands in a big line. The individual, small alkenes are called **monomers**. This is called addition polymerisation.

**Example**

Poly(ethene) is made by the addition polymerisation of ethene.

*ethene monomers*          *a section of poly(ethene)*

Addition polymerisation reactions can be written like this...

*monomer*          *polymer*

...where the n stands for a very large number of repeating units (monomers) in the polymer — there can be as many as 10 000.

To find the monomer used to form an addition polymer, take the repeating unit and add a double bond.

**Example**

To find the monomer used to make the polymer below you first need to look for the repeating unit.

*polymer*          *repeating unit*

Then replace the horizontal carbon-carbon bond with a double bond and remove the unnecessary side bonds to find the monomer.

*repeating unit*          *monomer — propene*

**Learning Objectives:**

- Be able to describe the addition polymerisation of alkenes.

- Be able to deduce the repeat unit of an addition polymer obtained from a given monomer.

- Be able to identify the monomer that would produce a given section of an addition polymer.

- Understand the formation of a range of polymers using unsaturated monomer units based on the ethene molecule.

**Specification Reference 2.1.3**

**Tip:** The bit inside the brackets is the repeating unit of the polymer. The formula of the polymer is the bit with the brackets and the n.

**Exam Tip**
To pick up the marks in the exam you must show the bonds at the end of the molecule <u>crossing the brackets</u>. This shows that the polymer continues outside the brackets.

***Figure 1:*** *A molecular model of a polymer. This is poly(chloroethene).*

# Different types of polymers

You can polymerise molecules other than basic alkenes. Different alkenes give polymers with different properties.

**Tip:** The names of polymers can be written with or without the brackets — e.g. poly(chloroethene) or polychloroethene.

**Tip:** Poly(chloroethene) is also known as polyvinyl chloride (PVC).

***Figure 2:*** *Objects made out of poly(chloroethene).*

**Tip:** Poly(tetrafluoroethene) is also known as Teflon®.

***Figure 3:*** *A Teflon® coated frying pan.*

**Exam Tip**
You could be asked to draw 1, 2 or even 3 repeating units in the exam, so make sure you read the question.

**Exam Tip**
If you're asked to name the monomer that forms a particular polymer, draw it out — then you can see what it is and name it using the rules on page 133.

## Examples

Poly(chloroethene) is made from chloroethene.

*Chloroethene* → *Poly(chloroethene)*

Poly(chloroethene) has a wide range of uses — for example, it's used to make water pipes, for insulation on electric wires and as a building material (e.g. many doors and window frames are made from poly(chloroethene)).

Poly(tetrafluoroethene) or PTFE is made from tetrafluoroethene.

*Tetrafluoroethene* → *Poly(tetrafluoroethene)*

Poly(tetrafluoroethene) is chemically inert and has non-stick properties. This makes it ideal as a coating for frying pans.

## Practice Questions — Application

Q1 Draw the repeating units of the polymers that would be formed from each of these alkenes:

a)  b)  c)

Q2 Draw the alkenes that would form each of these polymers:

a)  b)  c)

## Practice Questions — Fact Recall

Q1 What types of polymers are formed from alkenes?

Q2 Describe the process that leads to the formation of polymers from alkenes.

Q3 a) Suggest a use for poly(chloroethene).

b) Suggest a use for poly(tetrafluoroethene).

# 15. Disposing of Polymers

*Polymers are really useful — loads of things are made from them. But unfortunately, disposing of polymers once they've been used can be a tad tricky. Read on to find out why.*

## The widespread use of polymers

Synthetic polymers have loads of advantages, so they're incredibly widespread these days — we take them pretty much for granted. Just imagine what you'd have to live without if there were no polymers (see Figure 1).

**Figure 1:** *Some of the many items that are made out of synthetic polymers.*

## Biodegradability of polymers

One of the really useful things about many everyday polymers is that they're very unreactive. This means food doesn't react with the PTFE coating on pans, plastic windows don't rot, plastic crates can be left out in the rain and they'll be okay, and so on. But this lack of reactivity also leads to a problem. Most polymers aren't biodegradable, and so they're really difficult to dispose of.

## Disposing of waste plastics

In the UK over 2 million tonnes of plastic waste are produced each year. It's important to find ways to get rid of this waste while minimising environmental damage. There are various possible approaches (Figure 2).

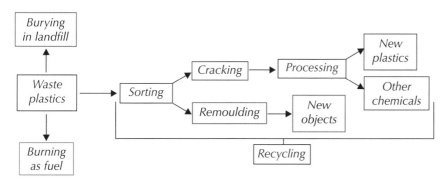

**Figure 2:** *The different methods for disposing of waste plastic.*

### Burying waste plastic

Landfill is one option for dealing with waste plastics. This means taking waste to a landfill site, compacting it, and then covering it with soil. It is generally used when the plastic is:

- Difficult to separate from other waste.

- Not in sufficient quantities to make separation financially worthwhile.

- Too difficult technically to recycle.

But because the amount of waste we generate is becoming more and more of a problem, there's a need to reduce landfill as much as possible.

**Learning Objectives:**

- Understand the benefits of processing alkenes to produce polymers and plastics.

- Be able to outline the processing of waste polymers by separation into types and recycling, combustion for energy production and use as a feedstock for cracking in the production of plastics and other chemicals.

- Be able to outline the role of chemists in minimising environmental damage by removing toxic waste products and developing biodegradable and compostable polymers.

- Understand the increased political and social desire to reduce plastic waste, to recycle or to use plastics for energy production.

- Understand the development of new degradable plastics produced from renewable resources.

**Specification Reference 2.1.3**

**Figure 3:** *A landfill site — burying waste plastic is one way of disposing of it.*

## Recycling plastics

Because many plastics are made from non-renewable oil fractions, it makes sense to recycle plastics as much as possible. There's more than one way to recycle plastics. After sorting into different types some plastics (poly(propene), for example) can be melted and remoulded, while others can be cracked into monomers which can be used to make more plastics or other chemicals. Plastic products are usually marked to make sorting easier. The different numbers show different polymers.

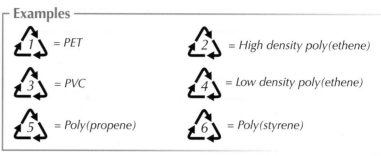

┌─ **Examples** ─────────────────────────────

　1 = PET　　　　　2 = High density poly(ethene)

　3 = PVC　　　　　4 = Low density poly(ethene)

　5 = Poly(propene)　　6 = Poly(styrene)

*Figure 4: The recycling symbol on the bottom of a plastic bottle.*

**Tip:** See page 31 for more on neutralisation reactions.

## Burning waste plastic

If recycling isn't possible for whatever reason, waste plastics can be burned — and the heat can be used to generate electricity. This process needs to be carefully controlled to reduce toxic gases. For example, polymers that contain chlorine (such as PVC) produce HCl when they're burned — this has to be removed. Waste gases from the combustion are passed through scrubbers which can neutralise gases such as HCl by allowing them to react with a base.

# Making biodegradable polymers

Scientists can now make biodegradable polymers — ones that naturally decompose. Biodegradable polymers decompose pretty quickly in certain conditions — because organisms can digest them. You might get asked about 'compostable' polymers as well as 'biodegradable' ones. These two terms mean more or less the same thing — 'compostable' just means it has to decay fairly quickly, "at the speed of compost".

Biodegradable polymers can be made from materials such as starch (from maize and other plants) and from the hydrocarbon isoprene (2-methyl-1,3-butadiene). So, biodegradable polymers can be produced from renewable raw materials or from oil fractions.

**Tip:** See page 4 for more on how society makes decisions about things like recycling and waste plastic.

### Advantages of using renewable raw materials

Using renewable raw material has several advantages:

- Renewable raw materials aren't going to run out like oil will.
- When polymers biodegrade, carbon dioxide (a greenhouse gas) is produced. If your polymer is plant-based, then the $CO_2$ released as it decomposes is the same $CO_2$ absorbed by the plant when it grew. But with an oil-based biodegradable polymer, you're effectively transferring carbon from the oil to the atmosphere.
- Over their 'lifetime' some plant-based polymers save energy compared to oil-based plastics.

But whatever raw material you use, at the moment the energy for making polymers usually comes from fossil fuels.

(HOW SCIENCE WORKS)

**Tip:** Releasing extra $CO_2$ into the atmosphere adds to the greenhouse effect and warms the Earth. See page 208 for loads more on the greenhouse effect.

## Disadvantages of using biodegradable plastics

Although biodegradable plastics sound like a fab idea, there are a few disadvantages of using biodegradable plastics over the standard non-biodegradable ones.

Even though they're biodegradable, these polymers still need the right conditions before they'll decompose. You couldn't necessarily just put them in a landfill and expect them to perish away — because there's a lack of moisture and oxygen under all that compressed soil. You need to chuck them on a big compost heap. This means that you still need to collect and separate the biodegradable polymers from non-biodegradable plastics. At the moment, they're also more expensive than oil-based equivalents.

## Uses of biodegradable plastics

There are various potential uses — e.g. plastic sheeting used to protect plants from the frost can be made from poly(ethene) with starch grains embedded in it. In time the starch is broken down by microorganisms and the remaining poly(ethene) crumbles into dust. There's no need to collect and dispose of the old sheeting.

## Other things scientists can do

Developing biodegradable plastics isn't the only thing that chemists can do to decrease the environmental damage caused by waste plastics. Other potential developments to solve the problem include:

- Introducing photodegradable polymers (polymers which can be chemically broken down by light).

- Developing better techniques for cracking polymers so that recycling polymers becomes more efficient.

- Finding new ways of making polymers from plant-based substances to reduce the use of finite raw materials like crude oil.

- Using processes with higher atom economy to reduce the amount of waste produced during manufacturing processes.

- Developing new, more efficient ways of sorting and recycling polymers.

**Exam Tip**
Weighing up the advantages and disadvantages of things is an important skill in Chemistry. You may be asked to do it in your exam, so make sure it's a skill you've mastered.

*Figure 5:* A compostable plastic bag.

**Tip:** See pages 115-117 for more on atom economy and why high atom economy processes are important.

## Practice Questions — Fact Recall

Q1 a) Explain why it is good for everyday polymers to be unreactive.

b) What problem does the fact that plastics are unreactive cause?

Q2 Give two reasons why plastics might be put into landfill.

Q3 a) Give two ways in which plastics can be recycled.

b) How is the sorting of plastics made easier?

Q4 Burning plastic produces toxic gases.

a) What toxic gas is produced when poly(chloroethene) is burnt?

b) How can this toxic gas be removed?

Q5 Suggest two things that biodegradable polymers can be made from.

Q6 Give three advantages of making plastic from renewable raw materials rather than non-renewable materials such as oil.

Q7 Suggest two disadvantages of using biodegradable polymers.

**Learning Objectives:**

- Know that an electrophile is an electron pair acceptor.

- Be able to describe how heterolytic fission leads to the mechanism of electrophilic addition in alkenes.

- Be able to describe addition reactions of alkenes with:

  (i) halogens to form dihalogenoalkanes, including the use of bromine to detect the presence of a double C=C bond as a test for unsaturation.

  (ii) hydrogen halides to form halogenoalkanes.

  (iii) steam in the presence of an acid catalyst to form alcohols.

  (iv) hydrogen in the presence of a suitable catalyst, i.e. Ni, to form alkanes.

- Be able to outline the use of alkenes in the industrial production of organic compounds.

- Understand the manufacture of margarine by catalytic hydrogenation of unsaturated vegetable oils using hydrogen and a nickel catalyst.

**Specification Reference 2.1.3**

# 16. Reactions of Alkenes

*Remember those alkenes from page 133 — well they're back and this time they're reacting.*

## Electrophilic addition reactions

**Electrophilic addition** reactions aren't too complicated. The double bond in an alkene opens up and atoms are added to the carbon atoms. Electrophilic addition reactions happen because the double bond has got plenty of electrons and is easily attacked by **electrophiles**. Electrophiles are electron-pair acceptors — they're usually a bit short of electrons, so they're attracted to areas where there's lots of them about.

> **Examples**
>
> Here are a few examples of electrophiles.
>
> *Positively charged ions are electrophiles.* $\longrightarrow NO_2^+$
>
> $H^+$
>
> $$H-\overset{\overset{\displaystyle H}{|}}{\underset{\underset{\displaystyle H}{|}}{C}}-\overset{\overset{\displaystyle H}{|}}{\underset{\underset{\displaystyle H}{|}}{C}}\overset{\delta+}{\phantom{.}}\overset{\delta-}{Br}$$
>
> *Polar molecules can also be electrophiles — the δ+ atom is attracted to places with lots of electrons.*

The double bond is also nucleophilic — it's attracted to places that don't have enough electrons.

You need to learn the mechanism for electrophilic addition. Here is the general electrophilic addition reaction equation.

$$H_2C=CH_2 + X–Y \rightarrow CH_2XCH_2Y$$

$$\overset{H}{\underset{H}{>}}\overset{1}{C}=\overset{2}{C}\overset{<H}{\underset{H}{}}$$
$$X\overset{\delta+}{—}Y\overset{\delta-}{}$$

*The carbon-carbon double bond repels the electrons in the X–Y bond, which polarises the X–Y bond (or the bond could already be polar, like in HBr).*

Two electrons from the carbon-carbon double bond attack the δ+ X atom, creating a new bond between carbon 1 and the X atom. The X–Y bond breaks (heterolytic fission) and the electrons from the bond are taken by the Y atom to form a negative ion with a lone pair of electrons. Carbon 2 is left electron deficient — when the double bond was broken carbon 1 took the electrons to form a bond with the X atom, which left carbon 2 as a positively charged **carbocation** intermediate.

$$\overset{H}{\underset{H}{>}}\overset{1}{C}=\overset{2}{C}\overset{<H}{\underset{H}{}} \longrightarrow H-\overset{\overset{\displaystyle H}{|}}{\underset{\underset{\displaystyle X}{|}}{\overset{1}{C}}}-\overset{\overset{\displaystyle H}{|}}{\underset{+}{\overset{2}{C}}}-H$$
$$X\overset{\delta+}{\underset{\Large\downarrow}{—}}Y\overset{\delta-}{} \qquad\qquad :\overline{Y}$$

**Tip:** A carbocation is an organic ion containing a positively charged carbon atom.

The Y⁻ ion then acts as a **nucleophile**, attacking the positively charged carbocation intermediate, donating its lone pair of electrons and forming a new bond with carbon 2.

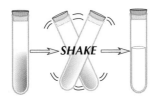

So overall, the X–Y molecule has been added to the alkene across the double bond to form a saturated compound.

**Exam Tip**
You <u>must</u> draw the curly arrows coming from the <u>lone pair</u> of electrons or from the <u>bond</u>. If you don't — you won't get the marks for the mechanism in the exam.

# Testing for unsaturation

Alkenes react with halogens to form dihalogenoalkanes. This reaction forms the basis of a test that can be used to distinguish between compounds that contain a double bond (like alkenes) and compounds that don't (like alkanes). When you shake an alkene with orange bromine water, the solution quickly turns from orange to colourless (see Figure 1).

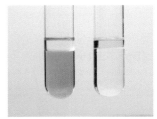

**Figure 2:** Bromine water has been added to two test tubes. The one on the right contains a compound with a C=C that has decolourised the bromine water. The one on the left contains a substance that doesn't react with bromine.

Figure 1: Adding bromine water to a solution containing a carbon-carbon double bond turns the bromine water colourless.

Bromine is added across the double bond to form a colourless dibromoalkane — this happens by electrophilic addition.

┌─ Example ─────────

When you shake ethene with orange bromine water, the solution turns from orange to colourless. Here's the equation for this reaction:

$$H_2C=CH_2 + Br_2 \rightarrow CH_2BrCH_2Br$$

Here's the mechanism...

*The double bond repels the electrons in $Br_2$, polarising Br–Br. This is called an induced dipole.*

*Heterolytic (unequal) fission of $Br_2$. The closer Br gives up its bonding electrons to the other Br and bonds to the C atom.*

...and bonds to the other C atom, forming 1,2-dibromoethane.

*You get a positively charged carbocation intermediate. The Br⁻ now zooms over...*

**Exam Tip**
You could get asked to draw the mechanism for the reaction between bromine water and any alkene — it might not be ethene. It's not too hard though — the mechanism is the same for all alkenes, and you'll always end up with a Br atom added to each of the carbon atoms that were double bonded. Simple as that.

**Tip:** Chlorine and iodine react with alkenes like this too.

# Synthesising halogenoalkanes

Alkenes undergo electrophilic addition reactions with hydrogen halides to form halogenoalkanes.

**Example**

This is the reaction between ethene and hydrogen bromide.

$$H_2C=CH_2 + HBr \rightarrow C_2H_5Br$$

It's an electrophilic addition reaction and the mechanism is the same as the one for the addition of halogens on pages 142-143.

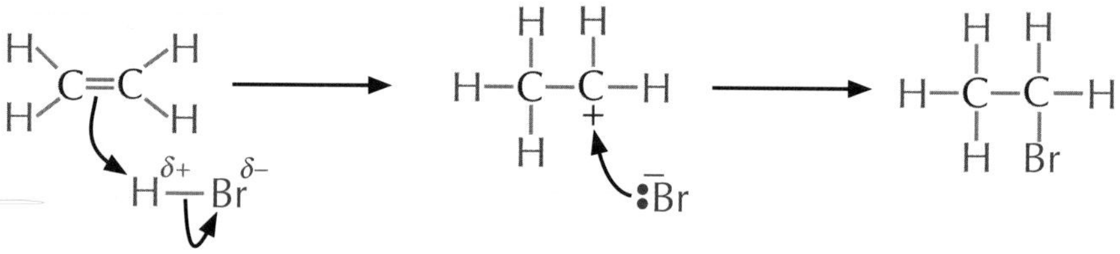

If the HBr adds to a symmetrical alkene like ethene, only one product can be formed. But if the HBr adds to an unsymmetrical alkene, there are two possible products.

**Example**

If you add hydrogen bromide to propene, the bromine atom could add to either the first carbon or the second carbon. This means you could produce 1-bromopropane or 2-bromopropane.

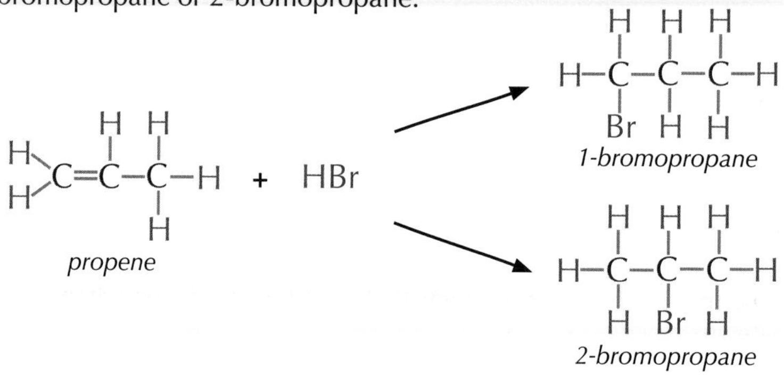

*1-bromopropane*

*propene*

*2-bromopropane*

The mechanism of the reaction is exactly the same, but two products can form because the hydrogen can add onto either of the carbons in the double bond.

**Example**

Here's how hydrogen bromide reacts with 2-methylbut-2-ene:

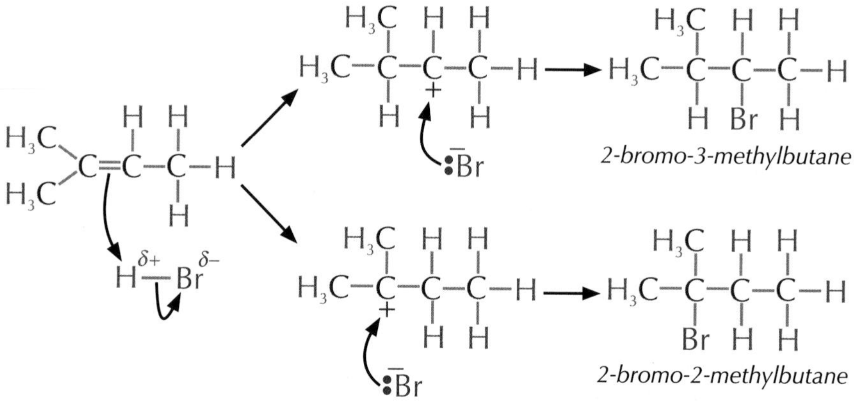

*2-bromo-3-methylbutane*

*2-bromo-2-methylbutane*

# Synthesising ethanol

Steam hydration of ethene is used industrially to produce ethanol. Ethene can be hydrated by steam at 300 °C and a pressure of 60 atm. It needs an acid catalyst — usually solid phosphoric(V) acid. The reaction's reversible and the reaction yield is low — only about 5%. This sounds rubbish, but you can recycle the unreacted ethene gas, making the overall yield a much more profitable 95%. Here's the equation for producing ethanol from alkenes:

$$H_2C{=}CH_{2(g)} + H_2O_{(g)} \underset{\substack{300\ ^\circ C \\ 60\ atm}}{\overset{H_3PO_4}{\rightleftharpoons}} CH_3CH_2OH_{(g)}$$

**Tip:** This is also an electrophilic addition reaction. You don't need to worry about the mechanism though — it's a bit different because there's a catalyst involved.

# Producing alkanes

Ethene will react with hydrogen gas to produce ethane. It needs a nickel catalyst and a temperature of 150 °C though. Here's the equation for the reaction:

$$H_2C{=}CH_2 + H_2 \xrightarrow[150\ ^\circ C]{Ni} CH_3CH_3$$

Margarine's made by 'hydrogenating' unsaturated vegetable oils. By removing some double bonds, you raise the melting point of the oil so that it becomes solid at room temperature.

*Figure 3:* Margarine is made by hydrogenating unsaturated vegetable oils.

## Practice Questions — Application

Q1  When propene is added to bromine water, the solution decolourises.

a)  Write an equation for the reaction that is occuring.

b)  Name and outline the mechanism for this reaction.

c)  Bromine does not decolourise when added to an unknown chemical. What does this tell you about the unknown compound?

Q2  Outline the mechanism for the reaction between but-2-ene and hydrogen bromide.

Q3  Draw the two different products that could be produced when hydrogen chloride reacts with but-1-ene.

Q4  The structure of penta-1,3-diene is shown below:

```
      H       H
      |       |
 H─C─C=C─C=C
      |   |   |    H
      H   H   H    H
```

Draw the products formed when this alkene reacts with HBr.

**Tip:** Q4 is a bit tricky so here's a hint. If there are two double bonds in an alkene, the addition could occur at either or both of the double bonds, so you'll get more than two products.

## Practice Questions — Fact Recall

Q1  What is an electrophile?

Q2  Give two examples of electrophiles.

Q3  What can you use bromine water to test for?

Q4  What could you react with ethene to produce bromoethane?

Q5  Write the equation for the hydration of ethene by steam. Include the conditions for this reaction in your answer.

Q6  What can you do to increase the yield of ethanol production by steam hydration?

## Section Summary

Make sure you know...

- That a functional group is a group of atoms responsible for the characteristic reactions of a compound.
- What molecular formulas, structural formulas, displayed formulas, empirical formulas, general formulas, homologous series and skeletal formulas are and how to use them.
- What structural isomerism is and what chain, positional and functional group structural isomers are.
- What stereoisomers are and how to work them out from molecular formulas.
- That E/Z isomerism and cis-trans isomerism are types of stereoisomerism, and why they occur.
- How to calculate the theoretical and percentage yields of a reaction.
- What atom economy is and how to calculate the percentage atom economy of a reaction.
- Why addition reactions have 100% atom economies and why substitution reactions are less efficient.
- That reactions can have a high percentage yield but a low atom economy and why this can be a problem.
- That a hydrocarbon is a compound that contains only hydrogen and carbon.
- What alkanes and cycloalkanes are and how to name them.
- Why atoms form a tetrahedral shape around each carbon atom in alkanes.
- Why long or linear alkanes have higher boiling points than short or branched alkanes.
- That alkanes make excellent fuels because they release lots of energy when they burn.
- How to write equations for the complete and incomplete combustion of alkanes.
- Why carbon monoxide (CO) is toxic to humans.
- That crude oil is used as a source of hydrocarbons and how they are separated by fractional distillation.
- That cracking can be used to break long-chain alkanes into shorter, more useful alkanes and alkenes.
- Why straight-chain alkanes are processed into branched and cyclic hydrocarbons.
- What fossil fuels are used for and how their increased use is leading to climate change.
- Why it's important to develop plant-based alternatives to fossil fuels.
- The disadvantages of using crop-based alternative fuels.
- What heterolytic and homolytic fission are.
- That a radical is a species with an unpaired electron.
- What curly arrows show in reaction mechanisms and how to use them in diagrams.
- How halogenoalkanes are formed from alkanes in free radical substitution reactions.
- The mechanism of free radical substitution including initiation, propagation and termination.
- Why you can get a mixture of products in free radical substitution reactions.
- What alkenes and cycloalkenes are and how to name them.
- The structure of a C=C double bond in terms of pi and sigma bonds.
- Why atoms form a trigonal planar shape around each carbon of the C=C double bond of alkenes.
- How alkenes can join together to form addition polymers.
- How to work out the repeating unit of a polymer given its monomer and how to work out the monomer of a polymer given its repeating unit.
- That different alkenes join together to form polymers with different properties.
- The ways of processing waste polymers and their disadvantages.
- Why it is important for chemists to develop biodegradable and compostable polymers.
- That an electrophile is an electron-pair acceptor.
- The mechanism of electrophilic addition in alkenes and how alkenes react with halogens, halides, steam and hydrogen.
- How margarine is made by catalytic hydrogenation of alkenes.

# Exam-style Questions

**1** The acyl chlorides are a homologous series of compounds with the general formula $C_nH_{2n-1}OCl$.

**(a) (i)** What is a homologous series?

*(1 mark)*

**(ii)** Give the molecular formula of propanoyl chloride.

*(1 mark)*

**(b)** Ethanoyl chloride ($CH_3COCl$) is used in the production of methyl ethanoate ($CH_3COOCH_3$). The equation for this reaction is shown below:

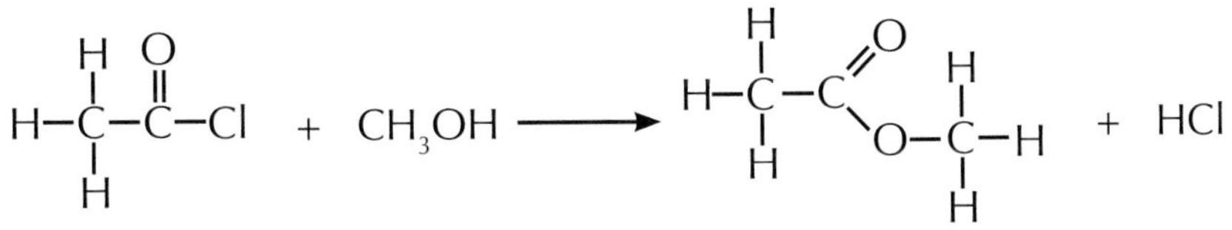

**(i)** How much methyl ethanoate would you expect to be produced from 10.0 g of ethanoyl chloride?

*(2 marks)*

**(ii)** Calculate the percentage yield if 7.20 g of methyl ethanoate is produced.

*(1 mark)*

**(iii)** The percentage atom economy for this reaction is around 67%. Give one advantage of using reactions with high atom economies.

*(1 mark)*

**(c)** Methyl ethanoate can also be produced from ethanoic acid ($CH_3COOH$) via the reaction shown below:

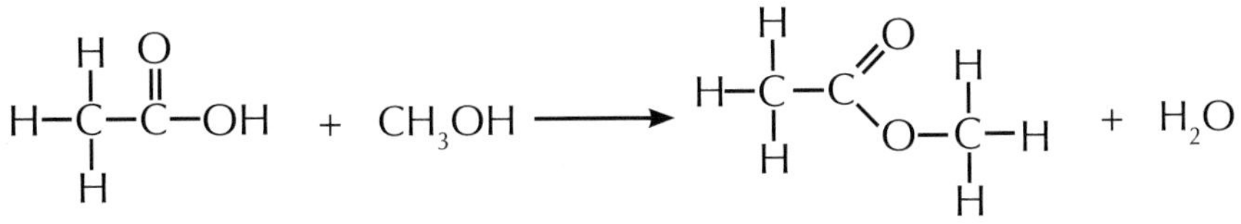

**(i)** Calculate the percentage atom economy for this reaction.

*(2 marks)*

**(ii)** Methyl ethanoate has multiple structural isomers. What is meant by the term 'structural isomer'?

*(1 mark)*

**(iii)** Draw displayed formulas for a functional group isomer and a positional isomer of methyl ethanoate.

*(2 marks)*

**2** 2,2,4-trimethylpentane is a branched alkane widely used in petrol. It is an isomer of the straight-chain alkane octane.

(a) (i) Draw the displayed formula of 2,2,4-trimethylpentane.

*(1 mark)*

(ii) The boiling point of 2,2,4-trimethylpentane is 372 K. Would you expect the boiling point of octane to be higher or lower than this? Explain your answer.

*(4 marks)*

(iii) Fuel manufacturers often convert octane to 2,2,4-trimethylpentane using isomerisation. Explain why.

*(1 mark)*

(b) Alkanes make excellent fuels because when they burn, they release lots of energy.

(i) Write an equation for the complete combustion of 2,2,4-trimethylpentane.

*(2 marks)*

(ii) Explain why 2,2,4-trimethylpentane releases more energy per mole when it is burnt than pentane does.

*(2 marks)*

(c) Alkanes are used as fuel in household appliances. Use your knowledge of combustion to explain the importance of an adequate supply of oxygen to the appliances.

*(3 marks)*

**3** When bromine is exposed to UV light, the Br–Br bond breaks and two radicals are formed.

(a) (i) What are radicals?

*(1 mark)*

(ii) What name is given to the type of bond fission that produces radicals?

*(1 mark)*

(b) Bromine reacts with ethane under UV light to form bromoethane.

(i) Write an equation for the formation of bromoethane.

*(1 mark)*

(ii) Outline the mechanism for this reaction, naming each step.

*(7 marks)*

(c) (i) Suggest two halogenoalkanes other than bromoethane that could be produced during this reaction.

*(2 marks)*

(ii) Suggest how the yield of bromoethane could be increased.

*(1 mark)*

**4**    The scheme below shows some reactions involving propene ($C_3H_6$):

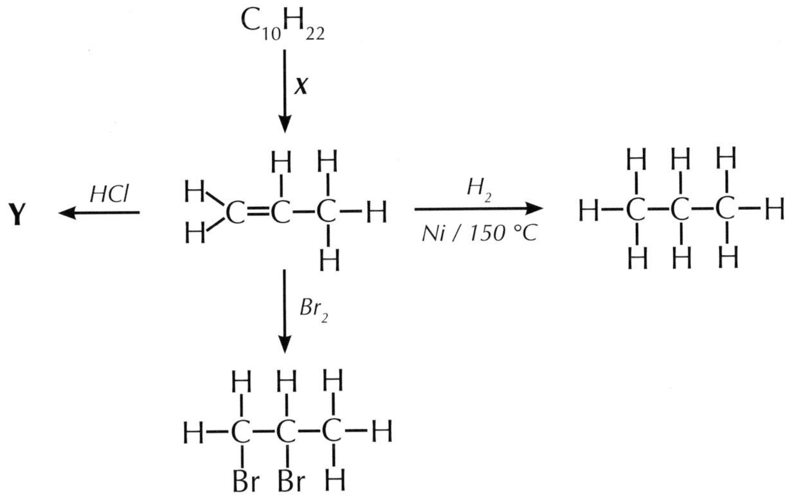

$$C_{10}H_{22}$$

$$\Big\downarrow X$$

**(a)**    Propene can be produced from decane ($C_{10}H_{22}$) by process **X**.

**(i)**   Identify process **X**.

*(1 mark)*

**(ii)**  Describe the conditions usually used for process **X**.

*(1 mark)*

**(iii)** Why is it economically beneficial to convert long-chain alkanes like decane into shorter-chain alkanes and alkenes, like propene?

*(2 marks)*

**(b)**    Alkenes like propene are susceptible to attack by electrophiles.

**(i)**   Draw a diagram to illustrate the structure of a carbon-carbon double bond.

*(2 marks)*

**(ii)**  Using your diagram from part (b) (i), explain why alkenes are susceptible to attack by electrophiles.

*(2 marks)*

**(c)**    When propene is added to bromine water, 1,2-dibromopropane is produced.

**(i)**   Outline the mechanism for this reaction, including dipoles where relevant.

*(4 marks)*

**(ii)**  State what you would observe when this reaction takes place.

*(1 mark)*

**(d)**    When propene reacts with HCl, molecule **Y** is formed.

Suggest two possible structures for molecule **Y**.

*(2 marks)*

**5** This question is about alkenes and their polymers.

**(a)** The structure of 1-bromo-1,3-butadiene is shown below:

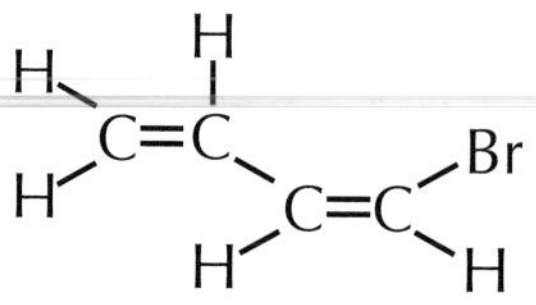

1-bromo-1,3-butadiene shows stereoisomerism.

**(i)** What is stereoisomerism?

*(2 marks)*

**(ii)** Circle the bond in 1-bromo-1,3-butadiene which enables it to show E/Z isomerism.

*(1 mark)*

**(iii)** Draw one other E/Z isomer of 1-bromo-1,3-butadiene and state whether the isomer you have drawn is the E-isomer or the Z-isomer.

*(2 marks)*

**(b)** Polyvinylacetate (PVA) is a synthetic polymer. It is one of the main components of PVA glue. The repeating unit of PVA is shown below:

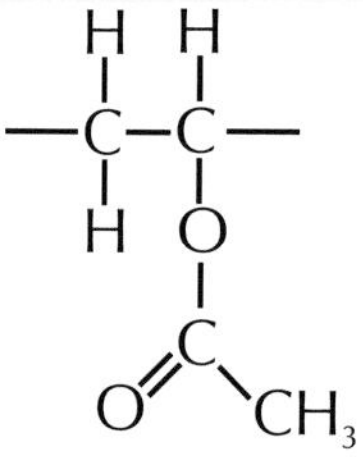

**(i)** What type of polymer is PVA?

*(1 mark)*

**(ii)** Draw the structure of the monomer that gives rise to PVA.

*(1 mark)*

**(c)** Alkene-based polymers are extremely useful, but disposing of waste polymers is a big problem.

**(i)** What three methods are currently available for disposing of waste polymers?

*(1 mark)*

**(ii)** Discuss the advantages and disadvantages of using biodegradable polymers.

*(4 marks)*

**6** Humans are heavily dependent on fossil fuels.
- Give two reasons why it is important for us to find alternatives to fossil fuels.
- Suggest two plant-based fuels which can be used as a source of energy and explain how they are made.
- Discuss the advantages and disadvantages of using plant-based fuels.

*(10 marks)*

# 1. Alcohols and their Uses

*This is a pretty important section — examiners love real life applications of chemistry and this topic is packed full of them. But before we get on to all that fun stuff here's a bit more nomenclature for you to learn.*

## Nomenclature of alcohols

The **alcohol** homologous series has the general formula $C_nH_{2n+1}OH$. Alcohols are named using the same IUPAC naming rules as alkanes (see pages 118-119) but the suffix -ol is added in place of the -e on the end of the name. You also need to indicate which carbon atom the alcohol functional group is attached to — the carbon number(s) comes before the -ol suffix. If there are two –OH (hydroxyl) groups the molecule is a -diol and if there are three it's a -triol.

### Learning Objectives:

- Use IUPAC rules of nomenclature for systematically naming alcohols.
- Be able to classify alcohols into primary, secondary and tertiary alcohols.
- Know how to explain, in terms of hydrogen bonding, the water solubility and the relatively low volatility of alcohols.
- Know that ethanol is used in alcoholic drinks and as a solvent in the form of methylated spirits.
- Know that methanol is used as a petrol additive to improve combustion.
- Know that methanol is gaining increasing importance as a feedstock in the production of organic chemicals.

**Specification Reference 2.1.1, 2.2.1**

---

#### Examples

*ethanol*

The longest continuous carbon chain is 2 carbon atoms, so the stem is ethane.

There's one –OH attached to the carbon chain so the suffix is -ol.

There's only one carbon atom it could be attached to (carbon atom 1) so there's no need to put a number.

So, the alcohol is called ethanol.

The longest continuous carbon chain is 3 carbon atoms, so the stem is propane.

There's one –OH attached to the carbon chain so the suffix is -ol.

It's attached to the second carbon so there's a 2 before the -ol.

There's also a methyl group attached to the second carbon so there's a 2-methyl- prefix.

The alcohol is called 2-methylpropan-2-ol.

*2-methylpropan-2-ol*

The longest continuous carbon chain is 2 carbon atoms, so the stem is ethane.

There are two –OH groups attached to the carbon chain so the suffix is -diol.

There's one –OH attached to each carbon atom so there's a 1,2- before the -diol.

So, the alcohol is called ethane-1,2-diol.

*ethane-1,2-diol*

**Tip:** In all the molecules in this section the alcohol functional group (–OH) is the most important one — that's why all the names end in -ol. If the alcohol functional group isn't the most important group then the molecule gets a hydroxy- prefix instead. For example, 1-hydroxypropanone.

# Primary, secondary and tertiary alcohols

An alcohol is primary, secondary or tertiary, depending on which carbon atom the hydroxyl group –OH is bonded to. Primary alcohols are given the notation 1° and the –OH group is attached to a carbon with one alkyl group attached (see Figure 1). Secondary alcohols are given the notation 2° and the –OH group is attached to a carbon with two alkyl groups attached. Tertiary alcohols are given the notation 3° (you can see where I'm going with this) and the –OH group is attached to a carbon with three alkyl groups attached.

**Tip:** Remember that an alkyl group is an alkane with a hydrogen removed, for example $CH_3$ or $CH_3CH_2$.

**Tip:** Alcohols can react in different ways depending on whether they are primary, secondary or tertiary — so it's important that you know the difference between them.

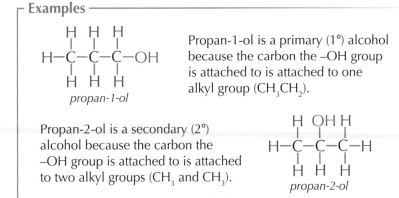

*primary alcohol*     *secondary alcohol*     *tertiary alcohol*

**Figure 1:** Diagrams of 1°, 2° and 3° alcohols. R = alkyl group.

--- Examples ---

*propan-1-ol*

Propan-1-ol is a primary (1°) alcohol because the carbon the –OH group is attached to is attached to one alkyl group ($CH_3CH_2$).

Propan-2-ol is a secondary (2°) alcohol because the carbon the –OH group is attached to is attached to two alkyl groups ($CH_3$ and $CH_3$).

*propan-2-ol*

**Figure 2:** A molecular model of propan-1-ol.

# The hydroxyl group

All alcohols contain a polar hydroxyl group (–OH) that has a δ– charge on the oxygen atom and a δ+ charge on the hydrogen atom. This polar group helps them form hydrogen bonds (see page 72), which gives them certain properties...

When you mix an alcohol with water, hydrogen bonds form between the –OH group and $H_2O$ — see Figure 3.

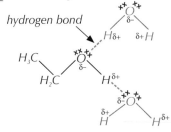

*hydrogen bond*

**Figure 3:** Hydrogen bonding of ethanol in water.

**Exam Tip**
If you're asked to draw hydrogen bonding in an exam don't forget to mark on the lone pairs of electrons and label the hydrogen bond and all the δ+ and δ– atoms.

If it's a small alcohol (e.g. methanol, ethanol or propan-1-ol), hydrogen bonding lets it mix freely with water — it's **miscible** with water. In larger alcohols, most of the molecule is made up of the non-polar carbon chain, which won't mix easily with water molecules. This means that as alcohols increase in size, their miscibility with water decreases.

Hydrogen bonding is the strongest kind of intermolecular force, so it gives alcohols high boiling points compared to non-polar compounds, e.g. alkanes of similar sizes.

**Tip:** Their relatively high boiling points mean that alcohols are liquids at room temperature.

The volatility of a substance is its tendency to evaporate (turn into a gas). Alcohols have a relatively low volatility because the hydrogen bonds between molecules need quite a lot of energy to break. This means that alcohols don't easily become gases.

# Uses of alcohols

There are a few uses of alcohols that you need to know about for the exam:

- Ethanol is the alcohol found in alcoholic drinks.
- Methylated spirits is an industrial solvent. It's basically ethanol, with some methanol and purple dye added to make it undrinkable and tax-exempt. Ethanol will dissolve polar, non-polar and some ionic compounds.
- Ethanol (this includes bioethanol, see page 129) is also being used increasingly as a fuel, particularly in countries with few oil reserves.
- Unleaded petrol contains 5% methanol and 15% MTBE (an ether made from methanol) to improve combustion.
- Methanol is important as a feedstock (starting point) for manufacturing organic chemicals, e.g. plastics and dyes.

**Figure 4:** *A bioethanol fuel pump. There's loads more on the use of bioethanol as a fuel on page 129.*

## Practice Questions — Application

Q1 Name the following alcohols.

a)

H H H OHH
| | | | |
H—C—C—C—C—C—H
| | | | |
H H H H H

b)

H H OHH
| | | |
H—C—C—C—C—H
| | | |
H H CH₃H

c)

H CH₃ H OH
| | | |
H—C—C—C—C—H
| | | |
H H CH₃H

d)

H H H CH₃H
| | | | |
H—C—C—C—C—C—H
| | | | |
H H CH₂ H OH
|
CH₂OH

Q2 State whether each of the alcohols in Question 1 parts a), b) and c) are primary (1°), secondary (2°) or tertiary (3°) alcohols.

Q3 Which alcohol is more miscible with water: propan-1-ol or octan-1-ol? Explain your answer.

Q4 Which of these molecules will have a higher boiling point: butane or butan-1-ol? Explain your answer.

**Tip:** Remember — name molecules so that the names include the lowest numbers possible.

**Tip:** When you're naming diols the stem of the name must come from the longest carbon chain that includes <u>both</u> hydroxy groups.

## Practice Questions — Fact Recall

Q1 What suffix is added to a molecule's name if an –OH functional group is the highest priority group in the molecule?

Q2 What is a secondary alcohol?

Q3 Explain why small alcohols mix easily with water.

Q4 Give three uses of alcohols.

**Exam Tip**
If an exam question asks for <u>three</u> uses of alcohols make sure you give them <u>three</u> uses. Put two uses and a doodle of a hedgehog and you won't be getting full marks...

# 2. Reactions of Alcohols

*Alcohols are really useful starting materials for making lots of other organic compounds as well as being pretty handy chemicals in their own right. This topic covers a few reactions involving alcohols that you need to know about...*

## Production of ethanol

There are two methods of producing ethanol that you need to know about:

### Steam hydration of ethene

At the moment most industrial ethanol is produced by steam hydration of ethene with a phosphoric acid catalyst (see page 145). The ethene comes from cracking heavy fractions of crude oil.

$$CH_2{=}CH_{2(g)} + H_2O_{(g)} \underset{\substack{300\ °C \\ 60\ atm}}{\overset{H_3PO_4}{\rightleftharpoons}} CH_3CH_2OH_{(g)}$$

$$\textit{ethene} \qquad\qquad\qquad \textit{ethanol}$$

But in the future, when crude oil supplies start running out, petrochemicals like ethene will be expensive — so producing ethanol by fermentation will become much more important...

### Industrial production of ethanol by fermentation

Fermentation is a process carried out by yeast in anaerobic conditions (without oxygen). Here's the equation for the reaction.

$$C_6H_{12}O_{6(aq)} \xrightarrow[\text{yeast}]{30\text{-}40°C} 2CH_3CH_2OH_{(aq)} + 2CO_{2(g)}$$

$$\textit{glucose} \qquad\qquad \textit{ethanol}$$

Yeast produces enzymes which convert sugars, such as glucose, into ethanol and carbon dioxide. The enzyme works at an optimum (ideal) temperature of 30-40 °C. If it's too cold, the reaction is slow — if it's too hot, the enzyme is denatured (damaged). Figure 2 shows how the rate of reaction of fermentation is affected by temperature.

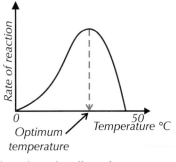

*Figure 2:* Graph to show the effect of temperature on fermentation.

When the solution reaches about 15% ethanol, the yeast dies. Fractional distillation is used to increase the concentration of ethanol. Fermentation is low-tech — it uses cheap equipment and renewable resources. The ethanol produced by this method has to be purified though.

***Figure 1:*** *Vat for the fermentation of yeast.*

# Dehydration of alcohols

Alkenes are really useful organic chemicals that can be used as starting products for lots of organic chemicals such as polymers (see page 137). You can make an alkene by heating an alcohol with an acid catalyst. This reaction eliminates water from the alcohol to form the alkene.

**Tip:** In a dehydration reaction water is lost from one of the reactants. It's the opposite of the hydration reaction on page 145.

---

**Example**

You can make ethene by eliminating water from ethanol in a dehydration reaction. The ethanol is mixed with an acid catalyst and heated to 170 °C. The ethene gas that is produced is collected over water (see Figure 3).

$$
\underset{\text{ethanol}}{H-\overset{\displaystyle H}{\underset{\displaystyle H}{C}}-\overset{\displaystyle H}{\underset{\displaystyle H}{C}}-OH} \quad \xrightarrow[\substack{acid\\catalyst}]{170\,°C} \quad \underset{\text{ethene}}{\overset{H}{\underset{H}{}}C=C\overset{H}{\underset{H}{}}} \quad + \quad H_2O
$$

---

The acid catalyst used for the dehydration of alcohols is either concentrated sulfuric acid ($H_2SO_4$) or concentrated phosphoric acid ($H_3PO_4$).

***Figure 3:*** *The apparatus for collecting gas over water.*

## Practice Questions — Fact Recall

Q1  What reaction conditions are needed to hydrate ethene using steam?

Q2  a)  Write down the equation for the production of ethanol by fermentation.

    b)  Why is it necessary for the reaction to take place between 30 °C and 40 °C?

Q3  a)  Explain why the ethanol produced by fermentation only has a concentration of 15%.

    b)  What can be done to increase the concentration of the ethanol?

Q4  a)  Write down the equation for the dehydration of ethanol.

    b)  Name the products of this reaction.

    c)  Name a catalyst that could be used to catalyse this reaction.

**Tip:** 'Collecting over water' (see Figure 3) is a way of capturing any gases produced by a reaction. A tube is set up that runs from the reaction vessel to an upside-down container filled with water. The gas travels down the tube and bubbles up to the top of the container, pushing water out at the same time.

# 3. Oxidising Alcohols

- Be able to describe the combustion of alcohols.

- Know that you can oxidise alcohols using $Cr_2O_7^{2-}/H^+$ (i.e. $K_2Cr_2O_7/H_2SO_4$).

- Be able to describe the oxidation of primary alcohols to form aldehydes and carboxylic acids.

- Know that when you oxidise a primary alcohol you can control the oxidation product using different reaction conditions.

- Be able to describe the oxidation of secondary alcohols to form ketones.

- Be able to describe the resistance to oxidation of tertiary alcohols.

**Specification Reference 2.2.1**

*Oxidising an alcohol creates a carbon-oxygen double bond. Substances that contain these carbon-oxygen double bonds are known as carbonyl compounds — they're great fun. Honest.*

## The basics

The simple way to **oxidise** alcohols is to burn them. It doesn't take much to set ethanol alight and it burns with a pale blue flame. The C–C and C–H bonds are broken as the ethanol is completely oxidised to make carbon dioxide and water. This is a **combustion** reaction (see page 122).

$$C_2H_5OH_{(l)} + 3O_{2(g)} \longrightarrow 2CO_{2(g)} + 3H_2O_{(g)}$$

But if you want to end up with something more interesting, you need a more sophisticated way of oxidising. You can use the oxidising agent acidified potassium dichromate(VI) ($K_2Cr_2O_7/H_2SO_4$) to mildly oxidise alcohols. In the reaction the orange dichromate(VI) ion is reduced to the green chromium(III) ion, $Cr^{3+}$ (see Figure 1). Primary alcohols are oxidised to **aldehydes** and then to **carboxylic acids**. Secondary alcohols are oxidised to **ketones** only. Tertiary alcohols won't be oxidised.

## Aldehydes, ketones and carboxylic acids

Aldehydes and ketones are carbonyl compounds — they have the functional group C=O. Their general formula is $C_nH_{2n}O$. Aldehydes have a hydrogen and one alkyl group attached to the **carbonyl** carbon atom...

*This is the aldehyde functional group.*

Aldehydes have the suffix -al. You don't have to say which carbon the functional group is on — it's always on carbon-1. Naming aldehydes follows very similar rules to the naming of alcohols (see page 151).

*Figure 1: Alcohol oxidation. As the alcohol is oxidised, the potassium dichromate(VI) is reduced to chromium(III) — so the solution turns from orange to green.*

**Tip:** Remember that a suffix comes at the end of a name and a prefix comes at the beginning.

**Tip:** A molecule has to contain at least 3 carbon atoms for it to be a ketone.

┌ **Examples** ─────────────────

*propanal*

The longest continuous carbon chain is 3 carbon atoms, so the stem is propane.
So, the aldehyde is called propanal.

The longest continuous carbon chain is 4 carbon atoms, so the stem is butane.

There's a methyl group attached to the second carbon atom so there's a 2-methyl- prefix.

So, the aldehyde is called 2-methylbutanal.

*2-methylbutanal*

Ketones have two alkyl groups attached to the carbonyl carbon atom.

*This is the ketone functional group.*

The suffix for ketones is -one. For ketones with five or more carbons, you always have to say which carbon the functional group is on. (If there are other groups attached, such as methyl groups, you have to say it for four-carbon ketones too.)

Examples

H─C─C─C─H (propanone structure with H O H on top, H H on bottom)

*propanone*

The longest continuous carbon chain is 3 carbon atoms, so the stem is propane.

So, the ketone is called propanone.

**Figure 2:** *The ketone propanone (also known as acetone) is commonly used as a nail varnish remover.*

The longest continuous carbon chain is 5 carbon atoms, so the stem is pentane.

The carbonyl is found on the second carbon atom.

So, the ketone is called pentan-2-one.

H─C─C─C─C─C─H (pentan-2-one structure)

*pentan-2-one*

Carboxylic acids have a COOH group at the end of their carbon chain.

H─C─C─C─OH (structure with carboxylic acid functional group circled)

*This is the carboxylic acid functional group.*

The suffix for carboxylic acids is -oic, and you also add the word 'acid' to the end of the name.

Examples

H─C─C─C─OH (propanoic acid structure)

*propanoic acid*

The longest continuous carbon chain is 3 carbon atoms, so the stem is propane.

So, the carboxylic acid is called propanoic acid.

The longest continuous carbon chain is 3 carbon atoms, so the stem is propane.

There's a COOH group at each end of the carbon chain so it has a -dioic acid suffix.

So, the carboxylic acid is called propanedioic acid.

HO─C─C─C─OH (propanedioic acid structure)

*propanedioic acid*

**Tip:** The carboxylic acid functional group is written as COOH and not CO$_2$H to show that the two oxygens are different — one is part of a carbonyl group (CO) and the other is part of an OH group.
The same idea applies to aldehydes — you always write the functional group out as CHO (not COH) so it doesn't look like an alcohol.

**Exam Tip**
Don't get all these functional groups mixed up in the exam — you could lose easy marks. The only way to learn them is practise, practise and more practise.

# Oxidation of primary alcohols

A primary alcohol is first oxidised to an aldehyde. This aldehyde can then be oxidised to a carboxylic acid. You can use the notation [O] to represent an oxidising agent — this saves you having to write down acidified potassium dichromate(VI) every time you write out a reaction, which is handy. This means you can write equations like this:

$$R-CH_2-OH + [O] \longrightarrow R-\overset{O}{\underset{}{C}}-H + [O] \longrightarrow R-\overset{O}{\underset{}{C}}-OH$$

*primary alcohol*       *aldehyde*       *carboxylic acid*

$$+ \; H_2O$$

You can control how far the alcohol is oxidised by controlling the reaction conditions.

## Oxidising primary alcohols to aldehydes

Gently heating ethanol with potassium dichromate(VI) solution and sulfuric acid in a test tube should produce "apple" smelling ethanal (an aldehyde).

**Tip:** Make sure you balance the oxidising agents when you're writing these equations.

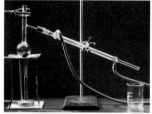

$$\underset{\text{ethanol}}{H-\overset{\displaystyle H}{\underset{\displaystyle H}{C}}-\overset{\displaystyle H}{\underset{\displaystyle H}{C}}-OH} \;+\; [O] \;\xrightarrow[\text{distillation}]{H_2SO_4}\; \underset{\text{ethanal}}{H-\overset{\displaystyle H}{\underset{\displaystyle H}{C}}-\overset{O}{\overset{\|}{C}}-H} \;+\; H_2O$$

However, it's really tricky to control the amount of heat and the aldehyde is usually oxidised to form "vinegar" smelling ethanoic acid. To get just the aldehyde, you need to get it out of the oxidising solution as soon as it's formed. You can do this by gently heating excess alcohol with a controlled amount of oxidising agent in distillation apparatus (see Figures 3 and 4), so the aldehyde (which boils at a lower temperature than the alcohol) is distilled off immediately.

**Figure 3:** Distillation apparatus.

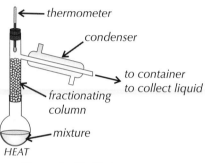

*Figure 4:* Distillation apparatus.

## Oxidising primary alcohols to carboxylic acids

To produce the carboxylic acid, the alcohol has to be vigorously oxidised.

**Tip:** Heating the alcohol under reflux means that, although you still make an aldehyde first, it stays in the reaction vessel with the oxidising agent — so it oxidises further to give a carboxylic acid.

$$\underset{\text{ethanol}}{H-\overset{\displaystyle H}{\underset{\displaystyle H}{C}}-\overset{\displaystyle H}{\underset{\displaystyle H}{C}}-OH} \;+\; 2[O] \;\xrightarrow{\text{reflux}}\; \underset{\text{ethanoic acid}}{H-\overset{\displaystyle H}{\underset{\displaystyle H}{C}}-\overset{O}{\overset{\|}{C}}-OH} \;+\; H_2O$$

The alcohol is mixed with excess oxidising agent and heated under **reflux** (see Figures 5 and 6). Heating under reflux means you can increase the temperature of an organic reaction to boiling without losing volatile solvents, reactants or products. Any vapourised compounds are cooled, condense and drip back into the reaction mixture. Handy, hey.

**Figure 5:** Refluxing apparatus.

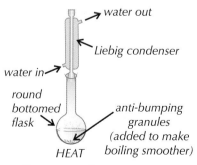

*Figure 6:* Refluxing apparatus.

# Oxidation of secondary alcohols

Refluxing a secondary alcohol with acidified dichromate(VI) will produce a ketone.

$$R_1 \!-\! \overset{\displaystyle R_2}{\underset{\displaystyle H}{\overset{|}{\underset{|}{C}}}} \!-\! OH \ + \ [O] \ \xrightarrow[\substack{acidic \\ conditions}]{reflux} \ R_1 \!-\! \overset{\displaystyle O}{\overset{\|}{C}} \!-\! R_2 \ + \ H_2O$$

secondary alcohol          ketone

**Tip:** Remember that [O] represents the oxidising agent (here that's the acidified potassium dichromate(VI)).

┌─ **Example** ─────────────────────────────────

$$H \!-\! \overset{H}{\underset{H}{\overset{|}{\underset{|}{C}}}} \!-\! \overset{OH}{\underset{H}{\overset{|}{\underset{|}{C}}}} \!-\! \overset{H}{\underset{H}{\overset{|}{\underset{|}{C}}}} \!-\! H \ + \ [O] \ \xrightarrow[\substack{acidic \\ conditions}]{reflux} \ H \!-\! \overset{H}{\underset{H}{\overset{|}{\underset{|}{C}}}} \!-\! \overset{O}{\overset{\|}{C}} \!-\! \overset{H}{\underset{H}{\overset{|}{\underset{|}{C}}}} \!-\! H \ + \ H_2O$$

propan-2-ol          propanone

└──────────────────────────────────────────────

Ketones can't be oxidised easily, so even prolonged refluxing won't produce anything more.

# Oxidation of tertiary alcohols

Tertiary alcohols don't react with acidified potassium dichromate(VI) at all — the solution stays orange. The only way to oxidise tertiary alcohols is by burning them.

**Exam Tip**
You might get a more complicated molecule than this in the exam, but just remember — if it's a primary or secondary alcohol and you treat it with acidified potassium dichromate, the hydroxyl groups will turn into carbonyl groups.

**Tip:** You can distinguish tertiary alcohols from primary and secondary alcohols by heating with acidified potassium dichromate(VI). The solution will stay orange if it's a tertiary alcohol, but will turn green if a primary or secondary alcohol is present.

## Practice Question — Application

Q1 Name the following molecules:

a)
$$H \!-\! \overset{H}{\underset{H}{\overset{|}{\underset{|}{C}}}} \!-\! \overset{H}{\underset{H}{\overset{|}{\underset{|}{C}}}} \!-\! \overset{H}{\underset{H}{\overset{|}{\underset{|}{C}}}} \!-\! \overset{O}{\overset{\|}{C}} \!-\! H$$

b)
$$H \!-\! \overset{O}{\overset{\|}{C}} \!-\! OH$$

c)
$$H \!-\! \overset{H}{\underset{H}{\overset{|}{\underset{|}{C}}}} \!-\! \overset{H}{\underset{H}{\overset{|}{\underset{|}{C}}}} \!-\! \overset{O}{\overset{\|}{C}} \!-\! \overset{H}{\underset{H}{\overset{|}{\underset{|}{C}}}} \!-\! \overset{H}{\underset{H}{\overset{|}{\underset{|}{C}}}} \!-\! H$$

d)
$$H \!-\! \overset{H}{\underset{H}{\overset{|}{\underset{|}{C}}}} \!-\! \overset{O}{\overset{\|}{C}} \!-\! \overset{H}{\underset{H}{\overset{|}{\underset{|}{C}}}} \!-\! \overset{H}{\underset{H}{\overset{|}{\underset{|}{C}}}} \!-\! \overset{H}{\underset{H}{\overset{|}{\underset{|}{C}}}} \!-\! \overset{H}{\underset{H}{\overset{|}{\underset{|}{C}}}} \!-\! H$$

Q2 Draw the structures of the organic products of the following reactions.

a) A reaction between butan-2-ol and acidified potassium dichromate(VI) under reflux.

b) A reaction between butan-1-ol and acidified potassium dichromate(VI) using distillation apparatus.

c) A reaction between butan-1-ol and acidified potassium dichromate(VI) under reflux.

## Practice Questions — Fact Recall

Q1 Write an equation for the complete combustion of ethanol.

Q2 What are the functional groups of aldehydes, ketones and carboxylic acids?

Q3 Write a general equation for the reaction of a primary alcohol with an oxidising agent under reflux.

**Exam Tip**
It's really important that you learn the conditions required to produce both aldehydes and carboxylic acids. It can be pretty easy to mix them up but make sure you don't — you'll be expected to know them for the exam.

# 4. Esterification and Esters

## Learning Objectives:

- Describe the esterification of alcohols with carboxylic acids in the presence of an acid catalyst.

- Use IUPAC rules of nomenclature for systematically naming esters.

**Specification Reference 2.1.1, 2.2.1**

**Tip:** Esterification reactions are also <u>condensation</u> reactions because they release water.

*Here's another crazy functional group for you to learn about — esters.*

## Esterification reactions

If you heat a carboxylic acid with an alcohol in the presence of a strong acid catalyst, you get an **ester**. It's called an **esterification** reaction.

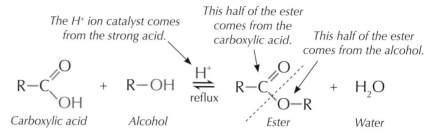

Concentrated sulfuric acid ($H_2SO_4$) is usually used as the acid catalyst but other strong acids such as $HCl$ or $H_3PO_4$ can also be used.

## Naming esters

You've just seen that an ester is formed by reacting an alcohol with a carboxylic acid. Well, the name of an ester is made up of two parts — the first bit comes from the alcohol, and the second bit from the carboxylic acid.

To name an ester, just follow these steps:

1.  Look at the alkyl group that came from the alcohol. This is the first bit of the ester's name.

2.  Now look at the part that came from the carboxylic acid. Swap its '-oic acid' ending for 'oate' to get the second bit of the name.

3.  Put the two parts together.

**Figure 1:** *Model showing the structure of the ester ethyl ethanoate.*

**Exam Tip**
Sometimes examiners will try and throw you by drawing esters the opposite way round, e.g.

$$\text{H}-\underset{\underset{\text{H}}{|}}{\overset{\overset{\text{H}}{|}}{\text{C}}}-\text{O}-\underset{}{\overset{\overset{\text{O}}{||}}{\text{C}}}-\underset{\underset{\text{H}}{|}}{\overset{\overset{\text{H}}{|}}{\text{C}}}-\underset{\underset{\text{H}}{|}}{\overset{\overset{\text{H}}{|}}{\text{C}}}-\text{H}$$

Try not to get confused when naming esters — always think about the position of the O and C=O groups rather than just thinking about left and right.

--- Example ---

Ethanoic acid reacts with methanol to produce the ester shown below:

1.  This part of the ester came from the alcohol. It's a methyl group so the first part of the ester's name is methyl-.

2.  This part of the ester came from the carboxylic acid. It came from ethanoic acid so the second part of the ester's name is -ethanoate.

3.  So this ester is methyl ethanoate.

## Practice Question — Application

Q1 a) Name the two esters shown below.

b) Write an equation for the esterification reaction used to form each of these esters.

(i)

(ii)

# 5. Halogenoalkanes

*Halogenoalkanes pop up a lot in chemistry so it's important that you know exactly what they are and why they're important.*

## What are halogenoalkanes?

A **halogenoalkane** is an alkane with at least one halogen atom in place of a hydrogen atom.

**Examples**

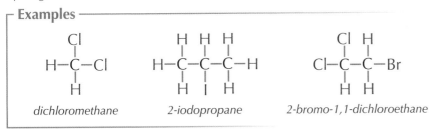

| dichloromethane | 2-iodopropane | 2-bromo-1,1-dichloroethane |

## Naming halogenoalkanes

You name halogenoalkanes in exactly the same way that alkanes are named (see pages 118-119) but you have to add in a prefix before the name of the alkane (see Figure 1). The prefixes are always placed in alphabetical order.

| Halogen | Prefix |
|---------|--------|
| Fluorine | *fluoro-* |
| Chlorine | *chloro-* |
| Bromine | *bromo-* |
| Iodine | *iodo-* |

**Figure 1:** *Prefixes for naming halogenoalkanes.*

**Examples**

The longest carbon chain is 1 carbon atom, so the stem is methane.

There's one chlorine atom attached to the carbon chain so it has a chloro- prefix: chloromethane.

*chloromethane*

The longest carbon chain is 2 carbon atoms, so the stem is ethane.

There's one bromine atom attached to the second carbon atom so it has a bromo- prefix.

There are two chlorine atoms attached to the first carbon so it also has the prefix dichloro-.

So the molecule is 2-bromo-1,1-dichloroethane.

*2-bromo-1,1-dichloroethane*

## Chlorofluorocarbons

Chlorofluorocarbons (CFCs) are well-known halogenoalkanes. They contain only chlorine, fluorine and carbon — all the hydrogens have been replaced. They're very stable, volatile, non-flammable and non-toxic. They were used a lot — e.g. in fridges, aerosol cans, dry cleaning and air-conditioning — until scientists realised they were destroying the ozone layer. See page 211 for more about the ozone layer.

**Learning Objectives:**

- Use IUPAC rules of nomenclature for systematically naming halogenoalkanes.
- Know that CFCs were developed as aerosols, refrigerants, and in air-conditioning because of their low reactivity, volatility and non-toxicity.
- Know that CFCs have caused environmental damage to the ozone layer.
- Be able to outline the role of green chemistry in minimising damage to the environment by promoting biodegradable alternatives to CFCs, such as hydrocarbons and HCFCs.
- Know the use of $CO_2$ as a blowing agent for expanded polymers.
- Know the uses of chloroethene and tetrafluoroethene to produce the plastics PVC and PTFE.

**Specification Reference 2.1.1, 2.2.2**

**Tip:** The carbon atoms in this molecule are numbered so that the lowest possible numbers are in the name. 2-bromo-1,1-dichloroethane has smaller numbers than 1-bromo-2,2-dichloroethane.

Trichlorofluoromethane and chlorotrifluoromethane are both CFCs.

$$Cl-\overset{\overset{\displaystyle Cl}{|}}{\underset{\underset{\displaystyle F}{|}}{C}}-Cl \qquad F-\overset{\overset{\displaystyle F}{|}}{\underset{\underset{\displaystyle Cl}{|}}{C}}-F$$

*trichlorofluoromethane*       *chlorotrifluoromethane*

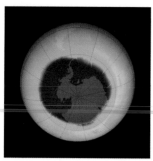

***Figure 2:*** *Antarctic ozone hole, 2009. On the diagram, green indicates areas with a high ozone concentration and blue indicates areas with a low ozone concentration.*

### The Montreal Protocol

**HOW SCIENCE WORKS**

The Montreal Protocol of 1989 was an international treaty to phase out the use of CFCs and other ozone-destroying halogenoalkanes by the year 2000. There were a few permitted uses such as in medical inhalers and in fire extinguishers used in submarines. Scientists supported the treaty, and worked on finding alternatives to CFCs.

### HCFCs and HFCs

HCFCs (hydrochlorofluorocarbons) and HFCs (hydrofluorocarbons) are being used as temporary alternatives to CFCs until safer products are developed. Hydrocarbons are also used.

**Tip:** The residence time of a compound is how long it spends in the atmosphere before being broken down. CFCs have long residence times which means they can destroy much more ozone than HCFCs can.

The problem with CFCs is that they hang around in the atmosphere causing disruption for ages — the have an average **residence time** of around 90 years. HCFCs are broken down in the atmosphere in 10-20 years. They still damage the ozone layer, but their effect is much smaller than CFCs. HFCs are broken down in the atmosphere too and they don't contain chlorine, so they don't affect the ozone layer.

**Tip:** To make an <u>expanded polymer</u> you bubble gas through liquid plastic (to make a foam) before letting it set. The substance used to create the bubbles (e.g. carbon dioxide) is called a <u>blowing agent</u>.

Unfortunately, HFCs and HCFCs are greenhouse gases (see page 208) — they contribute towards the warming of the Earth. Some hydrocarbons are being used in fridges but these are greenhouse gases too. Nowadays, most aerosols have been replaced by pump spray systems or use nitrogen as the propellant. Many industrial fridges and freezers now use ammonia as the coolant gas, and carbon dioxide is used to make expanded polymers.

These substances do have drawbacks, but they're currently the least environmentally damaging of all the alternatives. The ozone holes still form in the spring but it's now naturally repairing itself — so things are looking up.

## Polymer halogenoalkanes

**Tip:** You can use expanded polystyrene (an expanded polymer) to package fragile items.

The plastics PVC (made from chloroethene) and PTFE (made from tetrafluoroethene) are halogenoalkanes. Look back at page 138 and make sure you know how they're made, and some of their uses.

### Practice Question — Application

Q1 Draw skeletal formulas for the following halogenoalkanes:
a) 1-bromobutane            b) 2,3-difluoropentane
c) 1-bromo-2-chloropropane    d) 1-iodohexane

**Tip:** Don't worry if you see halogenoalkanes called haloalkanes. It's just an evil conspiracy to confuse you.

### Practice Questions — Fact Recall

Q1 What is a chlorofluorocarbon (CFC)?

Q2 Explain why CFCs were used a lot before we knew that they damaged the environment.

Q3 Name one type of chemical that is used as an alternative to CFCs.

# 6. More Halogenoalkanes

*Halogenoalkanes are really useful starting points for loads of organic reactions. They're especially useful because they can undergo nucleophilic substitution.*

## Polarity of halogenoalkanes

Halogens are much more electronegative than carbon.
So, the carbon-halogen bond is **polar**.

> **Example**
>
> $-\overset{\displaystyle |}{\underset{\displaystyle |}{C}}\!\overset{\delta+}{\phantom{.}}\!-\!\overset{\delta-}{Br}$
>
> The bromine atom is more electronegative than the carbon atom and so withdraws electron density from the carbon-bromine bond. This leaves the carbon atom with a partial positive charge and the bromine atom with a partial negative charge.

The $\delta+$ carbon doesn't have enough electrons. This means it can be attacked by a **nucleophile**. A nucleophile's an electron-pair donor. It donates an electron pair to somewhere without enough electrons.

> **Examples**
>
> Here are some nucleophiles that will react with halogenoalkanes.
>
> :CN         :NH$_3$         :OH
>
> *cyanide ion*    *ammonia*    *hydroxide ion*
>
> The pairs of dots represent lone pairs of electrons.
> Water's a nucleophile too, but it reacts slowly.

There are examples of reactions where nucleophiles react with halogenoalkanes on the next few pages.

## Nucleophilic substitution reactions

Mechanisms are diagrams that show how a reaction works. They show how the bonds in molecules are made and broken, how the electrons are transferred and how you get from the reactants to the products. The first mechanism we deal with is the **nucleophilic substitution reaction**. In a nucleophilic substitution reaction, a nucleophile attacks a polar molecule, kicks out a functional group and settles itself down in its place. The equation for the overall reaction of a general nucleophilic substitution reaction is:

$$CH_3CH_2X + Nu^- \rightarrow CH_3CH_2Nu + X^-$$

And here's how it all works:

*The carbon-halogen bond is polar. The tiny charges on the atoms are shown by $\delta+$ and $\delta-$ signs.*

*The X stands for one of the halogens (F, Cl, Br or I).*

*The Nu$^-$ stands for a nucleophile. The lone pair of electrons has a negative charge (as electrons are negatively charged).*

The lone pair of electrons on the nucleophile attacks the slightly positive charge on the carbon — this is shown by a black curly arrow.

In mechanisms, curly arrows always show the movement of an electron pair. The lone pair of electrons creates a new bond between the nucleophile and the carbon.

The carbon can only be bonded to four other atoms so the addition of the nucleophile breaks the bond between the carbon and the halogen — this is shown by another curly arrow. The pair of electrons from the carbon-halogen bond are taken by the halogen and become a lone pair.

**Tip:** The bond breaking between the carbon atom and the halogen atom is <u>heterolytic</u> bond breaking.

# Hydrolysis of halogenoalkanes

In **hydrolysis** reactions, molecules are split into two parts by water molecules (which also split apart). Halogenoalkanes can be hydrolysed to make alcohols.

**Tip:** <u>Refluxing</u> is a method for heating a reaction to boiling point without losing volatile solvents, reactants or products (see page 158).

┌─ Example ─────────────────

Bromoethane can be hydrolysed to ethanol in a nucleophilic substitution reaction. You can use water as the nucleophile in this reaction, but it would go pretty slowly. The reaction works much better if you use warm aqueous sodium hydroxide or potassium hydroxide instead. Here's the equation for this reaction:

$$CH_3CH_2Br + {}^-OH \xrightarrow{\text{reflux}} CH_3CH_2OH + Br^-$$

And here's the general equation for this type of reaction:

$$R–X + {}^-OH \rightarrow ROH + X^-$$

**Tip:** This reaction is usually called hydrolysis, even though it's ⁻OH ions from the alkali that are reacting, not water molecules. That's because the product and the mechanism are the same whichever you use.

R represents an alkyl group. X stands for one of the halogens (F, Cl, Br or I). As it's a nucleophilic substitution reaction, the nucleophile (⁻OH) kicks out the halogen (X) from the R–X molecule and takes its place. Here's how it happens:

1. The $C^{\delta+}$ from a polar C–Br bond attracts a lone pair of electrons from an OH⁻ ion.

3. The C–Br bond breaks heterolytically — both the electrons are taken by the Br.

4. A new bond forms between the C and the OH⁻ ion.

2. The OH⁻ ion acts as a nucleophile — it provides a pair of electrons for the $C^{\delta+}$.

5. The Br⁻ falls off as the OH bonds to the carbon.

**Tip:** When you're drawing mechanisms make sure the charges balance. That way you'll know if you've lost track of any electrons along the way. In this example, the left hand side has one negative charge on the hydroxide ion and the right hand side has one negative charge from a bromide ion — so it's balanced.

# Bond enthalpy and hydrolysis

How quickly different halogenoalkanes are hydrolysed depends on bond enthalpy — see page 180 for more on this. Weaker carbon-halogen bonds break more easily — so they react faster. Iodoalkanes have the weakest bonds, so they hydrolyse the fastest. Fluoroalkanes have the strongest bonds, so they're the slowest at hydrolysing (see Figure 1).

| bond | bond enthalpy kJ mol$^{-1}$ |
|------|------|
| C–F | 467 |
| C–Cl | 346 |
| C–Br | 290 |
| C–I | 228 |

*Faster hydrolysis as bond enthalpy decreases (the bonds are getting weaker).*

*Figure 1: Carbon-halogen bond enthalpies.*

**Tip:** If you've got a molecule with more than one halogen in it, the halogen with the lowest bond enthalpy will get replaced first.

## Comparing hydrolysis rates of halogenoalkanes

On page 164 you saw how to hydrolyse a halogenoalkane using a warm alkali, like sodium hydroxide. You can use water as the nucleophile instead (the reaction will just be slower) — then the overall reaction looks like this:

$$R–X + 2H_2O \rightarrow R–OH + H_3O^+ + X^-$$

If you put silver nitrate solution in the mixture too, the silver ions will react with the halide ions as soon as they form, giving a silver halide precipitate (see pages 94-95). This is the equation for that reaction:

$$Ag^+_{(aq)} + X^-_{(aq)} \rightarrow AgX_{(s)}$$

To compare the reactivities, set up four flasks each containing a different halogenoalkane, ethanol (as a solvent) and dilute silver nitrate solution. You can 'measure' the rates of the reactions by timing how quickly each silver halide is precipitated, using the good old 'timing how long it takes the cross to disappear method' (not its official name...). To do this, stick a piece of paper with a cross on it under each flask and measure how long it takes until you can't see the cross any more (see Figure 2).

**Tip:** To hydrolyse halogenoalkanes with high bond enthalpies you need to use harsher reaction conditions — for example, a higher temperature.

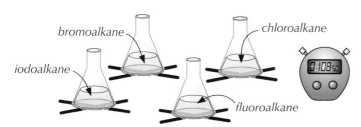

bromoalkane

chloroalkane

iodoalkane

fluoroalkane

*Figure 2: Experimental set-up for measuring the rate of reaction of hydrolysis.*

**Tip:** You need to use an iodoalkane, a bromoalkane, a chloroalkane and a fluoroalkane. They should be the same in all other respects to make it a fair test.

If all the conditions are the same (including the temperature, concentration of reactants, etc) then you'll find that iodoalkanes react quickly to form yellow precipitates, bromoalkanes are a bit slower to react (forming cream precipitates), and chloroalkanes take absolutely ages to react, forming white precipitates. Fluoroalkanes usually don't react at all.

You can do this experiment using an alkali as the nucleophile (see page 164) instead of water if you want. All you need to do is add a couple of extra steps to the method:

- Add the NaOH solution to the halogenoalkane. The ⁻OH ion acts as the nucleophile.

- Add dilute nitric acid to neutralise any spare ⁻OH ions before adding the silver nitrate solution (or else the silver nitrate will react with the ⁻OH ions to form a silver oxide precipitate, which messes up your results).

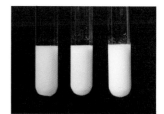

*Figure 3: The result of adding silver nitrate to a chloroalkane, a bromoalkane and an iodoalkane.*

Q1  Draw the mechanism for the hydrolysis of chloroethane by warm
aqueous sodium hydroxide. The structure of chloroethane is
shown below.

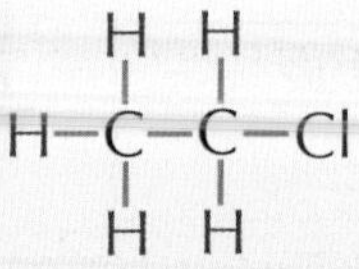

$$H-\underset{\underset{H}{|}}{\overset{\overset{H}{|}}{C}}-\underset{\underset{H}{|}}{\overset{\overset{H}{|}}{C}}-Cl$$

Q2  Which of the following reactions would be quickest?
Explain your answer.

A:  $CH_3CH_2Cl + H_2O \rightarrow CH_3CH_2OH + HCl$

B:  $CH_3CH_2Br + H_2O \rightarrow CH_3CH_2OH + HBr$

C:  $CH_3CH_2I + H_2O \rightarrow CH_3CH_2OH + HI$

Q3  Draw the mechanism for the reaction of 1-chlorobutane with
a $^-CN$ nucleophile. The molecule 1-chlorobutane is shown below.

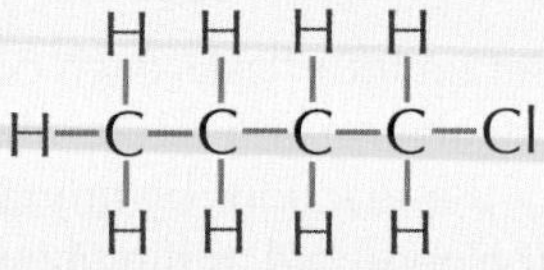

$$H-\underset{\underset{H}{|}}{\overset{\overset{H}{|}}{C}}-\underset{\underset{H}{|}}{\overset{\overset{H}{|}}{C}}-\underset{\underset{H}{|}}{\overset{\overset{H}{|}}{C}}-\underset{\underset{H}{|}}{\overset{\overset{H}{|}}{C}}-Cl$$

Q4  Draw the mechanism for the reaction of iodopropane with ammonia.
The reaction is done in a sealed tube in warm ethanol.
The reactants are shown below.

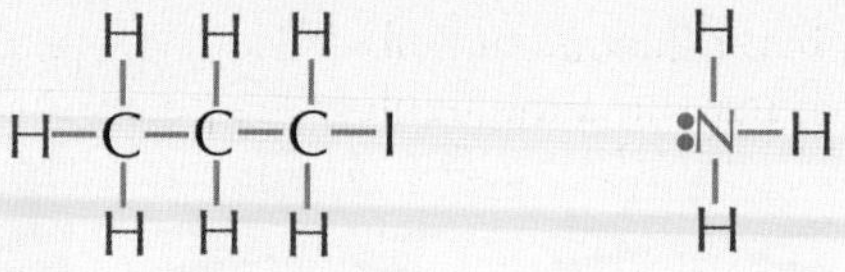

$$H-\underset{\underset{H}{|}}{\overset{\overset{H}{|}}{C}}-\underset{\underset{H}{|}}{\overset{\overset{H}{|}}{C}}-\underset{\underset{H}{|}}{\overset{\overset{H}{|}}{C}}-I \qquad \overset{\overset{H}{|}}{\underset{\underset{H}{|}}{:N-H}}$$

## Practice Questions — Fact Recall

Q1  Briefly describe a nucleophilic substitution reaction.

Q2  Name a substance that you could react with bromoethane to
produce ethanol.

Q3  Explain why fluoroalkanes are hydrolysed more slowly than other
halogenoalkanes.

Q4  Write an equation for the reaction of bromoethane with hydroxide ions.

Q5  Describe an experiment that you could perform to determine which
halogenoalkane, 1-iodopentane or 1-chloropentane, has the fastest
rate of reaction for hydrolysis.

# 7. Infrared Spectroscopy

*Infrared spectroscopy is an analytical technique which can help you to identify a compound. The bonds of different functional groups absorb different frequencies of infrared light. This means we can use an infrared spectrum of a molecule to identify its functional groups.*

## The basics

In **infrared (IR) spectroscopy**, a beam of IR radiation is passed through a sample of a chemical. The IR radiation is absorbed by the covalent bonds in the molecules, increasing their vibrational energy. Bonds between different atoms absorb different frequencies of IR radiation. Bonds in different places in a molecule absorb different frequencies too — so the O–H bond in an alcohol and the O–H in a carboxylic acid absorb different frequencies. Figure 1 shows what frequencies different bonds absorb — you don't need to learn this data, but you do need to understand how to use it. Wavenumber is the measure used for the frequency (it's just 1/wavelength).

| Functional group | Where it's found | Frequency / Wavenumber (cm⁻¹) | Type of absorption |
|---|---|---|---|
| C–H | most organic molecules | 2800 – 3100 | strong, sharp |
| O–H | alcohols | 3200 – 3550 | strong, broad |
| O–H | carboxylic acids | 2500 – 3300 | medium, broad |
| C=O | aldehydes, ketones, carboxylic acids | 1680 – 1750 | strong, sharp |

*Figure 1: Bond absorption for different functional groups.*

An infrared spectrometer produces a graph that shows you what frequencies of radiation the bonds in a molecule are absorbing. So you can use it to identify the functional groups in a molecule. The peaks show you where radiation is being absorbed — the 'peaks' on IR spectra are upside-down.

### Examples

The structure of ethanal is shown on the right:

This is the infrared spectrum of ethanal:

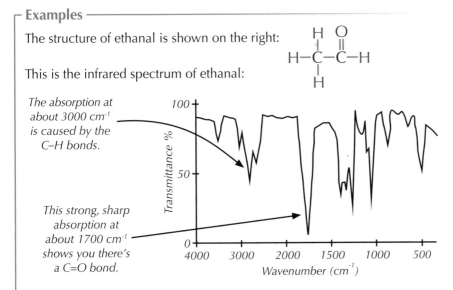

*The absorption at about 3000 cm⁻¹ is caused by the C–H bonds.*

*This strong, sharp absorption at about 1700 cm⁻¹ shows you there's a C=O bond.*

**Learning Objectives:**

- Know that the absorption of infrared radiation causes covalent bonds to vibrate.
- Be able to identify an alcohol from an absorption peak of the O–H bond using an infrared spectrum of an organic compound.
- Be able to identify an aldehyde or ketone from an absorption peak of the C=O bond using an infrared spectrum of an organic compound.
- Be able to identify a carboxylic acid from an absorption peak of the C=O bond and a broad absorption peak of the O–H bond using an infrared spectrum of an organic compound.
- Know that modern breathalysers measure ethanol in the breath by analysis using infrared spectroscopy.

**Specification Reference 2.2.3**

**Tip:** The 'type of absorption' column in Figure 1 tells you what the peak on the infrared spectrum will look like.

**Exam Tip**
You'll get a table like the one in Figure 1 on the data sheet in your exam. So there's no need to memorise all those numbers — yay.

Here is the structure and the infrared spectrum of ethanoic acid.

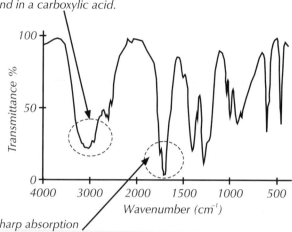

*ethanoic acid*

*This medium, broad absorption at about 3000 cm⁻¹ shows you there's an O–H bond in a carboxylic acid.*

*This strong, sharp absorption at about 1720 cm⁻¹ shows you there's a C=O bond.*

This also means that you can tell if a functional group has changed during a reaction. For example, if you oxidise an alcohol to an aldehyde you'll see the O–H absorption disappear from the spectrum, and a C=O absorption appear.

# An application of IR spectroscopy

If a person's suspected of drink driving, they're breathalysed. First a very quick test is done by the roadside — if it says that the driver's over the limit, they're taken into a police station for a more accurate test using infrared spectroscopy. The amount of ethanol vapour in the driver's breath is found by measuring the intensity of the peak corresponding to the C–H bond in the IR spectrum. It's chosen because it's not affected by any water vapour in the breath.

*Figure 2: A man undergoing a drink-driving breath test at a police station.*

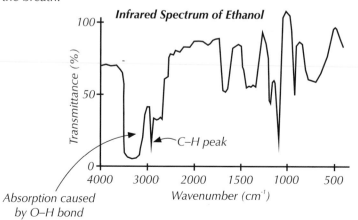

*Infrared Spectrum of Ethanol*

C–H peak

*Absorption caused by O–H bond*

## Practice Questions — Application

Q1  The spectrum below is the infrared spectrum of a carboxylic acid with $M_r = 74$.

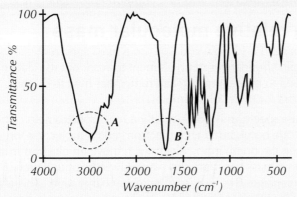

a) Identify the bonds that create the peaks marked **A** and **B** in the diagram.

b) Draw the displayed formula of the molecule.

Q2  The spectrum below shows the infrared spectrum for an unknown molecule. Use the spectrum to identify one important bond that can be found in the molecule.

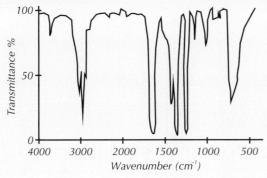

Q3  One of the infrared spectrums below is the infrared spectrum of propan-2-ol. Identify which spectrum (**A** or **B**) it is.

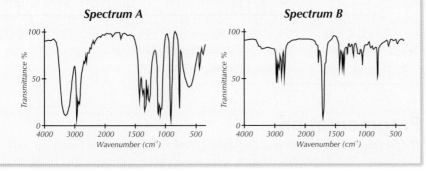

**Tip:** You can use the data table on page 167 to help you with all of these questions.

**Tip:** Remember that displayed formulas have to show <u>all</u> of the bonds present in a molecule.

## Practice Questions — Fact Recall

Q1  Give a brief explanation of how an infrared spectrum is created.

Q2  Describe one application of infrared spectroscopy.

- Be able to outline the use of mass spectrometry in the determination of relative isotopic masses.

- Be able to interpret mass spectra of elements in terms of isotopic abundances.

- Be able to use the molecular ion peak in a mass spectrum of an organic molecule to determine its molecular mass.

- Be able to use molecular ion peaks and fragmentation peaks to identify structures (limited to unipositive ions).

- Be able to suggest the identity of the major fragment ions, i.e. m/z = 29 as $CH_3CH_2^+$, in a given mass spectrum (limited to alkanes, alkenes and alcohols).

- Know that a mass spectrum is essentially a fingerprint for the molecule that can be identified by computer using a spectral database.

- Be able to outline the use of mass spectrometry as a method for identifying elements, i.e. use in the Mars space probe and in monitoring levels of environmental pollution, such as lead.

**Specification Reference 2.2.3**

# 8. Mass Spectrometry

*This topic deals with another analytical technique — mass spectrometry. Mass spectrometry uses the mass of a compound to identify it.*

## Finding relative molecular mass

You saw on pages 11-12 how you can use a **mass spectrum** showing the relative isotopic abundances of an element to work out its relative atomic mass. You need to make sure you can remember how to do this. You can also get mass spectra for molecular samples.

A mass spectrum is produced by a mass spectrometer. The molecules in the sample are bombarded with electrons and a molecular ion, $M^+_{(g)}$, is formed when the bombarding electrons remove an electron from the molecule. On a mass spectrum the y-axis gives the abundance of the ions, often as a percentage. The x-axis is the mass/charge ratio. This is just the molecular mass of the ion divided by its charge.

To find the relative molecular mass of a compound you look at the molecular ion peak (the M peak). For the spectrums that you'll see, the M peak is the one with the highest mass/charge ratio. The mass/charge value of the molecular ion peak is the molecular mass of the compound (assuming the ion has 1+ charge, which it normally will have).

### Example

Here's the mass spectrum of pentane ($CH_3CH_2CH_2CH_2CH_3$).

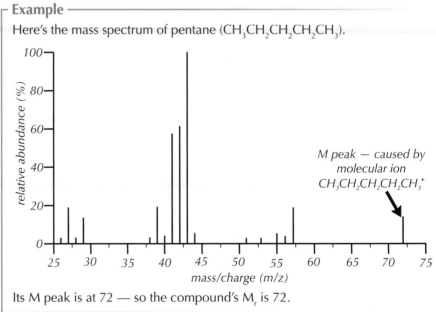

M peak — caused by molecular ion $CH_3CH_2CH_2CH_2CH_3^+$

Its M peak is at 72 — so the compound's $M_r$ is 72.

## Fragmentation

The bombarding electrons make some of the molecular ions break up into fragments. The fragments that are ions show up on the mass spectrum, making a fragmentation pattern. Fragmentation patterns are actually pretty cool because you can use them to identify molecules and even their structure.

For propane ($CH_3CH_2CH_3$), the molecular ion is $CH_3CH_2CH_3^+$, and the fragments it breaks into include $CH_3^+$ ($M_r = 15$) and $CH_3CH_2^+$ ($M_r = 29$).

$$CH_3CH_2CH_3^+ \nearrow \searrow$$

$CH_3CH_2\bullet$ + $CH_3^+$
*free radical*     *ion*

$CH_3CH_2^+$ + $CH_3\bullet$
*ion*     *free radical*

**Tip:** Only the ions show up on the mass spectrum — the free radicals are 'lost' because they are uncharged.

To work out the structural formula, you've got to work out what ion could have made each peak from its m/z value. (You can assume that the m/z value of a peak matches the mass of the ion that made it.)

**Examples**

**The mass spectrum below is for a molecule with the molecular formula $C_2H_6O$. Use the mass spectrum to work out the structure of the molecule.**

**Exam Tip**
For A-Level it's only the m/z values you're interested in — ignore the heights of the bars.

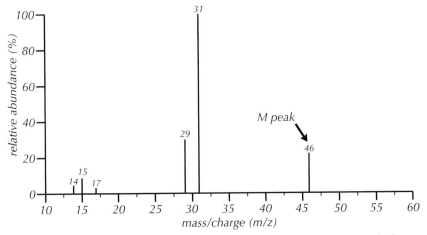

**Tip:** The little numbers above the peaks here are their exact m/z values.

First you need to identify the fragments — you can use Figure 1 to help you identify some common ions.

- This molecule's got a peak at 15 m/z, so it's likely to have a $CH_3$ group.
- It's also got a peak at 17 m/z, so it's likely to have an OH group.
- To find the other fragments you just have to add combinations of 12 (the mass of carbon), 1 (the mass of hydrogen) and 16 (the mass of oxygen) until you come up with sensible fragment ions.

Other ions are matched to the peaks here:

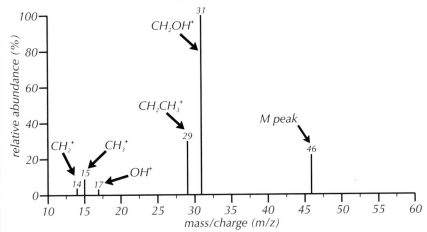

| Fragment | m/z |
|---|---|
| $CH_3^+$ | 15 |
| $CH_2CH_3^+$ | 29 |
| $CH_2CH_2CH_3^+$ | 43 |
| $OH^+$ | 17 |
| $C=O^+$ | 28 |
| $COCH_3^+$ | 43 |

*Figure 1: Common fragment ions.*

**Exam Tip**
You won't be given a common fragments table in the exam. But don't worry — if you can't remember an m/z value, you can work it out by finding the $M_r$ of the ion (e.g. $OH^+ = 16 + 1 = 17$).

**Exam Tip**
Getting your head around these mass spectra is always difficult at first — get loads of practice in before the exam and you'll soon pick it up.

**Exam Tip**
Don't worry if you can't assign every line to a fragment — just make sure you assign most of them and that your final molecule <u>makes sense</u>.

The next step is piecing them together to form a molecule with the correct $M_r$. Ethanol has all the fragments on this spectrum.

Ethanol's formula is $C_2H_6O$, and its molecular mass is 46 — the same as the m/z value of the M peak. So, this is the mass spectrum of ethanol.

# Differentiating between similar molecules

Even if two different compounds contain the same atoms, you can still tell them apart with mass spectrometry because they won't produce exactly the same set of fragments.

┌ **Example** ─────────────────────────────

The formulas of propanone and propanal are shown below.

*propanone*          *propanal*

They've got the same $M_r$, but different structures, so they produce some different fragments.

**Propanone**

**Propanal**

***Figure 2:*** *Mass spectrometer.*

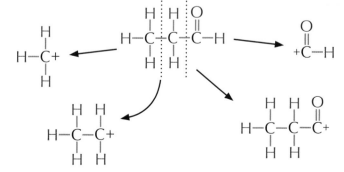

**Tip:** For example, the mass spectrum of propanone will have a peak at 43 m/z (thanks to the $CH_3CO^+$ ion), but the spectrum of propanal won't. And the mass spectrum of propanal will have a peak at 29 m/z (because of the $CH_3CH_2^+$ ion), but the spectrum of propanone won't.

Every compound produces a different mass spectrum — so the spectrum's like a fingerprint for the compound. Large computer databases of mass spectra can be used to identify a compound from its spectrum.

# Applications of mass spectrometry

Mass spectrometry is actually used by scientists out there in the real world. Here are a couple of examples.

- Probes to Mars have carried small mass spectrometers to study the composition of the surface of Mars and to look for elements and compounds that might suggest that life existed on the planet.

- Mass spectrometry can also be used to measure the levels of pollutants present in the environment, e.g. the amount of lead (or pesticides) entering the food chain. If lead is present in a sample of material, the mass spectrum will have a peak at 207.2 m/z, the $A_r$ of lead.

**Figure 3:** *Mars Exploration Rover. These rovers carry mass spectrometers to analyse rock samples.*

## Practice Questions — Application

Q1 Write down some possible fragment ions of propan-1-ol. The structure of propan-1-ol is shown on the right.

$$H-\overset{\displaystyle H}{\underset{\displaystyle H}{C}}-\overset{\displaystyle H}{\underset{\displaystyle H}{C}}-\overset{\displaystyle H}{\underset{\displaystyle H}{C}}-OH$$

Q2 Use the mass spectrum below to work out the structure of the molecule. HINT: The molecule is an alkene.

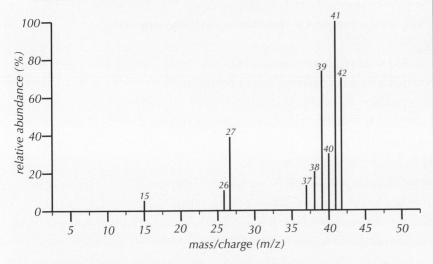

Q3 Identify a fragment ion that will appear in the mass spectrum of butan-2-ol but won't appear in the mass spectrum of butan-1-ol.

> **Tip:** You can use the table on page 171 to help with this question if you like.

> **Tip:** If you look at any real-life mass spectra from computer databases you might see a small peak one unit to the right of the M peak. This is called the M+1 peak and it's caused by the presence of the carbon isotope $^{13}C$ — but you don't need to worry about it for A-Level.

## Practice Questions — Fact Recall

Q1 Where would you find the M peak on a mass spectrum?

Q2 What information does the m/z value of the M peak give you?

Q3 If you have a peak at 15 m/z, what is the most likely fragment ion for an organic compound?

Q4 Give two applications of mass spectrometry.

# Section Summary

Make sure you know...

- How to name alcohols.
- What primary, secondary and tertiary alcohols are and how to spot them.
- How hydrogen bonding affects the water solubility and volatility of alcohols.
- That ethanol is used in alcoholic drinks, as a solvent in the form of methylated spirits and as a fuel.
- That methanol is used as a petrol additive and as a starting point for making other organic chemicals.
- How ethene reacts with steam in the presence of an acid catalyst.
- How ethanol can be made industrially by fermenting glucose.
- How water can be eliminated from alcohols to form alkenes.
- How to describe the combustion of alcohols.
- What aldehydes, ketones and carboxylic acids are.
- That you can oxidise alcohols using acidified potassium dichromate(VI).
- How to oxidise primary alcohols to form aldehydes and carboxylic acids.
- How to oxidise secondary alcohols to form ketones.
- That tertiary alcohols can only be oxidised by burning.
- How to make an ester by reacting an alcohol with a carboxylic acid in the presence of an acid catalyst.
- How to name esters.
- How to name halogenoalkanes.
- That CFCs are volatile, non-toxic, non-flammable and not very reactive.
- That CFCs were used as aerosols, refrigerants, and in dry cleaning and air-conditioning.
- That CFCs damage the ozone layer.
- That scientists are working to find less harmful alternatives to CFCs (e.g. hydrocarbons, HFCs and HCFCs).
- That carbon dioxide is now used as a blowing agent for expanded polymers.
- That chloroethene and tetrafluoroethene are used to make the plastics PVC and PTFE.
- That carbon–halogen bonds are polar so they can be attacked by nucleophiles.
- That a nucleophile is an electron pair donor.
- The basic mechanism for a nucleophilic substitution reaction.
- That the hydrolysis of a halogenoalkane is a nucleophilic substitution reaction.
- The mechanism for the reaction of a halogenoalkane with a hot aqueous alkali.
- That the hydrolysis rate of halogenoalkanes depends on the bond enthalpy of the carbon–halogen bond.
- That absorption of infrared radiation causes covalent bonds to vibrate.
- How to identify an alcohol, an aldehyde, a ketone and a carboxylic acid from the absorption peaks on an infrared spectrum.
- That modern breathalysers measure ethanol in the breath using infrared spectroscopy.
- How mass spectrometry can be used to find relative isotopic masses.
- How to interpret the mass spectrum of an element in terms of isotopic abundance.
- How to use the molecular ion peak on a mass spectrum to determine the molecular mass of a molecule.
- How to use the fragmentation pattern of a mass spectrum to identify the structure of a molecule.
- That a molecule that can be identified by using a computer to compare its mass spectrum to a spectral database.
- About the real-life applications of mass spectrometry e.g. in the Mars space probe and in monitoring levels of pollutants, such as lead.

# Exam-style Questions

**1** Ethanol is a simple alcohol that can be used as a solvent and as a starting point for many organic synthesis reactions. Its structure is shown below.

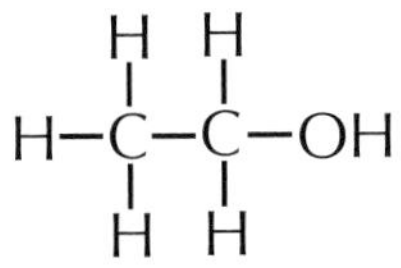

$$H-\underset{\underset{H}{|}}{\overset{\overset{H}{|}}{C}}-\underset{\underset{H}{|}}{\overset{\overset{H}{|}}{C}}-OH$$

**(a)** Ethanol can be made by reacting bromoethane with warm aqueous sodium hydroxide.

**(i)** Write the equation for this reaction.

*(1 mark)*

**(ii)** Draw the mechanism for the reaction between bromoethane and hydroxide ions.

*(3 marks)*

**(iii)** Ethanol can also be made by reacting iodoethane with aqueous sodium hydroxide. Which of the reactions would proceed more quickly? Explain your answer.

*(3 marks)*

**(b)** Industrially, ethanol can be produced by steam hydration or by fermentation.

**(i)** Suggest the conditions needed for the production of ethanol by steam hydration.

*(2 marks)*

**(ii)** Write down the equation for the production of ethanol by fermentation and suggest the conditions needed for the reaction to occur.

*(2 marks)*

**(iii)** The steam hydration method of producing ethanol is currently used more than the fermentation method. Explain, in terms of the raw materials used, why the production of ethanol by fermentation may become more important in the future.

*(2 marks)*

**(c)** Ethanol is miscible with water.

**(i)** Explain why ethanol is miscible with water.

*(1 mark)*

**(ii)** Explain why butan-1-ol is less miscible with water than ethanol.

*(1 mark)*

**(d)** Ethanol can be used to produce esters.

**(i)** Write an equation for the reaction between ethanol and propanoic acid. Name the ester formed in the reaction.

*(2 marks)*

**(ii)** Suggest the conditions needed for this reaction to take place.

*(1 mark)*

**2**    A scientist has synthesised a molecule — molecule **A**.
The molecule was synthesised by reacting ⁻OH ions with 1-bromopropane.
The structure of 1-bromopropane is shown below.

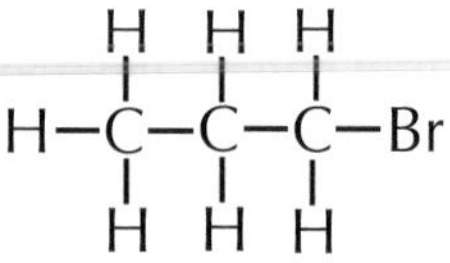

$$\begin{array}{ccccc} & H & H & H & \\ & | & | & | & \\ H- & C- & C- & C- & Br \\ & | & | & | & \\ & H & H & H & \end{array}$$

**2 (a) (i)**    Draw the displayed structure of molecule **A**.

*(1 mark)*

    **(ii)**    Name molecule **A**.

*(1 mark)*

  **(b)**    Suggest what reagents and conditions would be needed to produce a
carboxylic acid from molecule **A**.

*(2 marks)*

  **(c)**    The infrared spectrums of two unknown molecules are shown below.
One of them belongs to molecule **A**. Which infrared spectrum is of molecule **A**?
Explain your answer. You may use the table on page 167.

    In your answer, you should make clear how the structure fits with the information
given below.

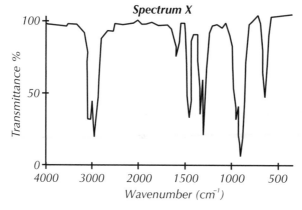

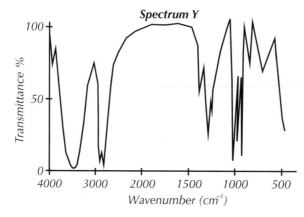

*(3 marks)*

**3**      Mass spectrometry and infrared spectrometry are two analytical techniques that are used to identify unknown compounds.

   **(a)**    Describe how infrared spectroscopy can help to catch drunk drivers.

*(2 marks)*

   **(b) (i)**   Briefly outline why mass spectrometry can be used to differentiate between similar molecules.

*(1 mark)*

   **(ii)**   Describe one practical application of mass spectrometry.

*(1 mark)*

   **(c)**    Molecule **J** is a hydrocarbon.  The mass spectrum of molecule **J** is shown below. Identify the structure of molecule **J**.  Explain your reasoning.

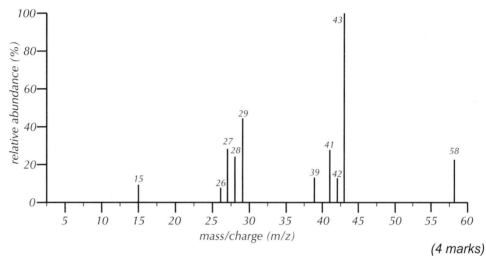

*(4 marks)*

   **(d)**    Molecule **K** contains only carbon, oxygen and hydrogen atoms. It has the infrared spectrum shown below.

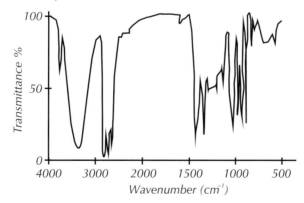

The mass spectrum of molecule **K** shows that the $M_r$ of the molecule is 74.

If you react molecule **K** with acidified potassium dichromate(VI) you produce a ketone.

Use your knowledge of organic chemistry and analytical techniques along with the table on page 167 to identify the structure of molecule **K**.  Explain your reasoning.

*(4 marks)*

# 1. Enthalpy Changes

*When chemical reactions happen, some bonds are broken and some bonds are made. More often than not, this'll cause a change in energy. The souped-up chemistry term for this is enthalpy change.*

## Enthalpy notation

**Enthalpy change**, $\Delta H$ (delta H), is the heat energy transferred in a reaction at constant pressure. The units of $\Delta H$ are kJ mol$^{-1}$. You write $\Delta H^{\ominus}$ to show that the elements were in their standard states (i.e. their states at a pressure of 100 kPa), and that the measurements were made under **standard conditions**. Standard conditions are 100 kPa (about 1 atm) pressure and a temperature of 298 K (25 °C). Sometimes the notation will also include a letter to signify whether the enthalpy change is for a reaction (r), combustion (c), or the formation of a new compound (f). See below for more on this notation.

## Conditions for enthalpy changes

You can't directly measure the actual enthalpy of a system. In practice, that doesn't matter, because it's only ever enthalpy change that matters. You can find enthalpy changes either by experiment or in textbooks. Enthalpy changes you find in textbooks are usually standard enthalpy changes — enthalpy changes under standard conditions (298 K and 100 kPa). This is important because changes in enthalpy are affected by temperature and pressure — using standard conditions means that everyone can know exactly what the enthalpy change is describing.

## The different types of $\Delta H$

### Standard enthalpy change of reaction

Standard enthalpy change of reaction, $\Delta H_r^{\ominus}$, is the enthalpy change when a reaction occurs in the molar quantities shown in the chemical equation, under standard conditions with all reactants and products in their standard states.

### Standard enthalpy change of formation

Standard enthalpy change of formation, $\Delta H_f^{\ominus}$, is the enthalpy change when 1 mole of a compound is formed from its elements in their standard states under standard conditions, e.g. $2C_{(s)} + 3H_{2(g)} + \frac{1}{2}O_{2(g)} \rightarrow C_2H_5OH_{(l)}$

### Standard enthalpy change of combustion

Standard enthalpy change of combustion, $\Delta H_c^{\ominus}$, is the enthalpy change when 1 mole of a substance is completely burned in oxygen under standard conditions with all reactants and products in their standard states.

## Exothermic reactions

Exothermic reactions give out energy to their surroundings. The products of the reaction end up with less energy than the reactants. This means that the enthalpy change for the reaction, $\Delta H$, will be negative.

Oxidation is exothermic. Here are two examples:

The combustion of a fuel like methane:

$$CH_{4(g)} + 2O_{2(g)} \rightarrow CO_{2(g)} + 2H_2O_{(l)} \qquad \Delta H_c^\ominus = -890 \text{ kJ mol}^{-1}$$

$\Delta H$ is negative so the reaction is **exothermic**.

The oxidation of carbohydrates, like glucose, in respiration is exothermic.

# Endothermic reactions

Endothermic reactions take in energy from their surroundings. This means that the products of the reaction have more energy than the reactants, so the enthalpy change for the reaction, $\Delta H$, is positive.

## Examples

The thermal decomposition of calcium carbonate is endothermic.

$$CaCO_{3(s)} \rightarrow CaO_{(s)} + CO_{2(g)} \qquad \Delta H_r^\ominus = +178 \text{ kJ mol}^{-1}$$

$\Delta H$ is positive so the reaction is **endothermic**.

The main reactions of photosynthesis are also endothermic — sunlight supplies the energy.

*Figure 1: Photosynthesis in plants is endothermic — the products have more energy than the reactants.*

# Enthalpy profile diagrams

Enthalpy profile diagrams show you how the enthalpy (energy) changes during a reaction (see Figure 2). A substance is most stable when it has lost all of its internal energy. So, lower positions on an enthalpy profile diagram will be more stable than higher positions.

The **activation energy**, $E_a$, is the minimum amount of energy needed to begin breaking reactant bonds and start a chemical reaction. On an enthalpy diagram, the $E_a$ is the difference between the highest point and the energy of the reactants (see Figure 2).

**Exam Tip**
There's quite a bit of maths in this section but you need to learn all the definitions too — you can be asked to write them down in an exam, and it's often the thing that people forget or get wrong.

**Tip:** On enthalpy profile diagrams $\Delta H$ arrows should point up for endothermic changes and down for exothermic changes.

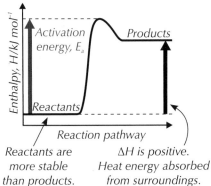

Endothermic reaction — Activation energy, $E_a$; Products; Reactants; Enthalpy, $H$/kJ mol$^{-1}$; Reaction pathway
*Reactants are more stable than products.* *$\Delta H$ is positive. Heat energy absorbed from surroundings.*

Exothermic reaction — Reactants; Activation energy, $E_a$; Products; Enthalpy, $H$/kJ mol$^{-1}$; Reaction pathway
*$\Delta H$ is negative. Heat energy released to surroundings.* *Products are more stable than reactants.*

**Figure 2:** *Enthalpy profile diagrams.*

## Practice Questions — Fact Recall

Q1 Give the notation for an enthalpy change under standard conditions.

Q2 Define the 'standard enthalpy change of a reaction'.

Q3 Describe the difference between exothermic and endothermic reactions.

Q4 a) Sketch an energy profile diagram for an endothermic reaction.

b) Draw an arrow on the diagram to show $E_a$ and explain the term.

- Explain exothermic
  and endothermic
  reactions in terms
  of enthalpy changes
  associated with the
  breaking and making
  of chemical bonds.

- Define and use the
  term average bond
  enthalpy.

- Be able to calculate
  an enthalpy change of
  reaction from average
  bond enthalpies.

  **Specification
  Reference 2.3.1**

# 2. Bond Enthalpies

*Reactions involve breaking and making bonds. The enthalpy change for a
reaction depends on which bonds are broken and which are made.*

## What are bond enthalpies?

In ionic bonding, positive and negative ions are attracted to each other. In
covalent molecules, the positive nuclei are attracted to the negative charge
of the shared electrons in a covalent bond. You need energy to break this
attraction. The amount of energy you need per mole is called the bond
dissociation enthalpy. (Of course it's got a fancy name — this is chemistry.)
Bond dissociation enthalpies always involve bond breaking in gaseous
compounds. This makes comparisons between different bond dissociation
enthalpies fair.

## Breaking and making bonds

When reactions happen, reactant bonds are broken and product bonds are
formed. You need energy to break bonds, so bond breaking is endothermic
($\Delta H$ is positive). Stronger bonds take more energy to break. Energy is
released when bonds are formed, so this is exothermic ($\Delta H$ is negative).
Stronger bonds release more energy when they form. The enthalpy change for
a reaction is the overall effect of these two changes. If you need more energy
to break bonds than is released when bonds are made, $\Delta H$ is positive. If it's
less, $\Delta H$ is negative.

┌─ **Example** ─────────────────────────────────────

Nitrogen reacts with hydrogen to form ammonia ($NH_3$) in this reaction:
$$N_2 + 3H_2 \rightarrow 2NH_3$$
The energy needed to break all the bonds in $N_2$ and $H_2$ = 2253 kJ mol$^{-1}$.

The energy released when forming the bonds in $NH_3$ = 2346 kJ mol$^{-1}$.

The amount of energy released is bigger than the amount needed, so the
reaction is exothermic and $\Delta H$ is negative. (See page 181 for full calculation.)

**Tip:** You can look
up the average bond
enthalpies for different
bonds in a data book,
or calculate them from
given data. In an exam
you'll be given any bond
enthalpies you need.

## Average bond enthalpies

We tend to use **average bond enthalpies** in calculations because the energy
required to break an individual bond can change depending on where it is.

┌─ **Example** ─────────────────────────────────────

Water ($H_2O$) has got two O–H bonds (see Figure 1). You'd think it'd take the
same amount of energy to break them both, but it doesn't.

The first bond, H–OH$_{(g)}$:       $E$(H–OH) = +492 kJ mol$^{-1}$

The second bond, H–O$_{(g)}$:       $E$(H–O) = +428 kJ mol$^{-1}$

(OH$^-$ is a bit easier to break apart because of the extra electron repulsion.)

So, the mean bond enthalpy for O–H bonds in water is:
$$\frac{492 + 428}{2} = +460 \text{ kJ mol}^{-1}.$$

The data book says the bond enthalpy for O–H is +463 kJ mol$^{-1}$. It's a bit
different than the one calculated above because it's the average for a much
bigger range of molecules, not just water. For example, it includes the O-H
bonds in alcohols and carboxylic acids too.

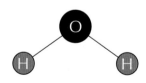

**Figure 1:** *The bonds in a
water molecule.*

So when you look up an average bond enthalpy, what you get is the energy needed to break one mole of bonds in the gas phase, averaged over many different compounds.

**Tip:** This definition of average bond energy is really important so make sure you learn it.

# Calculating enthalpy changes

In any chemical reaction, energy is absorbed to break bonds and given out during bond formation. The difference between the energy absorbed and released is the overall enthalpy change of reaction:

**Enthalpy change of reaction = Total energy absorbed – Total energy released**

- To calculate the overall enthalpy change for a reaction, first calculate the total energy needed to break the bonds in the reactants. You'll usually be given the average bond enthalpies for each type of bond, so just multiply each value by the number of each bond present. This total will be the total energy absorbed in the reaction.

- To find the total energy released by the reaction, calculate the total energy needed to form all the new bonds in the products. Use the average bond enthalpies to do this.

- The overall enthalpy change for the reaction can then be found by subtracting the total energy released from the total energy absorbed.

| Bond | Bond Enthalpy (Average value except where stated) |
|---|---|
| N≡N | +945 kJ mol⁻¹ |
| H–H | +436 kJ mol⁻¹ |
| N–H | +391 kJ mol⁻¹ |
| O=O | +498 kJ mol⁻¹ |
| O–H (water) | +460 kJ mol⁻¹ |

*Figure 2:* Table of bond enthalpies.

**Examples**

**Calculate the overall enthalpy change for the following reaction:**

$$N_2 + 3H_2 \rightarrow 2NH_3$$

Use the bond enthalpy values shown in Figure 2.

You might find it helpful to draw a sketch of the molecules in the reaction:

**Tip:** Draw sketches to show the bonds present in the reactants and products to make sure you include them all in your calculations.

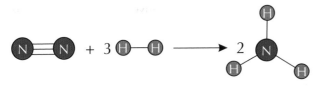

Bonds broken:   1 × N≡N bond broken   = 1 × 945 = 945 kJ mol⁻¹
               3 × H–H bonds broken  = 3 × 436 = 1308 kJ mol⁻¹

Total Energy Absorbed = 945 + 1308 = 2253 kJ mol⁻¹

Bonds formed:   6 × N–H bonds formed = 6 × 391 = 2346 kJ mol⁻¹
Total Energy Released = 2346 kJ mol⁻¹

Now you just subtract 'total energy released' from 'total energy absorbed':

Enthalpy change of reaction = 2253 – 2346 = –93 kJ mol⁻¹.

The negative sign tells you that the reaction is exothermic. More energy is released when the N–H bonds are made than is needed to break the N≡N and H–H bonds.

**Tip:** If you can't remember which value to subtract from which, just take the smaller number from the bigger one then add the sign at the end — positive if 'bonds broken' was the bigger number (endothermic), negative if 'bonds formed' was bigger (exothermic).

**Tip:** The $\frac{1}{2}O_2$ doesn't mean you're breaking ½ an O=O double bond — it means you're breaking ½ a mole of O=O double bonds.

**Exam tip**
Always double check you've multiplied the enthalpy values by the right number of bonds. It's really easy to make a mistake and end up losing marks.

**Tip:** You can ignore any bonds that don't actually change during the reaction. Just work out which bonds actually break and which new bonds form. You'll still get the same value if you break and form all of the bonds, but it'll save you time if you don't have to.

| Bond | Bond Enthalpy (Average value except where stated) |
|---|---|
| C–H | $+413$ kJ mol$^{-1}$ |
| C=C | $+612$ kJ mol$^{-1}$ |
| C–C | $+347$ kJ mol$^{-1}$ |
| C–O | $+358$ kJ mol$^{-1}$ |
| C–Cl | $+346$ kJ mol$^{-1}$ |
| C=O (in $CO_2$) | $+805$ kJ mol$^{-1}$ |
| C–N | $+286$ kJ mol$^{-1}$ |
| H–Cl | $+432$ kJ mol$^{-1}$ |
| Cl–Cl | $+243.4$ kJ mol$^{-1}$ |

***Figure 3:*** *Table of bond enthalpies.*

**Calculate the overall enthalpy change for the following reaction:**

$$H_{2(g)} + \frac{1}{2}O_{2(g)} \rightarrow H_2O_{(g)}$$

The molecules present are shown below:

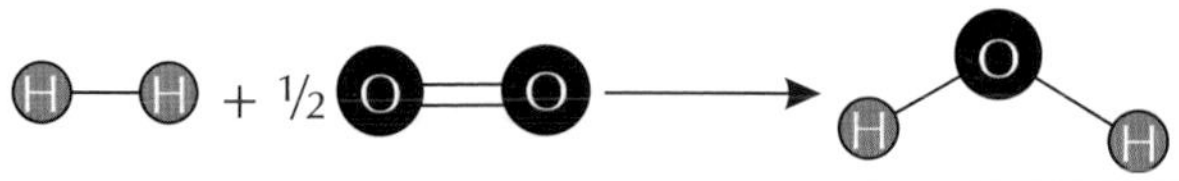

Bonds broken: 1 × H–H bond broken = 1 × 436 = 436 kJ mol$^{-1}$
½ × O=O bond broken = ½ × 498 = 249 kJ mol$^{-1}$

Total Energy Absorbed = 436 + 249 = 685 kJ mol$^{-1}$

Bonds formed: 2 × O–H bonds formed = 2 × 460 = 920 kJ mol$^{-1}$
Total Energy Released = 920 kJ mol$^{-1}$

Enthalpy change of reaction = 685 – 920 = –235 kJ mol$^{-1}$.

## Practice Questions — Application

Q1 Use the average bond enthalpies shown in Figures 2 and 3 to calculate the enthalpy changes for the following reactions:

a) 

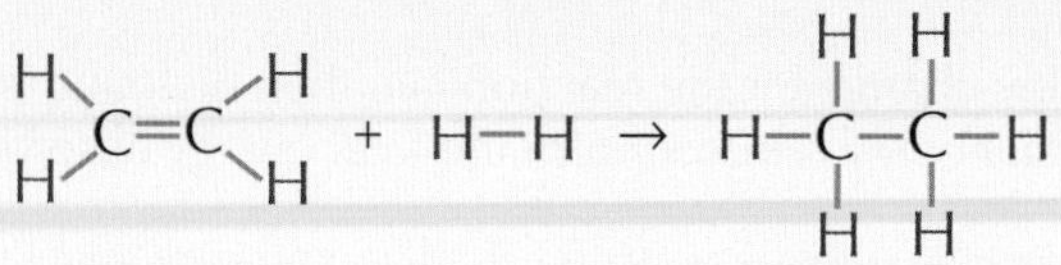

b) 

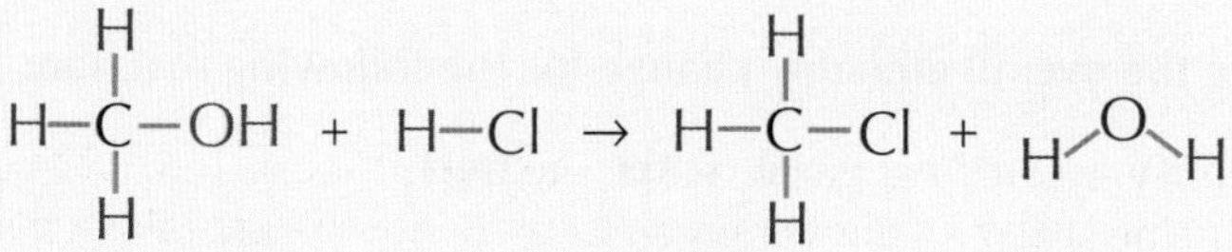

c) $C_3H_8 + 5O_2 \rightarrow 3CO_2 + 4H_2O$

d) $C_2H_5Cl + NH_3 \rightarrow C_2H_5NH_2 + HCl$

Q2 Calculate the enthalpy change for the complete combustion of ethene ($C_2H_4$) using the bond enthalpies given in Figures 2 and 3. (The products of complete combustion are $CO_2$ and $H_2O$.)

Q3 Calculate the enthalpy change for the formation of hydrogen chloride ($HCl_{(g)}$) from hydrogen ($H_{2(g)}$) and chlorine ($Cl_{2(g)}$) using the bond enthalpies given in Figures 2 and 3.

Q4 The enthalpy change for the following reaction is –181 kJ mol$^{-1}$:

$$2NO_{(g)} \rightarrow N_{2(g)} + O_{2(g)}$$

Use this value for $\Delta H_r$, along with the data in Figure 2, to estimate a value for the average bond enthalpy for the bond between nitrogen and oxygen in NO.

## Practice Questions — Fact Recall

Q1 Is bond breaking exothermic or endothermic?

Q2 In an exothermic reaction, which is larger — the energy required to make bonds or the energy required to break bonds?

Q3 What is average bond enthalpy?

Q4 Give the formula for calculating the enthalpy change of a reaction.

# 3. Measuring Enthalpy Changes

*A lot of the data we have on enthalpy changes has come from someone, somewhere, measuring the enthalpy change of a reaction in a lab.*

## Measuring enthalpy changes in the lab

To measure the enthalpy change for a reaction, you only need to know two things — the number of moles of the stuff that's reacting, and the change in temperature. How you go about doing the experiment depends on what type of reaction it is. Some reactions will quite happily take place in solution, such as neutralisation or displacement, and you can just stick a thermometer in to find out the temperature change. It's best to use an insulated container like a polystyrene beaker, so that you don't lose or gain much heat through the sides (see Figure 1).

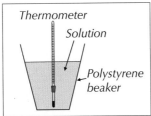

**Figure 1:** *Simple equipment used to measure the enthalpy change of reaction.*

Combustion reactions are trickier because the reactant is burned in air. A copper calorimeter containing a known mass of water is often used (see Figure 2). You burn a known mass of the reactant and record the temperature change of the water.

Ideally all the heat given out by the fuel as it burns would be absorbed by the water — allowing you to work out the enthalpy change of combustion (see page 178). In practice though, you always lose some heat (as you heat the apparatus and the surroundings).

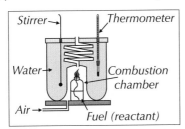

**Figure 2:** *A copper calorimeter used to measure the enthalpy change of combustion.*

A 'bomb' calorimeter, like the one shown in Figure 3, is a much more accurate piece of equipment, but works on the same principle.

## Using the equation $q = mc\Delta T$

The equation for enthalpy change is:

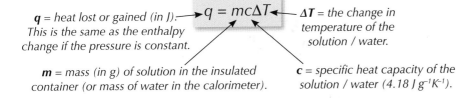

**q** = heat lost or gained (in J). This is the same as the enthalpy change if the pressure is constant.

$$q = mc\Delta T$$

$\Delta T$ = the change in temperature of the solution / water.

**m** = mass (in g) of solution in the insulated container (or mass of water in the calorimeter).

**c** = specific heat capacity of the solution / water (4.18 J g⁻¹K⁻¹).

**Learning Objective:**

- Be able to calculate enthalpy changes from appropriate experimental results directly, including use of the relationship: energy change = mcΔT.

    **Specification Reference 2.3.1**

**Figure 3:** *A bomb calorimeter.*

**Tip:** The specific heat capacity of a substance is the amount of heat energy it takes to raise the temperature of 1 g of that substance by 1 K.

## Calculating the standard enthalpy change of combustion

To calculate the standard enthalpy change of combustion, $\Delta H_c^{\ominus}$, using data from a laboratory experiment, follow these steps:

**Tip:** $\Delta H^{\ominus}$ is the standard enthalpy change of a reaction carried out at 100 kPa with all reactants and products in their standard states (see page 178). If the experiment was carried out under different conditions, this method wouldn't give you the value for $\Delta H^{\ominus}$.

**Step 1:** Calculate the amount of heat lost or gained during the combustion using $q = mc\Delta T$ and your measured or given values of $m$ and $\Delta T$. You'll then need to change the units of $q$ from joules to kilojoules.

**Step 2:** Calculate the number of moles of fuel that caused this enthalpy change, from the mass that reacted. Use the equation:

$$n = \frac{mass}{M}$$

$n$ is the number of moles of fuel burned.
$M$ is the fuel's molar mass (see page 15).

**Step 3:** Calculate the standard enthalpy change of combustion, $\Delta H_c^{\ominus}$ (in kJ mol$^{-1}$), using the actual heat change for the reaction, $q$ (in kJ), and the number of moles of fuel that burned, $n$. Use the equation:

$$\Delta H_c^{\ominus} = \frac{q}{n}$$

**Figure 4:** *A combustion reaction — glucose burning.*

--- Example ---

**Calculating the standard enthalpy change of combustion:**

In a laboratory experiment, 1.16 g of an organic liquid fuel was completely burned in oxygen. The heat formed during this combustion raised the temperature of 100 g of water from 295.3 K to 357.8 K. Calculate the standard enthalpy of combustion, $\Delta H_c^{\ominus}$, of the fuel. Its $M_r$ is 58.

**Step 1:** Calculate the amount of heat given out by the fuel using $q = mc\Delta T$. Remember that $m$ is the mass of water, not the mass of fuel.

$q = mc\Delta T$

$q = 100 \times 4.18 \times (357.8 - 295.3) = 26\ 125$ J

Change the amount of heat from J to kJ: $q = 26.125$ kJ.

**Step 2:** Find out how many moles of fuel produced this heat:

$$n = \frac{mass}{M} = \frac{1.16\ g}{58\ g\ mol^{-1}} = 0.02 \text{ moles of fuel.}$$

**Tip:** $M_r$ is the relative molecular mass — and it's exactly the same as the molar mass (M).

**Step 3:** The standard enthalpy of combustion involves 1 mole of fuel.

So $\Delta H_c^{\ominus} = \dfrac{q}{n} = \dfrac{-26.125\ kJ}{0.02\ mol} \approx -1306$ kJ mol$^{-1}$.

(Note: $q$ is negative because combustion is an exothermic reaction.)

The actual $\Delta H_c^{\ominus}$ of this compound is -1615 kJ mol$^{-1}$ — loads of heat has been lost and not measured. E.g. it's likely a fair bit would escape through the copper calorimeter and also the fuel might not combust completely.

**Exam Tip**
You'll often be asked to suggest why a measured enthalpy change value is different to one in a data book. It's usually to do with heat losses to the surroundings, but it can also be due to things like incomplete combustion.

## Calculating the standard enthalpy change of reaction

The standard enthalpy change of a reaction, $\Delta H_r^{\ominus}$, is calculated in a slightly different way. Instead of calculating the enthalpy change per mole of substance reacted, you need to find the enthalpy change for the number of moles shown in the balanced chemical equation. Step 1 is exactly the same as step 1 for calculating the standard enthalpy change of combustion. It's steps 2 and 3 that are a bit different...

**Step 2:** Calculate the number of moles of one of the reactants that caused this enthalpy change, from the mass of it that reacted. Use the equation $n = mass \div M$ again.

**Step 3:** Calculate the standard enthalpy change of reaction, $\Delta H_r^{\ominus}$
(in kJ mol⁻¹) using the actual heat change for the reaction, $q$ (in kJ),
and the number of moles that reacted, $n$, using the equation:

$\Delta H_r^{\ominus} = \dfrac{q}{n}$ (× number of moles reacting in balanced chemical equation)

---

**Example**

**Calculating the standard enthalpy change of reaction:**

30.0 g of ammonium chloride ($NH_4Cl_{(s)}$) is dissolved in water in a
polystyrene beaker. The temperature of the contents of the beaker decreases
from 298 K to 296 K. The total mass of the solution is 980 g. Calculate the
standard molar enthalpy change for the reaction.

The balanced reaction is: $NH_4Cl_{(s)} \rightarrow NH_4^{+}{}_{(aq)} + Cl^{-}{}_{(aq)}$

The molar mass, M, of $NH_4Cl = 14 + (4 \times 1) + 35.5 = 53.5$ g mol⁻¹.

**Step 1:** $q = mc\Delta T = 980 \times 4.18 \times (298 - 296) = 8192.8$ J $= 8.1928$ kJ

**Step 2:** $n = \dfrac{30.0 \text{ g}}{53.5 \text{ g mol}^{-1}} = 0.5607$ moles of $NH_4Cl$.

**Step 3:** The balanced reaction involves one mole of $NH_4Cl$ so:

$$\Delta H_r^{\ominus} = \frac{q}{n} = \frac{8.1928 \text{ kJ}}{0.5607 \text{ mol}} \approx +14.6 \text{ kJ mol}^{-1}.$$

**Tip:** When finding
the standard enthalpy
change of a reaction,
always write out a
balanced equation for
the reaction so you can
see the correct molar
quantities.

---

## Practice Questions — Application

Q1  0.05 mol of a compound dissolves in water, causing the temperature
of the solution to increase from 298 K to 301 K. The total mass of the
solution is 220 g. Calculate the enthalpy change for the reaction in
kJ mol⁻¹. Assume $c = 4.18$ J g⁻¹ K⁻¹.

Q2  A calorimeter, containing 200 g of water ($c = 4.18$ J g⁻¹ K⁻¹), was used
to measure the enthalpy change of combustion of pentane ($C_5H_{12(l)}$,
$M_r = 72$). 0.5 g of pentane was burnt, which increased the
temperature of the water by 29 K.

a) Calculate the enthalpy change of combustion of pentane.
Give your answer in kJ mol⁻¹.

b) Suggest reasons why this value may be different to the standard
enthalpy change of combustion of pentane given in a data book.

Q3  The standard enthalpy of combustion of octane ($C_8H_{18(l)}$, $M_r = 114$) is
−5512 kJ mol⁻¹. Some octane was burnt in a calorimeter containing
300 g of water ($c = 4.18$ J g⁻¹ K⁻¹). The temperature of the water went
up by 55 K. Calculate an estimate of the mass of propane burnt.

**Tip:** Remember — if
the temperature has
increased during
the reaction (i.e. it's
exothermic), you
need to use a negative
value for $q$ in your
calculations.

---

## Practice Questions — Fact Recall

Q1  What measurements need to be made in order to calculate the
enthalpy change for a reaction in a laboratory?

Q2  Sketch and label a calorimeter that could be used in the lab to
measure the enthalpy change of a combustion.

Q3  In the equation $q = mc\Delta T$, state what '$q$' stands for and give its units.

Q4  What conditions are needed to measure the standard enthalpy
change of a reaction, $\Delta H_r^{\ominus}$?

Q5  Explain how you would calculate $\Delta H_r^{\ominus}$ for a reaction, given a value
for $q$ and the number of moles, $n$, of a reactant used in the reaction.

- Use Hess' law to construct enthalpy cycles and carry out calculations to determine an enthalpy change of reaction from enthalpy changes of combustion, an enthalpy change of reaction from enthalpy changes of formation and an enthalpy change of reaction from an unfamiliar enthalpy cycle.

**Specification Reference 2.3.1**

# 4. Hess's Law

*For some reactions, there is no easy way to measure enthalpy changes in the lab. For these, we can use Hess's Law.*

## What is Hess's Law?

Hess's Law says that:

> The total enthalpy change of a reaction is always the same, no matter which route is taken.

This law is handy for working out enthalpy changes that you can't find directly by doing an experiment — for example, the enthalpy change of the reaction that breaks down $NO_2$ into $N_2$ and $O_2$. We can call this reaction 'route 1'. But we can also think of the reaction as $NO_2$ breaking down into NO and $O_2$, and then reacting further to form $N_2$ and $O_2$. This longer route, with an intermediate step, can be called 'route 2' (see Figure 1).

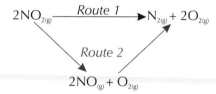

$$2NO_{2(g)} \xrightarrow{\text{Route 1}} N_{2(g)} + 2O_{2(g)}$$

*Route 2*

$$2NO_{(g)} + O_{2(g)}$$

**Figure 1:** *Two possible routes for the formation of nitrogen and oxygen from nitrogen dioxide.*

Hess's Law says that the total enthalpy change for route 1 is the same as for route 2. So if you know the enthalpy changes for the stages of route 2, you can calculate the enthalpy change for route 1, as shown in the example below.

---
### Example ---

**Use Hess's Law to calculate the enthalpy change, $\Delta H_r^\ominus$, for route 1 of the reaction shown below.**

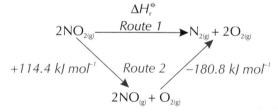

$$2NO_{2(g)} \xrightarrow[\text{Route 1}]{\Delta H_r^\ominus} N_{2(g)} + 2O_{2(g)}$$

$+114.4$ kJ mol$^{-1}$    *Route 2*    $-180.8$ kJ mol$^{-1}$

$$2NO_{(g)} + O_{2(g)}$$

The total enthalpy change for route 1 is the same as the total enthalpy change for route 2. So the enthalpy change for route 1 is the sum of the steps in route 2:

$\Delta H_r^\ominus = 144.4$ kJ $+ (-180.8$ kJ$) = -66.4$ kJ mol$^{-1}$.

---

## Using enthalpies of formation

You can find enthalpy changes of formation for hundreds of various compounds listed in textbooks. They're handy because you can use them (along with Hess's Law) to find enthalpy changes for all kinds of reactions.

You need to know $\Delta H_f^\circ$ for all the reactants and products that are compounds. The value of $\Delta H_f^\circ$ for elements is zero — the element's being formed from the element, so there's no change in enthalpy. The standard enthalpy changes are all measured at 298 K.

┌─ Examples ─────────────────────

**Calculate $\Delta H_r^\circ$ for this reaction using the enthalpies of formation in Figure 2:**

$$SO_{2(g)} + 2H_2S_{(g)} \rightarrow 3S_{(s)} + 2H_2O_{(l)}$$

| Compound | $\Delta H_f^\circ$ |
|---|---|
| $SO_{2(g)}$ | −297 kJ mol⁻¹ |
| $H_2S_{(g)}$ | −20.2 kJ mol⁻¹ |
| $H_2O_{(l)}$ | −286 kJ mol⁻¹ |

**Figure 2:** *Table of enthalpies of formation for three compounds.*

- Write under the reaction a list of all the elements present in the reaction, balanced in their correct molar quantities, as shown below:

*Reactants*　　　　　　　　*Products*

$$SO_{2(g)} + 2H_2S_{(g)} \longrightarrow 3S_{(s)} + 2H_2O_{(l)}$$

$$3S_{(s)} + 2H_{2(g)} + O_{2(g)}$$

*Elements*

- Enthalpies of formation ($\Delta H_f^\circ$) tell you the enthalpy change going from the elements to the compounds. The enthalpy change of reaction ($\Delta H_r^\circ$) is the enthalpy change going from the reactants to the products. Draw and label arrows to show this on your diagram:

*Reactants*　　$\Delta H_r^\circ$　　*Products*

$$SO_{2(g)} + 2H_2S_{(g)} \longrightarrow 3S_{(s)} + 2H_2O_{(l)}$$

$\Delta H_{f(reactants)}^\circ$　　　$\Delta H_{f(products)}^\circ$

$$3S_{(s)} + 2H_{2(g)} + O_{2(g)}$$

*Elements*

- The calculation is often simpler if you keep the arrows end to end, so make both routes go from the elements to the products. Route 1 gets there via the reactants (and includes $\Delta H_r^\circ$), whilst route 2 gets there directly. Label the enthalpy changes along each arrow, as shown below. There are 2 moles of $H_2O$ and 2 moles of $H_2S$, so their enthalpies of formation will need to be multiplied by 2. $\Delta H_f^\circ$ of sulfur is zero because it's an element, but you can still label it on the diagram.

*Reactants*　　$\Delta H_r^\circ$　　*Products*

$$SO_{2(g)} + 2H_2S_{(g)} \longrightarrow 3S_{(s)} + 2H_2O_{(l)}$$

*Route 1*

$\Delta H_{f[reactants]}^\circ = \Delta H_{f[SO_2]}^\circ + 2 \times \Delta H_{f[H_2S]}^\circ$　　$\Delta H_{f[products]}^\circ = 3 \times \Delta H_{f[S]}^\circ + 2 \times \Delta H_{f[H_2O]}^\circ$

$$3S_{(s)} + 2H_{2(g)} + O_{2(g)}$$

*Elements*

**Tip:** You don't have to pick a route that follows the direction of the arrows. If your route goes against an arrow you can just change the signs (so negative enthalpies become positive and positive enthalpies become negative). There's an example of this on pages 189-190.

- Use Hess's Law, Route 1 = Route 2, and plug the numbers from Figure 2 into the equation:

$$\Delta H_{f\,[SO_2]}^\circ + 2\Delta H_{f\,[H_2S]}^\circ + \Delta H_r^\circ = 3\Delta H_{f\,[S]}^\circ + 2\Delta H_{f\,[H_2O]}^\circ$$

$$-297 + (2 \times -20.2) + \Delta H_r^\circ = (3 \times 0) + (2 \times -286)$$

$$\Delta H_r^\circ = (3 \times 0) + (2 \times -286) - [-297 + (2 \times -20.2)] = -234.6 \text{ kJ mol}^{-1}.$$

| Compound | $\Delta H_f^\circ$ |
|---|---|
| $NH_4NO_{3(s)}$ | $-365$ kJ mol$^{-1}$ |
| $CO_{2(g)}$ | $-394$ kJ mol$^{-1}$ |
| $H_2O_{(l)}$ | $-286$ kJ mol$^{-1}$ |

*Figure 3: Table of enthalpies of formation for three compounds.*

**Calculate $\Delta H_r^\circ$ for this reaction using the enthalpies of formation in Figure 3:**

$$2NH_4NO_{3\,(s)} + C_{(s)} \rightarrow 2N_{2\,(g)} + CO_{2\,(g)} + 4H_2O_{(l)}$$

- Draw and label your diagram:

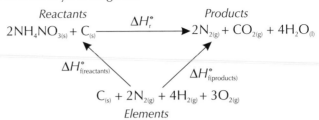

- Label the enthalpy changes along each arrow.

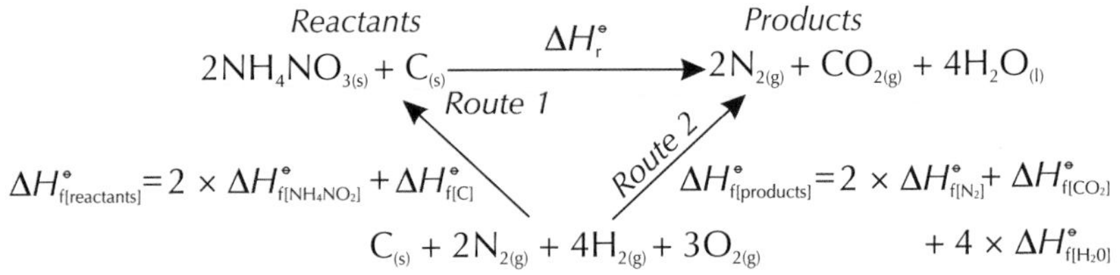

- Use Hess's Law, Route 1 = Route 2, and plug the numbers from Figure 3 into the equation:

$$2\Delta H_{f\,[NH_4NO_3]}^\circ + \Delta H_{f\,[C]}^\circ + \Delta H_r^\circ = 2\Delta H_{f\,[N_2]}^\circ + \Delta H_{f\,[CO_2]}^\circ + 4\Delta H_{f\,[H_2O]}^\circ$$

$$(2 \times -365) + 0 + \Delta H_r^\circ = 0 + -394 + (4 \times -286)$$

$$\Delta H_r^\circ = -394 + (-1144) - (-730) = -808 \text{ kJ mol}^{-1}.$$

| Compound | $\Delta H_f^\circ$ |
|---|---|
| $Mg(OH)_{2(s)}$ | $-925$ kJ mol$^{-1}$ |
| $H_2O_{(l)}$ | $-286$ kJ mol$^{-1}$ |
| $NaOH_{(aq)}$ | $-469$ kJ mol$^{-1}$ |
| $MgO_{(s)}$ | $-602$ kJ mol$^{-1}$ |
| $HCl_{(aq)}$ | $-167$ kJ mol$^{-1}$ |
| $MgCl_{2(s)}$ | $-641$ kJ mol$^{-1}$ |
| $NaCl_{(aq)}$ | $-407$ kJ mol$^{-1}$ |

*Figure 4: Table of enthalpies of formation for seven compounds.*

## Practice Questions — Application

**Q1** Use Hess's Law and the diagram below to calculate $\Delta H_r^\circ$ for the reaction between magnesium and water. The enthalpies of formation needed are given in Figure 4.

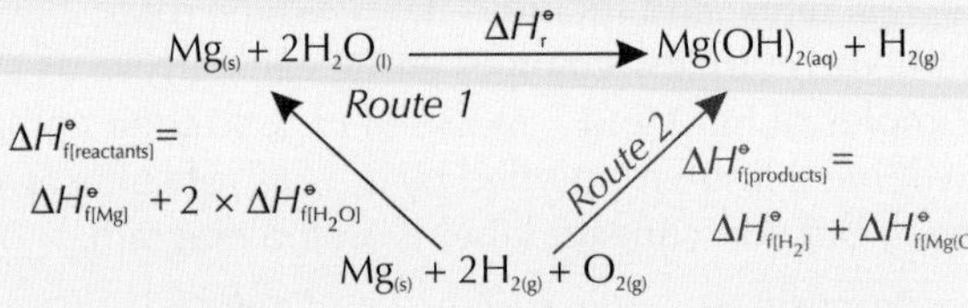

$$Mg_{(s)} + 2H_2O_{(l)} \xrightarrow{\Delta H_r^\circ} Mg(OH)_{2(aq)} + H_{2(g)}$$

*Route 1*

$\Delta H_{f[reactants]}^\circ = \Delta H_{f[Mg]}^\circ + 2 \times \Delta H_{f[H_2O]}^\circ$

*Route 2*

$\Delta H_{f[products]}^\circ = \Delta H_{f[H_2]}^\circ + \Delta H_{f[Mg(OH)_2]}^\circ$

$$Mg_{(s)} + 2H_{2(g)} + O_{2(g)}$$

**Q2** Calculate $\Delta H_r^\circ$ for the following reactions using Hess's Law, and the enthalpies of formation given in Figure 4:

a) $2Na_{(s)} + 2H_2O_{(l)} \rightarrow 2NaOH_{(aq)} + H_{2(g)}$

b) $MgO_{(s)} + 2HCl_{(aq)} \rightarrow MgCl_{2(s)} + H_2O_{(l)}$

c) $NaOH_{(aq)} + HCl_{(aq)} \rightarrow NaCl_{(aq)} + H_2O_{(l)}$

# Using enthalpies of combustion

You can use a similar method to find an enthalpy change from enthalpy changes of combustion, instead of using enthalpy changes of formation. There's a lovely example of this coming up on the next page...

**Calculate $\Delta H_f^\circ$ of ethanol using the enthalpies of combustion in Figure 5.**

- The desired reaction in this case is the formation of ethanol from its elements, so write out the balanced equation:

$$\text{Reactants} \qquad\qquad \text{Product}$$
$$2C_{(s)} + 3H_{2(g)} + \tfrac{1}{2}O_{2(g)} \longrightarrow C_2H_5OH_{(l)}$$

| Substance | $\Delta H_c^\circ$ |
|---|---|
| $C_{(s)}$ | $-394$ kJ mol$^{-1}$ |
| $H_{2(g)}$ | $-286$ kJ mol$^{-1}$ |
| $C_2H_5OH_{(l)}$ | $-1367$ kJ mol$^{-1}$ |

***Figure 5:*** *Table of enthalpies of combustion for three substances.*

- Figure 5 tells you the enthalpy change when each of the 'reactants' and 'products' is burned in oxygen. Add these combustion reactions to your diagram, making sure they are balanced, as shown below:

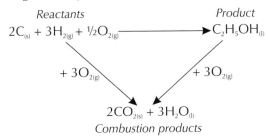

**Tip:** The products of a complete combustion are carbon dioxide ($CO_2$) and water ($H_2O$).

- Choose which reactions will form which route. Label the diagram with the enthalpy changes along each arrow as before (taking into account molar quantities):

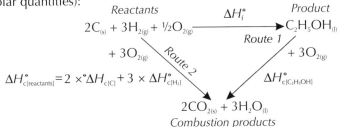

**Tip:** You can ignore the enthalpy change of combustion of oxygen in these calculations. Oxygen <u>doesn't have</u> an enthalpy change of combustion — you <u>can't</u> burn 1 mole of oxygen in oxygen.

- Use Hess's Law as follows:  Route 1 = Route 2

$$\Delta H_f^\circ[\text{ethanol}] + \Delta H_c^\circ[C_2H_5OH] = 2\Delta H_c^\circ[C] + 3\Delta H_c^\circ[H_2]$$
$$\Delta H_f^\circ[\text{ethanol}] + (-1367) = (2 \times -394) + (3 \times -286)$$
$$\Delta H_f^\circ[\text{ethanol}] = -788 + -858 - (-1367) = -279 \text{ kJ mol}^{-1}.$$

# Using enthalpies of reaction

You can also use Hess's Law to calculate enthalpy changes using a group of linked reactions, where all but one of the enthalpy changes for the reactions are known. The following example shows how to do this, this time choosing routes where the arrows don't run end to end.

**Example**

**Calculate $\Delta H_r^\circ$ for the reaction below using the data given in Figure 6.**

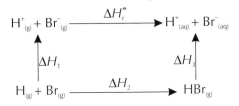

| Reaction | $\Delta H_r^\circ$ |
|---|---|
| $\Delta H_1$ | $+987$ kJ mol$^{-1}$ |
| $\Delta H_2$ | $-366$ kJ mol$^{-1}$ |
| $\Delta H_3$ | $-85$ kJ mol$^{-1}$ |

***Figure 6:*** *Table of enthalpies of reaction for three reactions.*

You are given three of the four enthalpies for these reactions, so use Hess's Law to find the unknown $\Delta H_r^{\ominus}$. First though, choose and label the two routes. For this example we will choose routes that go against the direction of the arrows, to show how this method works:

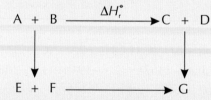

$$H^+_{(g)} + Br^-_{(g)} \xrightarrow[\text{Route 1}]{\Delta H_r^{\ominus}} H^+_{(aq)} + Br^-_{(aq)}$$

$$-\Delta H_1 \updownarrow \Delta H_1 \qquad\qquad \Delta H_3$$

$$H_{(g)} + Br_{(g)} \xrightarrow[\text{Route 2}]{\Delta H_2} HBr_{(g)}$$

The first step in the chosen route 2 goes against the direction of the arrow for $\Delta H_1$. The enthalpy change for a backwards reaction is exactly the same size as for the forwards reaction — but with the opposite sign. So the enthalpy change for the first step in route 2 will be $-\Delta H_1$, as shown.

Now just use Hess's Law as before:

Route 1 = Route 2

$\Delta H_r^{\ominus} = -\Delta H_1 + \Delta H_2 + \Delta H_3$

$\Delta H_r^{\ominus} = -987 + (-366) + (-85) = -1438$ kJ mol$^{-1}$.

| Element | $\Delta H_c^{\ominus}$ |
|---------|------------------------|
| $C_{(s)}$ | $-394$ kJ mol$^{-1}$ |
| $H_{2(g)}$ | $-286$ kJ mol$^{-1}$ |

**Figure 7:** Enthalpies of combustion for carbon and hydrogen.

## Practice Questions — Application

**Q1** Calculate $\Delta H_f^{\ominus}$ for the following organic compounds using Hess's Law, and the enthalpies of combustion given in Figure 7 and below:

a) propan-1-ol ($C_3H_7OH$): $\Delta H_c^{\ominus} = -2021$ kJ mol$^{-1}$.

b) ethane-1,2-diol ($C_2H_4(OH)_2$): $\Delta H_c^{\ominus} = -1180$ kJ mol$^{-1}$.

c) butan-2-one ($C_4H_8O$): $\Delta H_c^{\ominus} = -2442$ kJ mol$^{-1}$.

**Q2** The reaction scheme below involves 7 unknown substances, A-G:

$$A + B \xrightarrow{\Delta H_r^{\ominus}} C + D$$

$$\downarrow \qquad\qquad\qquad \downarrow$$

$$E + F \xrightarrow{\qquad\qquad} G$$

| Reaction | $\Delta H$ (kJ mol$^{-1}$) |
|----------|----------------------------|
| A + B → E + F | $-837$ |
| E + F → G | $+89$ |
| C + D → G | $+424$ |

Use Hess's Law, along with the data in the table, to calculate the enthalpy change, $\Delta H_r^{\ominus}$, for the reaction A + B → C + D.

# 5. Reaction Rates

*The rate of a reaction is how quickly the reaction happens.*

## Collision theory and activation energy

Particles in liquids and gases are always moving and colliding with each other. They don't react every time though — only when the conditions are right. **Collision theory** says that a reaction won't take place between two particles unless they collide in the right direction (they need to be facing each other the right way) and they collide with at least a certain minimum amount of kinetic (movement) energy.

The minimum amount of kinetic energy particles need to react is called the **activation energy**. The particles need this much energy to break the bonds to start the reaction. Reactions with low activation energies often happen pretty easily. But reactions with high activation energies don't. You need to give the particles extra energy by heating them.

## Enthalpy profile diagrams

To make things a bit clearer, we can draw an enthalpy profile diagram like the one shown below in Figure 1 (see page 179 for more on enthalpy profile diagrams).

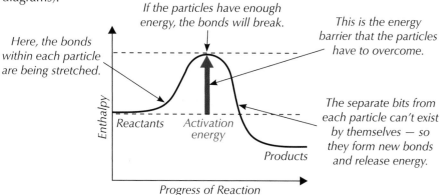

*If the particles have enough energy, the bonds will break.*

*This is the energy barrier that the particles have to overcome.*

*Here, the bonds within each particle are being stretched.*

*The separate bits from each particle can't exist by themselves — so they form new bonds and release energy.*

**Figure 1:** *An enthalpy profile diagram.*

Enthalpy profile diagrams can be used to work out the enthalpy change ($\Delta H$) of a reaction, and whether it is exothermic or endothermic (see pages 178-179). $\Delta H$ is the difference between the enthalpy of the reactants and the enthalpy of the products on the diagram. If the products have a lower enthalpy than the reactants, the reaction is exothermic. If the products have a higher enthalpy than the reactants, the reaction is endothermic.

**— Example —**

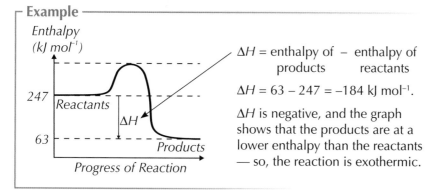

$\Delta H$ = enthalpy of − enthalpy of
 products     reactants

$\Delta H = 63 - 247 = -184$ kJ mol$^{-1}$.

$\Delta H$ is negative, and the graph shows that the products are at a lower enthalpy than the reactants — so, the reaction is exothermic.

**Learning Objectives:**

- Explain qualitatively the Boltzmann distribution and its relationship with activation energy.
- Describe qualitatively, using the Boltzmann distribution, the effect of temperature changes on the proportion of molecules exceeding the activation energy and hence the reaction rate.
- Describe qualitatively, in terms of collision theory, the effect of concentration changes on the rate of a reaction.
- Explain why an increase in the pressure of a gas, increasing its concentration, may increase the rate of a reaction involving gases.

**Specification Reference 2.3.2**

**Tip:** Remember, for <u>exothermic</u> reactions $\Delta H$ is <u>negative</u>. For <u>endothermic</u> reactions, $\Delta H$ is <u>positive</u>.

# Maxwell-Boltzmann distributions

Imagine looking down on Oxford Street when it's teeming with people. You'll see some people ambling along slowly, some hurrying quickly, but most of them will be walking with a moderate speed. It's the same with the molecules in a gas. Some don't have much kinetic energy and move slowly. Others have loads of kinetic energy and whizz along. But most molecules are somewhere in between. If you plot a graph of the numbers of molecules in a gas with different kinetic energies you get a **Maxwell-Boltzmann distribution**. The Maxwell-Boltzmann distribution is a theoretical model that has been developed to explain scientific observations (see page 1). It looks like this:

**Figure 2:** *James Clerk Maxwell, the Scottish physicist who studied the motion of gas molecules.*

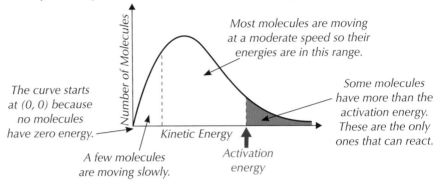

**Figure 3:** *A Maxwell-Boltzmann distribution curve showing the different kinetic energies of molecules in a gas.*

**Figure 4:** *Ludwig Boltzmann, the Austrian physicist who developed Maxwell's ideas on the energy distribution of gas molecules.*

## The effect of temperature on reaction rate

If you increase the temperature of a gas, the molecules will on average have more kinetic energy and will move faster. So, a greater proportion of molecules will have at least the activation energy and be able to react. This changes the shape of the Maxwell-Boltzmann distribution curve — it pushes it over to the right (see Figure 5). The total number of molecules is still the same, which means the area under each curve must be the same.

**Exam Tip**
You need to be able to draw distribution curves for different temperatures so remember — if the temperature **i**ncreases the curve moves to the r**i**ght, if it d**e**creases the curve moves to the l**e**ft.

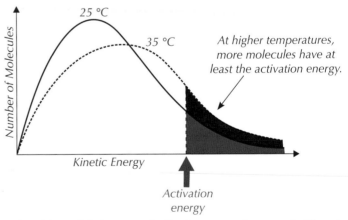

**Figure 5:** *Two Maxwell-Boltzmann distribution curves for a gas at different temperatures. Increasing the temperature of the gas shifts the distribution of the kinetic energies of the molecules.*

**Exam Tip**
When drawing Maxwell-Boltzmann distribution curves, make sure your line starts at the origin, but doesn't end touching the x-axis.

Because the molecules are flying about faster, they'll collide more often. This is another reason why increasing the temperature makes a reaction faster. So, small temperature increases can lead to large increases in reaction rate.

# The effect of concentration on reaction rate

If you increase the concentration of reactants in a solution, the particles will on average be closer together. If they're closer, they'll collide more often. If there are more collisions, they'll have more chances to react.

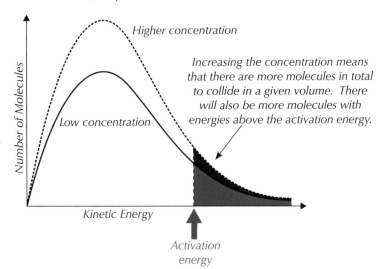

*Increasing the concentration means that there are more molecules in total to collide in a given volume. There will also be more molecules with energies above the activation energy.*

**Figure 6:** *Two Maxwell-Boltzmann distribution curves for a solution at different concentrations.*

If any of your reactants are gases, increasing the pressure will increase the rate of reaction. It's pretty much the same as increasing the concentration of a solution — at higher pressures, the particles will be closer together, increasing the chance of collisions. As a result there'll be more successful collisions.

**Tip:** Figure 6 refers to the number of molecules in a given volume. Changing the volume as well as the concentration means that two variables in the experiment have changed — you wouldn't be able to tell what was causing the change in the Maxwell-Boltzmann distribution. See page 221 for more on variables.

**Tip:** If one of the reactants is a solid, increasing its surface area makes the reaction faster too.

## Practice Questions — Application

Q1  Look at the enthalpy profile diagram below.

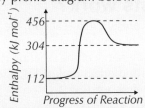

Is the reaction exothermic or endothermic? Explain your answer.

Q2  The two Maxwell-Boltzmann distribution curves shown in Figure 7 are for the same volume of the same gas. Which curve, A or B, is for the gas at a higher temperature? Explain your answer.

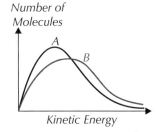

**Figure 7:** *Two Maxwell-Boltzmann distribution curves for a volume of gas at different temperatures.*

## Practice Questions — Fact Recall

Q1  What conditions are required for a collision between two particles to result in a reaction?

Q2  What does the term 'activation energy' mean?

Q3  Explain why a small increase in temperature can lead to a large increase in reaction rate.

Q4  Describe and explain the effect that increasing the concentration of a solution has on the rate of a reaction involving that solution.

## Learning Objectives:

- Know that a catalyst speeds up a reaction without being consumed by the overall reaction.
- Explain, using enthalpy profile diagrams, how a catalyst allows a reaction to occur via a different route giving rise to an increased reaction rate.
- Interpret catalytic behaviour in terms of the Boltzmann distribution.
- Explain that catalysts are often enzymes, generating specific products, and operating close to room temperatures and pressures.
- Explain that catalysts have great economic importance, e.g. iron in ammonia production, Ziegler–Natta catalyst in poly(ethene) production, platinum/palladium/rhodium in catalytic converters.
- Explain that catalysts affect the conditions needed for a reaction, (e.g. lowering temperatures and reducing energy demand and $CO_2$ emissions from burning of fossil fuels).
- Explain that catalysts enable different reactions to be used, with better atom economy and with reduced waste.

**Specification Reference 2.3.2**

**Tip:** See page 215 for more on <u>adsorption</u> and <u>desorption</u>.

# 6. Catalysts

*Sometimes you need to speed up a reaction, but you can't (or don't want to) increase the temperature, concentration or pressure any further. That's where catalysts come in.*

## What is a catalyst?

You can use **catalysts** to make chemical reactions happen faster. A catalyst increases the rate of a reaction by providing an alternative reaction pathway with a lower activation energy. The catalyst is chemically unchanged at the end of the reaction.

Catalysts are great. They don't get used up in reactions, so you only need a tiny bit of catalyst to catalyse a huge amount of stuff. They do take part in reactions, but they're remade at the end. Catalysts are very fussy about which reactions they catalyse. Many will usually only work on a single reaction. Catalysts save heaps of money in industrial processes.

> ### Example
>
> The Haber-Bosch process uses an iron catalyst to increase the rate of forming ammonia from nitrogen and hydrogen in the following reaction:
>
> $$N_{2(g)} + 3H_{2(g)} \rightleftharpoons 2NH_{3(g)}$$
>
> This reaction has a very high activation energy, due to a very strong N≡N bond in $N_2$. For the reaction rate to be high enough to make ammonia in any great quantity, the temperature and pressure would have to be extremely high — too high to be practical or profitable.
>
> In reality, the reaction is performed with the use of an iron catalyst, which increases the reaction rate at a workable temperature and pressure (around 400-500 °C and 20 MPa).

## How do catalysts work?

When a suitable catalyst is present in a reaction, the reactant molecules **adsorb** (bind) to the surface of the catalyst. This makes it easier to break the bonds, and so the activation energy of the reaction decreases. The broken reactant molecules then form product molecules, and **desorb** (break away from) the surface of the catalyst.

Enthalpy profiles (see Figure 1) and Maxwell-Boltzmann distribution curves (Figure 2 — next page) can help illustrate how catalysts work.

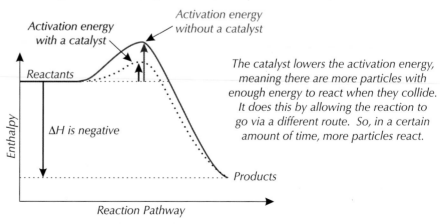

*The catalyst lowers the activation energy, meaning there are more particles with enough energy to react when they collide. It does this by allowing the reaction to go via a different route. So, in a certain amount of time, more particles react.*

**Figure 1:** *Enthalpy profile diagram for a reaction with and without a catalyst.*

With a catalyst present, the molecules still have the same amount of energy, so the Maxwell-Boltzmann distribution curve is unchanged. But because the catalyst lowers the activation energy, more of the molecules have energies above this threshold and are able to react, as shown in Figure 2.

**Tip:** Catalysts speed up the reaction in a different way to increasing temperature, concentration or pressure. These things all change the energy distribution but the addition of a catalyst does not.

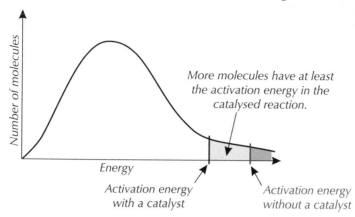

*More molecules have at least the activation energy in the catalysed reaction.*

*Activation energy with a catalyst*

*Activation energy without a catalyst*

**Figure 2:** *A Maxwell-Boltzmann distribution curve for a reaction with and without a catalyst.*

# Enzymes

Enzymes are biological catalysts — they're proteins that catalyse certain biochemical reactions. People have used enzymes for thousands of years — since way before we even knew what enzymes were. For example, enzymes produced by yeast are used to make bread and alcohol. More recent uses of enzymes include being added to washing powders to help break down stains (see Figure 3) and being used to partly digest baby food.

Many enzymes operate in conditions close to room temperature and pressure, so they're useful in industry because they can reduce the need for high temperature, fuel-guzzling processes. Enzymes tend to be very picky about what they catalyse, and most can only be used for very specific reactions. This can be useful too — it means they can select one molecule from a mixture and cause that to react without affecting the others. This has been exploited in the production of new drugs.

**Figure 3:** *Electron micrograph of biological washing powder granules. Some of the granules are partially opened and contain enzymes.*

# Catalysts in industry

Loads of industries rely on catalysts. They can dramatically lower production costs, and help make better products.

┌─ **Examples** ─────────────────

Using a catalyst changes the properties of poly(ethene).

|  | Made without a catalyst | Made with a catalyst (a Ziegler-Natta catalyst to be precise) |
|---|---|---|
| Properties of poly(ethene) | ▪ less dense ▪ less rigid | ▪ more dense ▪ more rigid ▪ higher melting point |

**Tip:** Interesting fact — the chemists Karl Ziegler and Giulio Natta shared the Nobel Prize for chemistry in 1963 for their work developing the Ziegler-Natta catalyst. Fascinating.

Catalysts are used loads in the petroleum industry too. They're used for cracking, isomerisation, and reforming alkanes (see pages 125-127).

Iron is used as a catalyst in ammonia production (see page 194).

# Catalysts and the environment

Using catalysts means that lower temperatures and pressures can be used. So energy is saved, meaning less $CO_2$ is released, and fossil fuel reserves are preserved. They can also reduce waste by allowing a different reaction to be used with a better atom economy. (See page 115 for more on atom economy.)

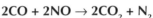

> **Example**
>
> Making the painkiller ibuprofen by the traditional method involves 6 steps and has an atom economy of 32%. Using catalysts it can be made in 3 steps with an atom economy of 77%.

**Figure 1:** *Tablets of the painkiller ibuprofen.*

Catalytic converters on cars are made from alloys of platinum, palladium and rhodium. They reduce the pollution released into the atmosphere by speeding up the following reaction:

$$2CO + 2NO \rightarrow 2CO_2 + N_2$$

But catalysts don't last forever. All catalysts eventually need to be disposed of. The trouble is, many contain nasty toxic compounds, which may leach into the soil if they're sent directly to landfill. So it's important to try to recycle them, or convert them to non-leaching forms. If catalysts contain valuable metals, such as platinum, it's worth recovering and recycling it — and there are special companies eager to do this. The decision whether to recycle the catalyst or to send it to landfill is made by balancing the economic and environmental factors.

*HOW SCIENCE WORKS*

## Practice Question — Application

**Q1** The enthalpy profile diagram shown below is for an uncatalysed chemical reaction to produce 'Product X'.

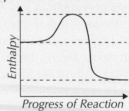

*Progress of Reaction*

A company wants to produce 'Product X' on a large scale. They are considering using a catalyst.

a) Draw a sketch to show how the addition of a catalyst would affect the enthalpy profile diagram for the reaction.

b) The uncatalysed reaction will only take place at temperatures above 1000 °C. Suggest how adding a catalyst would improve the industrial process.

**Tip:** 'Uncatalysed' just means that no catalyst has been used.

## Practice Questions — Fact Recall

**Q1** What is a catalyst?

**Q2** Explain why catalysts are used in many industrial processes.

**Q3** Explain how a catalyst can speed up the rate of a reaction.

**Q4** Explain why enzymes are used as catalysts in industry.

**Q5** Give an example of a product where the use of a catalyst in its production changes its properties.

**Exam Tip**
You need to be able to give a full description of what a catalyst is.

# 7. Reversible Reactions

*We usually think of a reaction as a one-way process to make products from reactants. In reality though, many reactions are reversible.*

## Dynamic equilibrium

Lots of chemical reactions are reversible — they go both ways. To show a reaction's reversible, you stick in a $\rightleftharpoons$.

> **Example**
>
> Hydrogen will react with iodine to produce hydrogen iodide:
>
> $$H_{2(g)} + I_{2(g)} \rightleftharpoons 2HI_{(g)}$$
>
> This reaction can go in either direction —
>
> forwards: $H_{2(g)} + I_{2(g)} \rightarrow 2HI_{(g)}$ ...or backwards: $2HI_{(g)} \rightarrow H_{2(g)} + I_{2(g)}$

As the reactants get used up, the forward reaction slows down — and as more product is formed, the reverse reaction speeds up. After a while, the forward reaction will be going at exactly the same rate as the backward reaction. The concentration of reactants and products won't be changing any more, so it'll seem like nothing's happening. It's a bit like you're digging a hole, while someone else is filling it in at exactly the same speed. This is called a **dynamic equilibrium**. A dynamic equilibrium can only happen in a **closed system**. This just means nothing can get in or out.

## Le Chatelier's principle

If you change the concentration, pressure or temperature of a reversible reaction, you're going to alter the position of equilibrium. This just means you'll end up with different amounts of reactants and products at equilibrium. If the position of equilibrium moves to the left, the backwards reaction is faster than the forwards reaction, and so you'll get more reactants.

> **Example**
>
> If the position of equilibrium in the reaction $H_{2(g)} + I_{2(g)} \rightleftharpoons 2HI_{(g)}$ shifts to the left, the backwards reaction is fastest, so more $H_2$ and $I_2$ are produced:
>
> $$H_{2(g)} + I_{2(g)} \rightleftharpoons 2HI_{(g)}$$

If the position of equilibrium moves to the right, the forwards reaction is faster than the backwards reaction, and so you'll get more products.

> **Example**
>
> If the position of equilibrium in the reaction $H_{2(g)} + I_{2(g)} \rightleftharpoons 2HI_{(g)}$ shifts to the right, the forwards reaction is fastest, so more HI is produced:
>
> $$H_{2(g)} + I_{2(g)} \rightleftharpoons 2HI_{(g)}$$

**Le Chatelier's principle** tells you how the position of equilibrium will change if a condition changes:

> If there's a change in concentration, pressure or temperature, the equilibrium will move to help counteract the change.

So, basically, if you raise the temperature, the position of equilibrium will shift to try to cool things down. And, if you raise the pressure or concentration, the position of equilibrium will shift to try to reduce it again. Catalysts have no effect on the position of equilibrium. They can't increase yield — but they do mean equilibrium is reached faster.

**Learning Objectives:**

- Explain that a dynamic equilibrium exists when the rate of the forward reaction is equal to the rate of the reverse reaction.
- Be able to state le Chatelier's principle.
- Be able to apply le Chatelier's principle to deduce qualitatively (from appropriate information) the effect of a change in temperature, concentration or pressure, on a homogeneous system in equilibrium.
- Be able to explain, from given data the importance in the chemical industry of a compromise between chemical equilibrium and reaction rate.

**Specification Reference 2.3.2**

**Tip:** $H_{2(g)} + I_{2(g)} \rightarrow 2HI_{(g)}$ is an example of a <u>homogeneous reaction</u> — the reactants and products are all in the same state (in this case they're all gases).

# Using Le Chatelier's principle

## Changing concentration

If you increase the concentration of a reactant, the equilibrium tries to get rid of the extra reactant. It does this by making more product. So the equilibrium's shifted to the right. If you increase the concentration of the product, the equilibrium tries to remove the extra product. This makes the reverse reaction go faster. So the equilibrium shifts to the left. Decreasing the concentrations has the opposite effect.

**Figure 1:** *Henri Le Chatelier, the French physical chemist who developed Le Chatelier's principle in the 1880s.*

---
**Examples**

Sulfur dioxide reacts with oxygen to produce sulfur trioxide:

$$2SO_{2(g)} + O_{2(g)} \rightleftharpoons 2SO_{3(g)}$$

If you increase the concentration of $SO_2$ or $O_2$, the equilibrium tries to get rid of it by making more $SO_3$, so the equilibrium shifts to the right. If you increase the concentration of $SO_3$, the equilibrium shifts to the left to make the backwards reaction faster to get rid of the extra $SO_3$.

In the Haber process, nitrogen reacts with hydrogen to produce ammonia:

$$N_{2(g)} + 3H_{2(g)} \rightleftharpoons 2NH_{3(g)}$$

If you increase the concentration of $N_2$ or $H_2$, the equilibrium shifts to the right and you'll make more $NH_3$. If you increase the concentration of $NH_3$, the equilibrium shifts to the left and you'll make more $N_2$ and $H_2$.

---

## Changing pressure

Changing the pressure only affects equilibria involving gases. Increasing the pressure shifts the equilibrium to the side with fewer gas molecules. This reduces the pressure. Decreasing the pressure shifts the equilibrium to the side with more gas molecules. This raises the pressure again.

**Tip:** If all the reactants and products are gases, and there are the same number of moles on each side of the equation, changing the pressure won't change the position of equilibrium.

---
**Examples**

When sulfur dioxide reacts with oxygen you get sulfur trioxide:

$$2SO_{2(g)} + O_{2(g)} \rightleftharpoons 2SO_{3(g)}$$

There are 3 moles on the left, but only 2 on the right. So, an increase in pressure shifts the equilibrium to the right, making more $SO_3$ and reducing the pressure. Decreasing the pressure favours the backwards reaction, so the equilibrium shifts to the left and more $SO_2$ and $O_2$ will be made to increase the pressure.

Methane reacts with water to produce carbon monoxide and hydrogen:

$$CH_{4(g)} + H_2O_{(g)} \rightleftharpoons CO_{(g)} + 3H_{2(g)}$$

There are 2 moles on the left and 4 on the right. So for this reaction an increase in pressure shifts the equilibrium to the left, making more $CH_4$ and $H_2O$. Decreasing the pressure shifts the equilibrium to the right to make more CO and $H_2$. This reaction is used in industry to produce hydrogen. It is best performed at a low pressure to favour the forwards reaction so that more $H_2$ is produced.

---

## Changing temperature

Increasing the temperature means adding heat energy. The equilibrium shifts in the endothermic (positive $\Delta H$) direction to absorb this energy. Decreasing the temperature removes heat energy. The equilibrium shifts in the exothermic (negative $\Delta H$) direction to try to replace the heat energy. If the forward reaction is endothermic, the reverse reaction will be exothermic, and vice versa.

This reaction's exothermic in the forward direction, which means it is endothermic in the backward direction.

$$Exothermic\rightarrow$$
$$2SO_{2(g)} + O_{2(g)} \rightleftharpoons 2SO_{3(g)} \qquad \Delta H = -197 \text{ kJ mol}^{-1}.$$
$$\leftarrow Endothermic$$

If you increase the temperature, the equilibrium shifts to the left (the endothermic direction) to absorb the extra heat. This means more $SO_2$ and $O_2$ are produced. If you decrease the temperature, the equilibrium shifts to the right (the exothermic direction) to produce more heat. This means more $SO_3$ is produced.

This reaction's endothermic in the forward direction (and so exothermic in the backward direction).

$$Endothermic\rightarrow$$
$$C_{(s)} + H_2O_{(g)} \rightleftharpoons CO_{(g)} + H_{2(g)} \qquad \Delta H = +131 \text{ kJ mol}^{-1}.$$
$$\leftarrow Exothermic$$

Increasing the temperature will shift the equilibrium to the right, producing more CO and $H_2$. Decreasing the temperature shifts the equilibrium to the left, producing more C and $H_2O$.

# Ethanol production

HOW SCIENCE WORKS

The industrial production of ethanol is a good example of why Le Chatelier's principle is important in real life. Ethanol is produced via a reversible exothermic reaction between ethene and steam:

$$C_2H_{4(g)} + H_2O_{(g)} \rightleftharpoons C_2H_5OH_{(g)} \qquad \Delta H = -46 \text{ kJ mol}^{-1}$$

The industrial conditions for the reaction are:

- a pressure of 60-70 atmospheres
- a temperature of 300 °C
- a phosphoric acid catalyst.

Because it's an exothermic reaction, lower temperatures favour the forward reaction. This means that at lower temperatures more ethene and steam is converted to ethanol — you get a better **yield**. But lower temperatures mean a slower rate of reaction. You'd be daft to try to get a really high yield of ethanol if it's going to take you 10 years. So the 300 °C is a compromise between maximum yield and a faster reaction.

Higher pressures favour the forward reaction, so a pressure of 60-70 atmospheres is used — high pressure moves the reaction to the side with fewer molecules of gas. Increasing the pressure also increases the rate of reaction. Cranking up the pressure as high as you can sounds like a great idea so far. But high pressures are expensive to produce. You need stronger pipes and containers to withstand high pressure. And, in this process, increasing the pressure can also cause side reactions to occur. So the 60-70 atmospheres is a compromise between maximum yield and expense. In the end, it all comes down to minimising costs.

Only a small proportion of the ethene reacts each time the gases pass through the catalyst. To save money and raw materials, the unreacted ethene is separated from the liquid ethanol and recycled back into the reactor. Thanks to this around 95% of the ethene is eventually converted to ethanol.

**Tip:** An enthalpy change given with a reversible reaction always refers to the forwards reaction, unless you're told otherwise.

**Exam Tip**
In an exam question, make it clear exactly how the equilibrium shift opposes a temperature change — i.e. by removing or producing heat.

**Tip:** A lot of questions in this section ask about the effect of increasing temperature, pressure and concentration. But their effect on reaction rate is different to their effect on the position of equilibrium. Make sure you're clear which one you're being asked about.

**Tip:** The yield is the amount of product you get from a reaction. Increasing the reaction rate will give you a higher yield in a given time, but you need to shift the equilibrium to increase the maximum yield.

Q1 An industrial process uses the following reversible reaction:

$$A_{(g)} + 2B_{(g)} \rightleftharpoons C_{(g)} + D_{(g)} \qquad \Delta H = -189 \text{ kJ mol}^{-1}.$$

a) Explain the effect of increasing the concentration of A on the position of the equilibrium.

b) Explain the effect of increasing the pressure on the position of the equilibrium.

c) Explain the effect of increasing the temperature on the position of the equilibrium.

d) Briefly outline the best reaction conditions (in terms of high or low concentration, pressure and temperature) to maximise the production of product D.

Q2 What will be the effect of increasing the pressure on the position of equilibrium of the following reaction?

$$H_{2(g)} + I_{2(g)} \rightleftharpoons 2HI_{(g)}$$

Explain your answer.

**Exam Tip**
You may get asked why the ideal conditions for a reaction aren't used in reality. Often the answer is to do with the cost of generating the conditions or their safety.

## Practice Questions — Fact Recall

Q1 What does it mean if a reaction is in dynamic equilibrium?

Q2 What is Le Chatelier's Principle?

Q3 How does the addition of a catalyst affect the position of equilibrium in a reversible reaction?

Q4 Ethanol is produced using a reaction that gives you a higher yield at a low temperature. Explain why a low temperature is not used to produce ethanol industrially.

## Section Summary

Make sure you know...

- That enthalpy change, $\Delta H$ (in kJ mol$^{-1}$), is the heat energy transferred in a reaction at constant pressure.

- That $\Delta H^\ominus$ is the enthalpy change for a reaction where the reactants and products are in their standard states and the measurements are made at 100 kPa pressure and a stated temperature (usually 298 K).

- That $\Delta H_r^\ominus$ is the enthalpy change when a reaction occurs in the molar quantities shown in the chemical equation, under standard conditions with all reactants and products in their standard states.

- That $\Delta H_f^\ominus$ is the enthalpy change when 1 mole of a compound is formed from its elements in their standard states under standard conditions.

- That $\Delta H_c^\ominus$ is the enthalpy change when 1 mole of a substance is completely burned in oxygen under standard conditions.

- That exothermic reactions give out energy, so $\Delta H$ is negative.

- That oxidation (e.g. the combustion of fuels and the reaction of carbohydrates in respiration) is an exothermic process.

- That endothermic reactions absorb energy, so $\Delta H$ is positive.

- That endothermic processes such as thermal decomposition and photosynthesis need an input of heat energy.

- How to draw and interpret an enthalpy profile diagram for a reaction, identifying the activation energy, the enthalpy change of the reaction, and whether the reaction is exothermic or endothermic.
- That the minimum amount of kinetic energy required for a reaction is called the activation energy.
- That average bond enthalpies tell us the energy needed to break one mole of bonds in the gas phase, averaged over many different compounds.
- How to use average bond enthalpies to calculate enthalpy changes for reactions, using the equation: Enthalpy change of reaction = Total energy absorbed – Total energy released.
- How to calculate the heat lost or gained ($q$) by a reaction in the laboratory using the equation $q = mc\Delta T$, where m is the mass of the reaction mixture, $c$ is its specific heat capacity, and $\Delta T$ is the temperature change due to the reaction.
- That Hess's Law says that:
  The total enthalpy change of a reaction is always the same, no matter which route is taken.
- How to use Hess's Law to calculate enthalpy changes for reactions from enthalpies of formation.
- How to use Hess's Law to calculate enthalpy changes for reactions from enthalpies of combustion.
- How to use Hess's Law to calculate enthalpy changes for reactions from other enthalpies of reaction.
- That the Maxwell-Boltzmann distribution describes the spread of energies of the molecules in a gas.
- How to draw and interpret Maxwell-Boltzmann distribution curves for gases at different temperatures.
- That even a small increase in temperature can increase the reaction rate, by increasing the number of molecules with energies above the activation energy so that more will react when they collide.
- That increasing the concentration of reactants (or the pressure if they're gases) will increase the reaction rate, because the molecules will be closer together and so more likely to collide and react.
- That a catalyst is a substance that increases the rate of a reaction by providing an alternative pathway with a lower activation energy, and is chemically unchanged at the end of the reaction.
- That catalysts affect the conditions needed for reactions or allow different reactions to be used.
- That enzymes are used in industry as catalysts.
- The economic importance of catalysts such as iron in ammonia production, the Ziegler-Natta catalyst in poly(ethene) production and platinum/palladium/rhodium in catalytic converters.
- That reversible reactions can reach an equilibrium, where the concentrations of reactants and products stay constant and the forwards and backwards reactions have the same reaction rate.
- Le Chatelier's principle states that "if there's a change in concentration, pressure or temperature, the equilibrium will move to help counteract the change."
- That a catalyst does not affect the position of equilibrium in a reversible reaction.
- That increasing the concentration of a reactant shifts the equilibrium to remove the extra reactant.
- That increasing the pressure shifts the equilibrium in favour of the reaction that produces the fewest moles of gas, in order to reduce the pressure.
- That increasing the temperature shifts the equilibrium in favour of the endothermic reaction, to remove the excess heat. (Low temperatures favour exothermic reactions.)
- Why there sometimes has to be a compromise between chemical equilibrium and reaction rate in industry.

# Exam-style Questions

**1** A chemical factory produces ethanol ($C_2H_5OH$) from ethene ($C_2H_4$) and water ($H_2O$) using the following reversible reaction:

$$C_2H_{4(g)} + H_2O_{(g)} \rightleftharpoons C_2H_5OH_{(g)} \qquad \Delta H = -46 \text{ kJ mol}^{-1}$$

The reaction is carried out under the following conditions:

Pressure = 60 atm
Temperature = 300 °C
Catalyst = phosphoric acid

**(a)** Without the phosphoric acid catalyst the rate of reaction is so slow that dynamic equilibrium takes a very long time to be reached.

Describe what it means for a reaction to be at dynamic equilibrium.

*(2 marks)*

**(b)** The process conditions for the reaction were chosen with consideration to Le Chatelier's principle. State Le Chatelier's principle.

*(2 marks)*

**(c)** Explain why the pressure chosen for the process is a compromise.

*(3 marks)*

**(d)** A leak in one of the pipes reduces the amount of $H_2O$ in the reaction mixture. Explain the effect this has on the maximum yield of ethanol.

*(3 marks)*

**2** Two gases react together in an exothermic reaction.
The reaction has an activation energy of 90 kJ mol$^{-1}$.
The enthalpy change for the reaction is −150 kJ mol$^{-1}$.

**(a) (i)** What is meant by the term 'activation energy'?

*(2 marks)*

**(ii)** Sketch the enthalpy profile diagram for the reaction.
Label your diagram to show the activation energy and the enthalpy change of the reaction.

*(3 marks)*

**(b)** The reactants are heated.
Explain the effect this will have on the rate of the reaction.

*(3 marks)*

**(c)**    Explain the effect that lowering the pressure has on the rate of the reaction.

*(3 marks)*

**(d)**    A catalyst is added to the reaction.

   **(i)**    Define the term catalyst.

*(1 mark)*

   **(ii)**    Explain how a catalyst increases the rate of reaction using an enthalpy profile diagram and a Boltzmann distribution curve.

       You should organise your answer and use the correct technical terms.

*(6 marks)*

   **(iii)**    Describe the processes that occur between the two gases and the catalyst during the reaction.

*(4 marks)*

**3**    The table below shows the standard enthalpy change of combustion, $\Delta H_c^{\ominus}$, for carbon, hydrogen and octane ($C_8H_{18(l)}$).

The standard enthalpy of formation of octane can be calculated from this data using Hess's Law.

|  | $\Delta H_c^{\ominus}$ |
|---|---|
| $C_{(s)}$ | $-394$ kJ mol$^{-1}$ |
| $H_{2(g)}$ | $-286$ kJ mol$^{-1}$ |
| $C_8H_{18(l)}$ | $-5470$ kJ mol$^{-1}$ |

**(a)**    State Hess's Law.

*(1 mark)*

**(b)**    Write out a balanced chemical equation for the complete combustion of octane.

*(1 mark)*

**(c) (i)**    Use your answers to parts **(a)** and **(b)**, and the data in the table above, to calculate the standard enthalpy change of formation of octane, $\Delta H_f^{\ominus}$.

*(3 marks)*

   **(ii)**    State whether the formation of octane is exothermic or endothermic. Explain your answer.

*(2 marks)*

**4** Alkenes are very important in the chemical industry.

**(a)** The structure of the alkene but-1-ene is shown below.

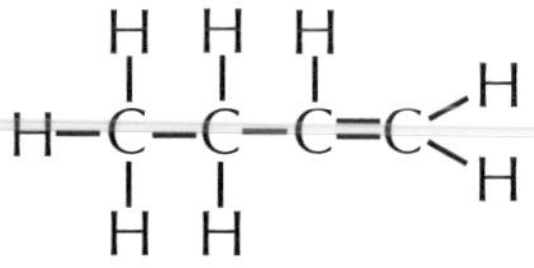

$$H-\overset{\overset{\displaystyle H}{|}}{\underset{\underset{\displaystyle H}{|}}{C}}-\overset{\overset{\displaystyle H}{|}}{\underset{\underset{\displaystyle H}{|}}{C}}-\overset{\overset{\displaystyle H}{|}}{C}=C\overset{H}{\underset{H}{<}}$$

But-1-ene will burn completely in oxygen to produce $CO_2$ and $H_2O$.

The table below shows bond enthalpies for the bonds present in the reactants and products of this combustion reaction.

| Bond | Bond Enthalpy (Average value except where stated) |
|---|---|
| C–H | +413 kJ mol$^{-1}$ |
| C=C | +612 kJ mol$^{-1}$ |
| C–C | +347 kJ mol$^{-1}$ |
| O=O | +498 kJ mol$^{-1}$ |
| C=O (in $CO_2$) | +805 kJ mol$^{-1}$ |
| O–H (in $H_2O$) | +460 kJ mol$^{-1}$ |

These bond enthalpies can be used to calculate the standard enthalpy change of combustion for but-1-ene.

**(i)** State the meaning of the term 'standard enthalpy change of combustion', $\Delta H_c^{\circ}$.

*(3 marks)*

**(ii)** Use the data in the table to calculate a value for the standard enthalpy change of combustion for but-1-ene.

*(3 marks)*

**(iii)** The standard enthalpy change of combustion for but-1-ene calculated from the average bond enthalpies is different to the value given in the data book. Suggest why.

*(1 mark)*

**(b)** 0.0215 mol of another alkene are burned. The energy released heats 200 cm$^3$ water from 21.0 °C to 53.8 °C.

(density of water = 1.00 g dm$^{-3}$, specific heat capacity of water = 4.18 J g$^{-1}$ K$^{-1}$)

**(i)** Calculate the amount of energy released in kJ when the alkene is burned.

*(2 marks)*

**(ii)** Calculate the enthalpy change of combustion, $\Delta H_c^{\circ}$, of the alkene. Give your answer to 3 significant figures.

*(2 marks)*

**(iii)** Explain, in terms of making and breaking bonds, why the combustion of the alkene is exothermic.

*(2 marks)*

**(iv)** The data book gives a value of –2058 kJ mol$^{-1}$ for the standard enthalpy change of this reaction.

Give two reasons why the experiment gives a different value.

*(2 marks)*

# 1. Green Chemistry

*You've already learnt a bit about sustainability, but now it's time to cover things in a bit more detail and learn what it really means to be 'green'.*

## Sustainability

Doing something sustainably means doing it without stuffing things up for the future. Sustainable chemistry (or 'green chemistry') means you don't use up all the Earth's resources, or put loads of damaging chemicals into the environment. Many of the chemical processes used in industry at the moment aren't very sustainable.

─ Example ──────────────

### The plastics industry
The raw materials used to make plastics often come from non-renewable crude oil, and the products themselves are usually non-biodegradable or hard to recycle when we're finished with them. So making plastics isn't very sustainable. (See pages 139-141 for more details.)

But there are things chemists can do to try and improve things. For example, they can ensure all the chemicals they use are as non-toxic as possible, use renewable resources and renewable energy sources, ensure that products and waste are biodegradable or recycleable and develop more efficient processes. More details on all of this below...

## Ensuring the chemicals involved are as non-toxic as possible

Many common chemicals are harmful — either to humans, other living things, the environment, or all three. Where possible, it's generally a good thing to use a safer alternative. For example...

- Lead (which can have some nasty effects on your health) used to be used in paint, petrol and for soldering. Alternatives are now used — paint and petrol use lead-free compounds, solder can be made with other metals.

- Some foams used in fire extinguishers are very good at putting out fires, but leave hazardous products behind, including some that deplete the ozone layer (see page 212). Again, alternatives are now available.

- Dry cleaners used to use a solvent based on chlorinated hydrocarbons, but these are known to be carcinogenic (i.e. they cause cancer). Safer alternatives are now available, such as liquid 'supercritical' carbon dioxide.

Sometimes redesigning a process means you can do without unsafe chemicals completely — e.g. instead of using harmful organic solvents, some reactions can be carried out with one of the reactants acting as a solvent.

## Using renewable raw materials

Loads of chemicals are traditionally made from non-renewable raw materials (e.g. crude oil fractions, or metal ores). But chemists can often develop alternative compounds (or alternative ways to make existing ones) involving renewable raw materials — e.g. some plastics are now made from plant products rather than oil fractions (see page 140 for more).

---

**Learning Objectives:**

- Be able to describe the principles of chemical sustainability:
(i) using industrial processes that reduce or eliminate hazardous chemicals and which involve the use of fewer chemicals.
(ii) designing processes with a high atom economy.
(iii) using renewable resources such as plant-based substances.
(iv) seeking alternative energy sources such as solar energy, rather than consuming finite resources such as fossil fuels.
(v) ensuring that any waste products produced are non-toxic, and can be recycled or biodegraded.

- Be able to explain that the apparent benefits of green chemistry may be offset by unexpected and detrimental side-effects.

- Be able to explain the importance of establishing international cooperation to promote the reduction of pollution levels.

- Be able to discuss issues of sustainability in contexts.

**Specification Reference 2.4.2**

*Figure 1:* Solar panels are used to produce electricity from sunlight.

*Figure 2:* Wind turbines are used to produce electricity from the wind.

**Tip:** See page 129 for more on biofuels and how they are made.

*Figure 3:* Deforestation to generate land for agriculture in the Democratic Republic of Congo.

**Tip:** International cooperation basically means different countries working together to reduce pollution.

## Using renewable energy sources

Many chemical processes use a lot of energy. Right now, most of that energy comes from fossil fuels, which will soon run out. But there are potential alternatives.

> **Examples**
>
> These can all be used as renewable alternatives to fossil fuels:
> - Plant-based fuels such as bioethanol or biodiesel (see page 129).
> - Solar power (see Figure 1) — ways to produce electricity from sunlight are developing rapidly.
> - Other renewable energy technologies — like geothermal, wave or wind energy (see Figure 2).

## Developing more efficient processes

You can improve sustainability by developing more efficient processes — for example, by using catalysts (see pages 194-196), or by picking reactions with higher atom economy, which produce less waste (see pages 115-117).

## Ensuring products and waste are biodegradable or recyclable

Chemists can try to create recyclable products. This is a good way to conserve raw materials. Waste should be kept to a minimum, and preferably be recyclable or biodegradable (see page 140).

Laws can be used to encourage change. For example, when you buy a new TV, the shop now has to agree to recycle your old TV set, with the TV manufacturers paying some of the cost. This creates an incentive to design products that are easier and cheaper to recycle.

# Disadvantages of greener chemistry

Pretty much everyone agrees that making the chemical industry more sustainable is a good thing. But sometimes making things 'greener' can cause unwanted knock-on effects.

> **Example**
>
> **Biofuels**
>
> Growing grain for biodiesel (or sugar cane for ethanol) means less land is available to grow food. So food gets more expensive — which will be worst for the urban poor, who already struggle to afford food (and can't grow their own). Also, large biofuel companies might buy up the most fertile land, forcing small farmers onto land with poorer crop yields.
>
> Alternatively, the land to grow biofuels might come from clearing forests (see Figure 3). Removing loads of trees means less $CO_2$ is absorbed in photosynthesis, so more stays in the atmosphere — the very problem that the use of biofuels is supposed to tackle. And that's not all — destroying existing, varied habitats and replacing them all with vast swathes of the same crop will reduce biodiversity and could cause soil degradation (loss of nutrients, etc.).

# The need for international cooperation

Pollution doesn't stop at national borders — rivers flow from one country to the next, and the atmosphere and oceans are constantly moving and mixing. This means that eventually everyone suffers from everyone else's dirty ways. So, international cooperation is important — there are already concerns about countries buying products made using polluting technologies from abroad, so that they can claim not to be producing the pollution themselves.

Various international treaties have been agreed. But usually, not all countries sign up because they're worried it will be bad for their economy (make things more expensive, cause job losses, and so on).

The Montreal Protocol on Substances that Deplete the Ozone Layer is probably the most successful 'green chemistry' global treaty to date — virtually everyone's signed up. Countries who signed up to this 'Montreal Protocol' agreed to phase out production of substances that damaged the ozone layer (see page 212). Similarly, most countries have signed the Stockholm Treaty on persistent organic pollutants (POPs). POPs are organic chemicals (e.g. some pesticides and fungicides) that accumulate in the fatty tissues of living organisms. They're passed up the food chain and are toxic to humans and other animals.

In 1992, the United Nations held a big conference about the environment and development (the 'Earth Summit') in Rio de Janeiro. Governments agreed to a set of 27 principles about sustainable development — the 'Rio Declaration'. These principles were all very sensible (e.g. don't cause environmental harm, develop in a sustainable way, and so on) but they aren't legally binding — so no punishment can be dished out when countries don't keep to the principles.

**Tip:** You don't need to memorise every detail of the examples on these pages, but you should understand the basic principles behind them.

**Tip:** See page 210 for more on the 'Kyoto Protocol' and how it aims to reduce global warming.

## Practice Questions — Application

Q1 A supermarket wants to be greener. It currently uses a diesel powered generator to make its electricity, imports most of its food from abroad and uses polyethene (a non-biodegradable plastic made from crude oil) to package its food. Suggest three things that the supermarket could do to reduce the amount of pollution it produces.

Q2 Ibuprofen can be produced by two different processes (A and B). Process A involves six steps and has an atom economy of 40%. Process B involves three steps and has an atom economy of 99%. Which process, A or B, is more sustainable? Explain your answer.

Q3 Hexachlorobenzene is a persistent organic compound (POP). It used to be used as a fungicide but was banned under the Stockholm Treaty. Explain why hexachlorobenzene was banned.

**Figure 4:** A wheat field. Hexachlorobenzene was used on wheat to prevent a fungal disease called bunt.

## Practice Questions — Fact Recall

Q1 What does 'sustainable chemistry' mean?

Q2 The production of plastics is not very sustainable. Explain why.

Q3 Suggest four things that can be done to help make industrial processes more sustainable.

Q4 Green chemistry can sometimes have negative consequences. Describe one example of this.

Q5 a) Explain why international cooperation is needed to reduce pollution.

b) Give one example of an international treaty that aims to reduce pollution.

c) Explain why not all countries have signed up to this treaty.

- Be able to explain that infrared radiation is absorbed by C=O, O–H and C–H bonds in $H_2O$, $CO_2$ and $CH_4$, and that these absorptions contribute to global warming.

- Be able to explain that the 'Greenhouse Effect' of a given gas is dependent both on its atmospheric concentration and its ability to absorb infrared radiation.

- Be able to outline the importance of controlling global warming resulting from atmospheric increases in greenhouse gases.

- Know that chemists collect data to confirm whether or not climate change is occurring, monitor measures to reduce the change and model the potential damage.

- Be able to outline the role of chemists in minimising climate change resulting from global warming by:
  (i) providing scientific evidence to governments to verify that global warming is taking place.
  (ii) investigating solutions to environmental problems, such as carbon capture and storage, CCS.
  (iii) monitoring progress against initiatives such as the Kyoto protocol.

  **Specification Reference 2.4.1**

# 2. Global Warming

*Global warming, the greenhouse effect and climate change seems to crop up in every subject, at every level. Here's the chemistry spin on them, including how chemists are involved in measuring, monitoring and fighting back.*

## Greenhouse gases

Some of the electromagnetic radiation from the Sun reaches the Earth and is absorbed. The Earth then re-emits it as infrared radiation (heat). Various gases in the **troposphere** (the lowest layer of the atmosphere) absorb some of this infrared radiation... and re-emit it in all directions — including back towards Earth, keeping us warm (see Figure 1). This is called the '**greenhouse effect**' (even though a real greenhouse doesn't actually work like this, annoyingly).

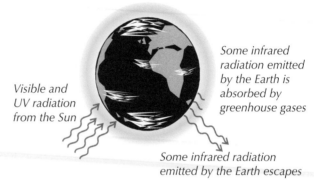

*Visible and UV radiation from the Sun*

*Some infrared radiation emitted by the Earth is absorbed by greenhouse gases*

*Some infrared radiation emitted by the Earth escapes*

**Figure 1:** *The greenhouse effect.*

The main **greenhouse gases** are water vapour, carbon dioxide and methane. The C=O, O–H and C–H bonds in these molecules absorb infrared (IR) radiation (see page 167) and this makes the bonds in the molecule vibrate more. This extra energy is passed on to other molecules in the air by collisions, giving the other molecules more kinetic energy and raising the overall temperature.

Not all greenhouse gases contribute the same amount to the greenhouse effect. The contribution of any particular gas depends on a number of factors, including:

- How much IR radiation one molecule of the gas absorbs.

- How much of that gas there is in the atmosphere — concentration in parts per million (ppm), say.

- How long the gas stays in the atmosphere for (this is called the residence time).

┌─ Example ──────────────────────────────
One methane molecule traps far more heat than one carbon dioxide molecule, but there's much less methane in the atmosphere, so its overall contribution to the greenhouse effect is smaller.
└────────────────────────────────────────

## What is global warming?

Over the last 150 years or so, the world's human population has shot up and we've become more industrialised. We've been burning fossil fuels, releasing tons of $CO_2$, and we've been chopping down forests which used to absorb $CO_2$ by photosynthesis.

Methane levels have also risen as we've grown more food. Cows produce large amounts of methane (from both ends). Paddy fields, in which rice is grown, kick out a fair bit of it too.

These human activities have caused a rise in greenhouse gas concentrations, which enhances the greenhouse effect. More heat is being trapped and the Earth is getting warmer — this is **global warming**.

*Figure 2:* Methane is released from cows...

*Figure 3:* ...and from paddy fields (fields where rice is grown).

# Consequences of global warming

Global warming won't just make everywhere a bit warmer and affect the skiing — warmer oceans will expand and massive ice-sheets in the polar regions could melt, causing sea levels to rise and leading to more flooding. The climate in any region of the world depends on a really complicated system of ocean currents, winds, etc. Global warming means there's more heat energy in the system. This could lead to stormier, less predictable weather. In some places there could be much less rainfall, with droughts and crop failures causing famines and forcing entire populations to become refugees. In other regions, increased rainfall and flooding could bring diseases like cholera.

# Evidence for global warming

Scientists have collected data to provide evidence for if and why global warming and climate change are happening, e.g. from analysing air samples and sea water samples. The evidence shows that the Earth's average temperature has increased dramatically in the last 50 years, and that $CO_2$ levels have increased at the same time — see Figure 4.

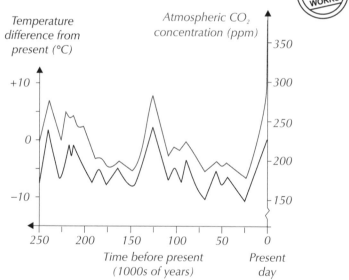

*Figure 4:* Graph showing the correlation between atmospheric $CO_2$ concentration and temperature.

The correlation between $CO_2$ and temperature is pretty clear, but there's been debate about whether rising carbon dioxide levels have caused the recent temperature rise. Just showing a correlation doesn't prove that one thing causes another — there has to be a plausible mechanism for how one change causes the other (in this case, the explanation is the enhanced greenhouse effect). There's now a consensus among climate scientists that the link is causal, and that recent warming is anthropogenic — this means that human activities are to blame.

**Tip:** Don't get confused — the greenhouse effect isn't a bad thing. In fact, without it the Earth would be too cold for us to live on. The problem comes when the greenhouse effect is <u>enhanced</u> by adding more greenhouse gases to the atmosphere. This causes global warming, which is where all the problems come in.

**Tip:** See pages 3-4 for more on how scientists collect evidence and use it to support their claims.

**Tip:** You don't need to memorise this graph — just notice that whenever atmospheric $CO_2$ increases, the temperature difference also increases. This is a correlation. See pages 223-224 for more on correlation.

# The response to global warming

Scientific evidence gathered by the Intergovernmental Panel on Climate Change (IPCC) persuaded most of the world's governments that global warming is happening. There's now global agreement that climate change could be very damaging for millions of people, the environment and economies, and that we should try to limit it. In 1997 the Kyoto protocol was signed — industrialised countries (including the UK) promised to reduce their greenhouse gas emissions to agreed levels.

## Monitoring global warming

Many chemists are now involved in monitoring greenhouse gas emissions to see if countries will meet the Kyoto targets (it looks like many won't). Chemists also continue to monitor the environment to see how it's changing now. The data they collect and analyse is used in climate models (a big load of equations run on a computer to simulate how the climate system works). Climate scientists use these models to predict future changes. It's a big job — when new factors affecting the climate are discovered by other scientists, the modellers have to 'tweak' their models to take this into account.

## Limiting global warming

Scientists are investigating various ways to help reduce carbon dioxide emissions. These include developing alternative fuels and using **carbon capture and storage** (CCS). CCS involves removing waste $CO_2$ from, say, power stations, and either:

- Injecting it as a liquid into the deep ocean.
- Storing it deep underground — one possibility is to use old oil- or gas-fields under the sea-bed.
- Reacting it with metal oxides to form stable, easily stored carbonate minerals, e.g. calcium carbonate.

**Figure 5:** *Equipment used to monitor air pollution.*

**Tip:** There's more on developing alternative fuel sources on page 129.

**Tip:** $CH_4$ has a 20 year GWP of 72. This means that if there were equal volumes of $CH_4$ and $CO_2$, the $CH_4$ would trap 72× more heat than the $CO_2$ over the course of 20 years.

**Tip:** ppm means parts per million and ppt means parts per trillion. 1 ppm is 1 million ($10^6$) times larger than 1 ppt — so don't get the two mixed up.

## Practice Question — Application

Q1  The global warming potential (GWP) of a gas is a measure of how much radiation one molecule of a gas absorbs relative to one molecule of $CO_2$ (which has a GWP of 1 by definition).
The GWPs and atmospheric concentrations of $CO_2$ and $SF_6$ are given in the table below:

| Gas | 20 year GWP | Atmospheric concentration |
|---|---|---|
| $CO_2$ | 1 | ~380 ppm |
| $SF_6$ | 16 300 | ~7.5 ppt |

Discuss the relative contributions of these two greenhouse gases to the greenhouse effect.

## Practice Questions — Fact Recall

Q1  What type of radiation do greenhouse gases absorb?

Q2  Give two factors that effect how much a particular greenhouse gas contributes to the greenhouse effect.

Q3  How is the greenhouse effect linked to global warming?

Q4  Explain why global warming is a problem.

Q5  How are chemists involved in efforts to limit global warming?

# 3. The Ozone Layer

*Molecules of ozone contain three oxygen atoms — hence the formula $O_3$. Most of the Earth's ozone is found in the ozone layer, which prevents harmful UV rays from reaching the Earth's surface. So it's pretty useful stuff.*

## What is the ozone layer?

The **ozone layer** is in a layer of the atmosphere called the stratosphere. It contains most of the atmosphere's ozone molecules, $O_3$. Ozone is formed when UV radiation from the Sun hits oxygen molecules. If the right amount of UV radiation is absorbed by an oxygen molecule, it splits into separate atoms or **free radicals**:

$$O_2 + h\nu \rightarrow O\bullet + O\bullet$$

*A quantum of UV radiation* — *An oxygen free radical*

The free radicals then combine with other oxygen molecules to form ozone molecules, $O_3$.

$$O_2 + O\bullet \rightarrow O_3$$

### Maintaining the ozone layer

UV radiation can also reverse the formation of ozone.

$$O_3 + h\nu \rightarrow O_2 + O\bullet$$

The radical produced then forms more ozone with an $O_2$ molecule, as shown above. So, the ozone layer is continuously being destroyed and replaced as UV radiation hits the molecules. The rate of formation of ozone is roughly the same as the rate of decomposition of ozone. As a result, an equilibrium is set up:

$$O_2 + O\bullet \rightleftharpoons O_3$$

This means that the concentration of ozone in the atmosphere stays fairly constant and the ozone layer is maintained.

## The protective role of the ozone layer

The UV radiation from the Sun is made up of different frequencies. These are grouped into three bands — UVA, UVB and UVC (see Figure 1):

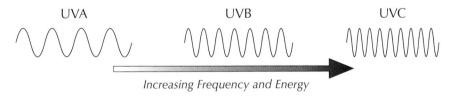

UVA          UVB          UVC

*Increasing Frequency and Energy*

**Figure 1:** *The relative frequency and energy of the three bands of UV.*

The ozone layer removes all the high energy UVC radiation and about 90% of the UVB. These types of UV radiation are harmful to humans and most other life on Earth. UVB can damage the DNA in cells and cause skin cancer. It's the main cause of sunburn too. UVA can also lead to skin cancer. Both UVA and UVB break down collagen fibres in the skin causing it to age faster.

When the skin's exposed to UV, it tans. This helps protect deeper tissues from the effects of the radiation. But UV radiation isn't all bad — in fact it's essential for us humans. We need it to produce vitamin D.

**Learning Objectives:**

- Be able to explain that ozone is continuously being formed and broken down in the stratosphere by the action of ultraviolet radiation.

- Using the chemical equilibrium $O_2 + O \rightleftharpoons O_3$:
  (i) be able to describe and explain how the concentration of ozone is maintained in the ozone layer, including the role of ultraviolet radiation.
  (ii) be able to outline the role of ozone in the absorption of harmful ultraviolet radiation and the essential benefit of this process for life on Earth.

- Understand that radicals, e.g. from CFCs, and $NO_x$ from thunderstorms or aircraft, may catalyse the breakdown of ozone.

**Specification Reference 2.4.1**

**Tip:** A free radical is a particle with an unpaired electron — see page 130 for more.

**Tip:** If you don't get enough sunlight, you won't produce enough vitamin D. This results in a disease known as rickets — so make sure you take a break from studying to enjoy the sunshine.

# Ozone depletion

In the 1970s and 1980s, scientists discovered that the ozone layer above Antarctica was getting thinner — in fact, it was decreasing very rapidly (see figure 2 and 3). The ozone layer over the Arctic has been found to be thinning too. These 'holes' in the ozone layer are bad because they allow more harmful UVB radiation to reach the Earth.

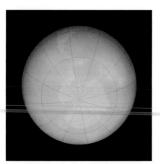

*Figure 2: Satellite image of the ozone layer over Antarctica in 1979.*

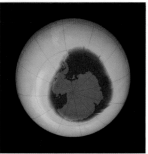

*Figure 3: Satellite image of the ozone layer over Antarctica in 2010. The purple shows the 'hole' in the ozone layer, where the concentration of ozone is much lower than it should be.*

## Chlorofluorocarbons

One of the causes of ozone break down are **chlorofluorocarbons** (CFCs). CFCs were used a lot in fridges, aerosol cans, air-conditioning and dry cleaning until scientists realised they were destroying the ozone layer. CFCs absorb UV radiation and undergo homolytic fission (see page 130) to form chlorine **free radicals**. For example:

$$CF_3Cl \xrightarrow{h\nu} CF_3\bullet + Cl\bullet$$

These free radicals destroy ozone molecules and are then regenerated to destroy more ozone. One chlorine atom can destroy 10 000 ozone molecules before it forms a stable compound.

Due to their ozone-depleting properties, CFCs were banned under the Montreal Protocol and CFCs have now been replaced in many applications. But there is still concern about ozone depletion because:

- CFCs take a long time to reach the stratosphere and have a very long residence time, so CFCs released before the ban will still be causing damage.
- CFCs are still being used in some countries that did not sign up to the Montreal Protocol.
- There are other substances besides CFCs which have ozone depleting properties that are still being used.

## Nitrogen monoxide free radicals

$NO\bullet$ free radicals from nitrogen oxides destroy ozone too — nitrogen oxides are produced by car and aircraft engines and thunderstorms. There are a few different oxides of nitrogen (e.g. $NO$, $NO_2$) but they can all be referred to as $NO_x$. $NO\bullet$ free radicals affect ozone in the same way as chlorine radicals.

## Equations for ozone depletion

The reactions of free radicals with ozone can be represented by equations, where R represents a free radical, e.g. $Cl\bullet$ or $NO\bullet$.

First the radical reacts with ozone to form an oxide and oxygen:

$$R + O_3 \rightarrow RO + O_2$$

The oxide then reacts with $O\bullet$ radicals, which are formed when UV light breaks down $O_2$. This regenerates the harmful radical which can then go on to break down more ozone.

$$RO + O\bullet \rightarrow R + O_2$$

Because the free-radical is regenerated at the end of the reaction, it effectively acts as a catalyst for the destruction of the ozone. The overall equation for this reaction is:

$$O_3 + O\bullet \rightarrow 2O_2$$

You can use these equations to show how any free radical reacts with ozone.

**Tip:** $NO\bullet$ and $Cl\bullet$ aren't the only culprits — free radicals are produced from other halogenoalkanes too.

**Exam Tip**
You could be asked about the reactions of free-radicals other than $NO\bullet$ and $Cl\bullet$ in the exam. Don't be put off though — you can use the same general equations.

**Exam Tip**
You need to know these equations for the exam — they come up a lot. So make sure you learn them off by heart.

## Examples

Here are the equations to show how Cl• free radicals react with ozone:

$$Cl\bullet + O_3 \rightarrow ClO + O_2$$
$$ClO + O\bullet \rightarrow Cl\bullet + O_2$$

And this is how NO• radicals react with ozone:

$$NO\bullet + O_3 \rightarrow NO_2 + O_2$$
$$NO_2 + O\bullet \rightarrow NO\bullet + O_2$$

For both these examples, the overall equation for the reaction is:

$$O_3 + O\bullet \rightarrow 2O_2$$

**Figure 4:** *A research station in Antarctica used to study the ozone layer.*

## Practice Question — Application

Q1 CFCs are the main cause of ozone depletion but many other chemicals, including bromotrifluoromethane ($CF_3Br$), also damage the ozone layer. Bromine radicals react with ozone in a similar way to chlorine radicals.

a) Suggest how bromine radicals could be formed from bromotrifluoromethane.

b) Write equations to show how bromine radicals would react with ozone.

c) Write an equation for the overall reaction that would occur when bromine radicals react with ozone.

## Practice Questions — Fact Recall

Q1 What is the chemical formula of ozone?

Q2 Where in the atmosphere is most of Earth's ozone found?

Q3 a) Write equations to show how ozone is formed from oxygen in the atmosphere.

b) What type of radiation is needed to form ozone?

c) This type of radiation can also degrade ozone. Write an equation for this degradation.

Q4 Explain why the ozone layer is important to life on Earth.

Q5 a) What does CFC stand for?

b) Give three uses of CFCs.

c) Explain why CFCs were banned under the Montreal Protocol.

Q6 a) Write equations to show how free radicals react with ozone (using R to represent a free radical).

b) Identify two types of free radical which are contributing to ozone depletion.

- For carbon monoxide, oxides of nitrogen and unburnt hydrocarbons:
  (i) be able to explain their formation from the internal combustion engine.
  (ii) be able to state the environmental concerns from their toxicity and contribution to low-level ozone and photochemical smog.
- Be able to outline how a catalytic converter decreases carbon monoxide and nitrogen monoxide emissions from internal combustion engines by:
  (i) adsorption of CO and NO to the catalyst surface.
  (ii) chemical reaction.
  (iii) desorption of $CO_2$ and $N_2$ from the catalyst surface.
- Be able to outline the use of infrared spectroscopy in monitoring air pollution.

**Specification Reference 2.4.1**

**Tip:** Incomplete combustion reactions can produce unburnt carbon (soot) and small amounts of carbon dioxide as well as carbon monoxide.

*Figure 1: Photochemical smog over Hong Kong.*

# 4. Air Pollution

*Unfortunately, the depletion of the ozone by CFCs isn't the only air pollution problem we need to worry about. There are other types of air pollution too...*

## Carbon monoxide pollution

Fuels from crude oil are used all the time, for things such as transport and in power stations. When pure alkanes burn completely, all you get is carbon dioxide and water. But if there's not enough oxygen, hydrocarbons combust incompletely, and you get carbon monoxide gas produced instead of carbon dioxide.

---
**Examples**

Here's the equation for **incomplete combustion** of methane:

$$CH_{4\,(g)} + 1\tfrac{1}{2}O_{2\,(g)} \rightarrow CO_{(g)} + 2H_2O_{(g)}$$

And here's how carbon monoxide forms when octane burns without enough oxygen:

$$C_8H_{18\,(g)} + 8\tfrac{1}{2}O_{2\,(g)} \rightarrow 8CO_{(g)} + 9H_2O_{(g)}$$

---

This can happen in internal combustion engines (as used in most cars on the planet), which is bad news — carbon monoxide gas is poisonous. Carbon monoxide molecules bind to the same sites on haemoglobin molecules in red blood cells as oxygen molecules. So oxygen can't be carried around the body.

## Other pollutants

Carbon monoxide's not the only pollutant gas that comes out of a car exhaust — other pollutants are released too. For example:

- Engines don't burn all the fuel molecules. Some of these come out as unburnt hydrocarbons.
- Oxides of nitrogen ($NO_x$) are produced when the high pressure and temperature in a car engine cause the nitrogen and oxygen atoms in the air to react together.

Oxides of nitrogen don't just contribute to the breaking down of the ozone layer. The hydrocarbons and nitrogen oxides react with sunlight to form ground-level ozone ($O_3$), which is a major component of smog. Specifically, it's part of **photochemical smog** — the dangerous chemicals that form when certain pollutant gases react with sunlight.

Ground-level ozone irritates people's eyes, aggravates respiratory problems and even damages our lungs (ozone isn't very nice stuff, unless it is high up in the atmosphere as part of the ozone layer). Luckily, carbon monoxide, unburnt hydrocarbons and oxides of nitrogen can be removed by catalytic converters on cars.

## Catalytic converters

**Catalytic converters** sit quietly in a car exhaust and get rid of pollutant gases like carbon monoxide, oxides of nitrogen and unburnt hydrocarbons by changing them to harmless gases, like water vapour and nitrogen, or to less harmful ones like carbon dioxide.

Solid heterogeneous catalysts can provide a surface for a reaction to take place on. Here's how it works:

- Reactant molecules arrive at the surface and bond with the solid catalyst. This is called **adsorption**.
- The bonds between the reactant's atoms are weakened and break up. This forms radicals. These radicals then get together and make new molecules.
- The new molecules are then detached from the catalyst. This is called **desorption**.

**Tip:** Most catalytic converters use rhodium, palladium or platinum as a catalyst.

**Tip:** A heterogenous catalyst is one that is in a different phase to the reactants.

--- Example ---

Here's how a catalytic converter changes the harmful gases nitrogen monoxide, NO, and carbon monoxide, CO, to nitrogen and carbon dioxide.

1. Adsorption of NO and CO to the catalyst.

2. A chemical reaction takes place and $N_2$ and $CO_2$ are formed.

3. Desorption of $N_2$ and $CO_2$ from the catalyst.

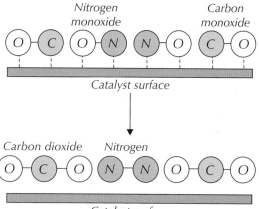

The overall equation for this reaction is:

$$2CO + 2NO \rightarrow 2CO_2 + N_2$$

**Tip:** Don't get the terms absorption and adsorption mixed up.

Absorption is when something is incorporated into something else.

Adsorption is when something just sticks to the surface of something else.

When the reactant molecules adsorb to the surface of the catalyst, the adsorption mustn't be too strong or the catalyst won't let go of the atoms after the reaction has taken place. However, the adsorption needs to be strong enough to weaken the bonds between the reactant molecules so that the new molecules can form. So a very precise strength of adsorption is needed for catalytic converters to work properly.

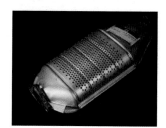

***Figure 2:*** *A catalytic converter.*

# Monitoring air pollution

You can use **infrared (IR) spectroscopy** to measure how much of a polluting gas is present in the air. Here's an outline of how infrared spectroscopy is used to check how much carbon monoxide there is:

- A sample of air is drawn into the spectrometer. A beam of infrared radiation of a certain frequency is passed through the sample. Any carbon monoxide that is present will absorb some of this radiation.
- At the same time, a beam of infrared radiation of the same frequency is passed through a sample of a gas that doesn't absorb any infrared, like $N_2$. This acts as a kind of control reading.
- The difference in the amount of infrared energy absorbed by the gases in the two chambers is a measure of the amount of carbon monoxide present in the air sample.

**Tip:** If you've forgotten what infrared spectroscopy is, go back and look at page 167.

***Figure 3:*** *An air quality monitoring station in Israel.*

You can use the same technique to monitor the levels of any polluting gas that can absorb infrared, like NO, $SO_2$ or $CH_4$. Only molecules containing at least two different atoms will absorb infrared radiation.

## Practice Questions — Application

**Tip:** See pages 122-123 for more on complete and incomplete combustion of alkanes.

Q1 Write equations for the following reactions:
  a) The complete combustion of ethane ($C_2H_6$).
  b) The complete combustion of butane ($C_4H_{10}$).
  c) The incomplete combustion of propane ($C_3H_8$).
  d) The incomplete combustion of pentane ($C_5H_{12}$).

Q2 When the pressure and temperature are high, nitrogen reacts with oxygen to form nitrogen dioxide ($NO_2$).
  a) Write an equation for this reaction.
  b) Where might this reaction take place?
  c) Give one reason why the release of $NO_2$ into the atmosphere is bad for the environment.

Q3 In catalytic converters, the surface area of the catalyst is as large as possible. Using your knowledge of how a catalytic converter works, explain why this is important.

**Figure 4:** The view through a catalytic converter. The mesh-like structure maximises the surface area of the catalyst.

## Practice Questions — Fact Recall

Q1 What are the products of:
  a) complete combustion?
  b) incomplete combustion?

Q2 Explain why carbon monoxide is poisonous.

Q3 Name two pollutants, other than carbon monoxide, which are produced by cars.

Q4 a) Name three pollutants that are removed from car exhausts by catalytic converters.
  b) Describe how a catalytic converter works.

Q5 Name a technique that can be used to measure how much of a polluting gas is present in the air?

# Section Summary

Make sure you know...

- That sustainable chemistry means not using up all the Earth's resources or putting loads of damaging chemicals into the environment.
- How chemists can make industrial processes more sustainable by...
  1. Ensuring that all the chemicals involved are as non-toxic as possible.
  2. Using renewable raw materials, such as plant based substances, instead of non-renewable raw materials such as crude oil fractions or metal ores.
  3. Developing renewable energy sources such as plant based fuels or solar power.
  4. Designing processes that have a high atom economy and so produce little waste.
  5. Ensuring that any products of reactions are either biodegradable or recyclable.
- That the advantages of greener chemistry can be reduced by negative side-effects (e.g. loss of farm land when growing biofuels).
- Why international cooperation is needed to tackle the problems of pollution and sustainability.
- That $H_2O$, $CO_2$ and $CH_4$ are greenhouse gases and contribute to the greenhouse effect.
- That the C=O, O–H and C–H bonds in greenhouse gases absorb infrared radiation and how this is linked to increases in temperature.
- That the contribution of a particular greenhouse gas to the greenhouse effect depends on how much radiation one molecule of the gas absorbs and the atmospheric concentration of the gas.
- That global warming is happening because the atmospheric concentration of greenhouse gases is increasing, enhancing the greenhouse effect.
- Why it is important to control global warming and the possible consequences if we don't.
- That chemists have collected data to confirm that global warming and climate change are occurring and have provided evidence to the world's governments.
- That chemists are continuing to collect data to monitor the progress of initiatives like the Kyoto protocol which aim to reduce climate change.
- What carbon capture storage (CCS) is and how it can be used to reduce waste $CO_2$ emissions.
- How ozone is continuously being formed and broken down in the stratosphere by UV radiation.
- That the concentration of ozone is maintained in the ozone layer because the rate of ozone formation is roughly the same as the rate of ozone degradation.
- That the ozone layer protects the Earth from harmful UVC and UVB rays.
- That radicals from chlorofluorcarbons (CFCs) and nitrogen oxides ($NO_x$) can catalyse the breakdown of ozone resulting in thinning of the ozone layer.
- That CFCs were once widely used but have since been banned under the Montreal Protocol due to their ozone depleting properties.
- The equations for the breakdown of ozone by free-radicals.
- That carbon monoxide is produced from the incomplete combustion of hydrocarbons in internal combustion engines (such as those found in most cars).
- Why carbon monoxide is toxic to humans.
- That unburnt hydrocarbons and nitrogen oxides ($NO_x$) are released by car exhausts and that they can react to form ground level ozone which contributes to photochemical smog.
- That carbon monoxide, unburnt hydrocarbons and nitrogen oxides are removed from car exhausts by catalytic converters.
- How a catalytic converter works — adsorption of the reactants to the surface of the catalyst, chemical reaction and desorption of the products.
- How infrared spectroscopy is used to measure how much of a polluting gas is present in the air.

# Exam-style Questions

**1**    Carbon dioxide is a greenhouse gas.  Greenhouse gases contribute to the greenhouse effect because they absorb infrared radiation.

**(a) (i)**    State which part of the carbon dioxide molecule absorbs infrared radiation.

*(1 mark)*

**(ii)**    What effect does the absorption of infrared radiation have on carbon dioxide molecules?

*(1 mark)*

**(b)**    Over the last few decades, the concentration of carbon dioxide in the atmosphere has increased dramatically, resulting in global warming.

**(i)**    Suggest two potential consequences of global warming.

*(2 marks)*

**(ii)**    Carbon capture and storage (CCS) has been suggested as a way of reducing carbon dioxide emissions.  Suggest three ways of storing carbon and preventing it from entering the atmosphere.

*(3 marks)*

**(c)**    $CO_2$ emissions are one reason why the use of fossil fuels as a source of energy is not sustainable.

**(i)**    Give another reason why the use of fossil fuels is not sustainable.

*(1 mark)*

**(ii)**    Suggest three alternative energy sources which could replace fossil fuels.

*(1 mark)*

**(iii)**    Other than developing greener energy sources, how else are chemists trying to increase sustainability in industry?

*(3 marks)*

**(d)**    Carbon dioxide is not the only greenhouse gas.  Many other gases are also contributing to the greenhouse effect and global warming.

**(i)**    Name two gases, other than carbon dioxide, which contribute to the greenhouse effect.

*(2 marks)*

**(ii)**    Suggest two factors which influence how much a particular gas contributes to the greenhouse effect.

*(2 marks)*

**2**     This question is about the ozone layer.

**(a)**    Ozone is created by UV light in the stratosphere.

**(i)**  Write equations to show how ozone ($O_3$) is formed in the stratosphere.

*(2 marks)*

**(ii)**  Without any human interference, the concentration of ozone in the stratosphere would remain roughly the same. Explain why.

*(2 marks)*

**(iii)**  Why is it important to humans that the ozone layer is maintained?

*(1 mark)*

The graph below shows the general trends in the amount of chlorine in the atmosphere and the amount of ozone in the atmosphere from 1980 to 2008.

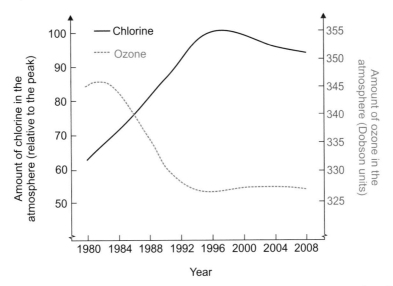

**(b)**    Between 1980 and 1996 the amount of chlorine steadily increased and the amount of ozone in the atmosphere generally decreased.

**(i)**  Name one source of chlorine free radicals.

*(1 mark)*

**(ii)**  Write equations to show how chlorine radicals react with ozone.

*(2 marks)*

**(c)**    In 1987 an international treaty known as the Montreal Protocol was signed. Under this treaty the use of the main ozone depleting substances was to be completely phased out by 1996.

**(i)**  Explain why international co-operation is needed if we are to prevent further damage to the ozone layer.

*(2 marks)*

**(ii)**  Using the information in the graph, explain whether or not the Montreal Protocol has been a successful initiative.

*(2 marks)*

**3**      Most modern cars use a type of engine known as an internal combustion engine.

**(a)**     Sometimes, combustion within an internal combustion engine is incomplete.

    **(i)**  Under what conditions does incomplete combustion occur?

*(1 mark)*

    **(ii)** Explain why incomplete combustion is potentially harmful.

*(2 marks)*

**(b)**     The high temperatures and pressures within an internal combustion engine can cause nitrogen to react with oxygen forming nitrogen monoxide (NO).

    **(i)**  Write a balanced equation to show how nitrogen monoxide is formed from nitrogen and oxygen.

*(1 mark)*

    **(ii)** Describe two negative consequences of releasing nitrogen monoxide into the atmosphere.

*(4 marks)*

**(c)**     Carbon monoxide and nitrogen monoxide are both removed from car exhausts by catalytic converters.

    **(i)**  Write a balanced equation to show how carbon monoxide and nitrogen monoxide are removed by catalytic converters.

*(1 mark)*

    **(ii)** Outline how a catalytic converter promotes this reaction.

 You should organise your answer and use correct technical terms.

*(4 marks)*

    **(iii)** Catalytic converters can be poisoned by lead. The lead binds to the surface of the catalyst. Using your knowledge of how a catalytic converter works, explain why lead poisoning decreases the efficiency of the catalytic converter.

*(1 mark)*

**(d)**     Cars fitted with catalytic converters still release gases that are harmful to the environment.

    **(i)**  Name one gas produced by catalytic converters that can have a damaging effect on the environment.

*(1 mark)*

    **(ii)** Explain why catalytic converters are still used despite producing this gas.

*(1 mark)*

# Practical Skills in Chemistry

# 1. Variables and Data

*When you're planning an experiment you need to think carefully about what things you're going to change, what things you're going to measure and how you're going to record your results.*

## Variables

You probably know this all off by heart but it's easy to get mixed up sometimes. So here's a quick recap. A **variable** is a quantity that has the potential to change, e.g. mass. There are two types of variable commonly referred to in experiments:

> **Independent variable** — the thing that you change in an experiment.

> **Dependent variable** — the thing that you measure in an experiment.

> **Tip:** When drawing graphs, the dependent variable should go on the y-axis, the independent variable on the x-axis.

> ### Example
>
> You could investigate the effect of temperature on rate of reaction using the apparatus in Figure 1 below:
>
>
>
> Thermometer — to check the temperature of the reaction mixture.
>
> Gas syringe — to measure the amount of gas given off over time.
>
> **Figure 1:** *Apparatus for measuring the rate of reaction.*
>
> - The independent variable will be temperature.
> - The dependent variable will be the amount of gas produced.
> - All the other variables must be kept the same. These include the concentration and volume of solutions, mass of solids, pressure, the presence of a catalyst and the surface area of any solid reactants.

## Types of data

Experiments always involve some sort of measurement to provide data. There are different types of data — and you need to know what they are.

### 1. Discrete data

You get discrete data by counting. E.g. the number of bubbles produced in a reaction would be discrete (see Figure 2). You can't have 1.25 bubbles. That'd be daft. Shoe size is another good example of a discrete variable.

**Figure 2:** *An acid-carbonate reaction. The number of bubbles produced is discrete data, but the volume of gas produced is continuous data.*

## 2. Continuous data

A continuous variable can have any value on a scale. For example, the volume of gas produced or the mass of products from a reaction. You can never measure the exact value of a continuous variable.

## 3. Categoric data

A categoric variable has values that can be sorted into categories. For example, the colours of solutions might be blue, red and green (see Figure 3). Or types of material might be wood, steel, glass.

## 4. Ordered (ordinal) data

Ordered data is similar to categoric, but the categories can be put in order. For example, if you classify reactions as 'slow', 'fairly fast' and 'very fast' you'd have ordered data.

***Figure 3:*** *Different coloured solutions. Colour is a type of categoric data.*

# Tables of data

Before you start your experiment, make a table to write your results in. You'll need to **repeat** each test at least three times to check your results are reliable (see page 225 for more on reliable results). Figure 4 (below) is the sort of table you might end up with when you investigate the effect of temperature on reaction rate. (You'd then have to do the same for different temperatures.)

**Tip:** To find the average of each set of repeated measurements you need to add them all up and divide by how many there are.

For example, for the average volume of gas evolved after 10 s, it's:

$8 + 7 + 8 \div 3 = 7.7$ cm$^3$

| Temperature | Time (s) | Volume of gas evolved (cm³) Run 1 | Volume of gas evolved (cm³) Run 2 | Volume of gas evolved (cm³) Run 3 | Average volume of gas evolved (cm³) |
|---|---|---|---|---|---|
| 20 °C | 10 | 8 | 7 | 8 | **7.7** |
| | 20 | 17 | 19 | 20 | **18.7** |
| | 30 | 28 | 20 | 30 | **29** |

***Figure 4:*** *Table of results showing the effect of temperature on the rate of reaction.*

Watch out for **anomalous results**. These are ones that don't fit in with the other values and are likely to be wrong. They're usually due to random errors, such as making a mistake when measuring. You should ignore anomalous results when you calculate averages.

**Tip:** Just because you ignore anomalous results in your calculations you shouldn't ignore them in your write-up. Try to find an explanation for what went wrong so that it can be avoided in future experiments.

---

**Example**

Look at the table in Figure 4 again — the volume of gas evolved after 30 s in Run 2 looks like it might be an anomalous result. It's much lower than the values in the other two runs. It could have been caused by the syringe plunger getting stuck.

The anomalous result has been ignored when the average was calculated — that's why the average volume of gas evolved after 30 s is 29 cm$^3$ ((28 + 30) ÷ 2 = 29), rather than 26 cm$^3$ ((28 + 20 +30) ÷ 3 = 26).

---

# 2. Graphs and Charts

*You'll usually be expected to make a graph of your results. Graphs make your data easier to understand — so long as you choose the right type.*

## Types of graphs and charts

### Bar charts

You should use a bar chart when one of your data sets is categoric or ordered data, like in Figure 1.

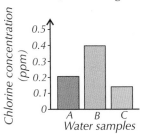

*Figure 1:* Bar chart to show chlorine concentration in water samples.

### Pie charts

Pie charts are normally used to display categoric data, like in Figure 2.

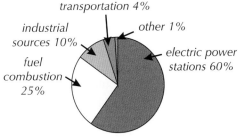

*Figure 2:* Pie chart to show sources of a country's sulfur dioxide emissions.

### Line Graphs

Line graphs are best when you have two sets of continuous data, like in Figure 3. Volume of gas and time are both continuous variables — you could get any value on the x or y-axis.

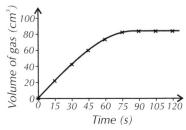

*Figure 3:* Line graph to show volume of gas evolved against time.

### Scatter graphs

Scatter graphs, like Figure 4, are great for showing how two sets of data are related (or correlated — see below for more on correlation). Don't try to join all the points — draw a line of best fit to show the trend.

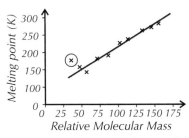

*Figure 4:* Scatter graph showing the relationship between $M_r$ and melting point of some alcohols.

> **Tip:** Use simple scales when you draw graphs — this'll make it easier to plot points.

> **Tip:** Whatever type of graph you make, you'll only get full marks if you:
>
> 1. Choose a sensible scale — don't do a tiny graph in the corner of the paper.
>
> 2. Label both axes — including units.
>
> 3. Plot your points accurately — using a sharp pencil.

> **Tip:** A line of best fit should have about half of the points above it and half of the points below. You can ignore any anomalous points like the one circled in Figure 4.

## Scatter graphs and correlation

Correlation describes the relationship between two variables — usually the independent one and the dependent one. Data can show positive correlation, negative correlation or no correlation (see Figure 5).

### Positive correlation

As one variable increases the other also increases.

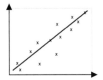

### Negative correlation

As one variable increases the other decreases.

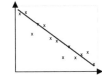

### No correlation

There is no relationship between the variables.

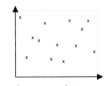

*Figure 5:* Scatter graphs showing positive, negative and no correlation.

> **Tip:** Computers can make it a lot quicker to collect, record and analyse big sets of data from experiments — but you've still got to understand what all the numbers and graphs they churn out mean.

# 3. Conclusions and Evaluations

*Once you've got your results nicely presented in graphical form you can start to draw a conclusion. But be careful — you may have a graph showing a lovely correlation, but that doesn't always tell you as much as you might think.*

## Correlation and cause

Ideally, only two quantities would ever change in any experiment — everything else would remain constant. But in experiments or studies outside the lab, you can't usually control all the variables. So even if two variables are correlated, the change in one may not be causing the change in the other. Both changes might be caused be a third variable.

┌─ **Example** ─────────────────

Some studies have found a correlation between drinking chlorinated tap water and the risk of developing certain cancers. So some people argue that this means water shouldn't have chlorine added. But it's hard to control all the variables between people who drink tap water and people who don't. It could be many lifestyle factors. Or, the cancer risk could be affected by something else in tap water — or by whatever the non-tap water drinkers drink instead.

## Drawing conclusions

The data should always support the conclusion. This may sound obvious but it's easy to jump to conclusions. Conclusions have to be specific — not make sweeping generalisations.

┌─ **Example** ─────────────────

The rate of an enzyme-controlled reaction was measured at 10 °C, 20 °C, 30 °C, 40 °C, 50 °C and 60 °C. All other variables were kept constant, and the results are shown in Figure 1.

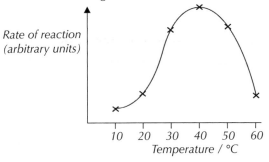

**Figure 1:** *Graph to show the effect of temperature on the rate of an enzyme-controlled reaction.*

A science magazine concluded from this data that enzyme X works best at 40 °C. The data doesn't support this. The enzyme could work best at 42 °C or 47 °C but you can't tell from the data because increases of 10 °C at a time were used. The rate of reaction at in-between temperatures wasn't measured. All you know is that it's faster at 40 °C than at any of the other temperatures tested.

Also, the experiment only gives information about this particular enzyme-controlled reaction. You can't conclude that all enzyme-controlled reactions happen faster at a particular temperature — only this one. And you can't say for sure that doing the experiment at, say, a different constant pressure, wouldn't give a different optimum temperature.

# Evaluations

There are a few terms that you need to understand. They'll be useful when you're evaluating how convincing your results are.

### 1. Valid results

Valid results answer the original question, using reliable data. For example, if you haven't controlled all the variables your results won't be valid, because you won't be testing just the thing you wanted to.

### 2. Accurate results

Accurate results are those that are really close to the true answer.

### 3. Precise results

These are results taken using sensitive instruments that measure in small increments.

> **Example**
>
> A pH measured with a meter (pH 7.692) will be more precise than pH measured with paper (pH 7).

**Tip:** It's possible for results to be precise but not accurate, e.g. a balance that weighs to 1/1000th of a gram will give precise results, but if it's not calibrated properly the results won't be accurate.

### 4. Reliable results

Reliable means the results can be consistently reproduced in independent experiments. And if the results are reproducible they're more likely to be true. If the data isn't reliable for whatever reason you can't draw a valid conclusion. For experiments, the more repeats you do, the more reliable the data. If you get the same result twice, it could be the correct answer. But if you get the same result 20 times, it'd be much more reliable. And it'd be even more reliable if everyone in the class got about the same results using different apparatus.

**Tip:** Part of the scientific process (see pages 1-4) involves other scientists repeating your experiment too — then if they get the same results you can be more certain they're reliable.

### 5. Percentage error

You may have to calculate the percentage error of a measurement. If you know the precision that the measuring equipment is calibrated to, just divide this by the measurement taken and multiply by 100, as shown below.

**Tip:** You should always choose appropriate measuring equipment for the precision you need to work with.

> **Example**
>
> A balance is calibrated to within 0.1 g, and you measure a mass as 4 g.
>
> The percentage error is: $(0.1 \div 4) \times 100 = 2.5\%$.
>
> Using a larger quantity reduces the percentage error —
> a mass of 40 g has a percentage error of: $(0.1 \div 40) \times 100 = 0.25\%$.

Most measuring equipment has the precision it's calibrated to written on it. Where it doesn't, you can usually use the scale as a guide (e.g. if a measuring cylinder has a 1 ml scale, it is probably calibrated to within 0.5 ml).

**Tip:** After evaluating your results, you can suggest improvements to the experiment — e.g. use more precise equipment or repeat the experiment more times.

# Risks, hazards and ethical considerations

In any experiment you'll be expected to show that you've thought about the risks and hazards. It's generally a good thing to wear an apron and goggles, but you may need to take additional safety measures, depending on the experiment. For example, anything involving nasty gases will need to be done in a fume cupboard.

You need to make sure you're working ethically too. This is most important if there are other people or animals involved. You have to put their welfare first.

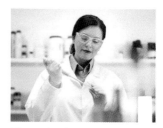

***Figure 2:*** *A scientist wearing protective clothing.*

# 1. Exam Structure and Technique

*Passing exams isn't all about revision — it really helps if you know how the exam is structured and have got your exam technique nailed so that you pick up every mark you can.*

**Exam Tip**
Make sure you have a good read through of this exam structure. It might not seem important now but you don't want to get any nasty surprises just before an exam.

## Exam structure

For OCR AS-Level Chemistry you're gonna have to sit through two exams (Unit F321 and Unit F322) and complete an internal assessment (Unit F323). This book covers Unit F321 in Unit 1 and F322 in Unit 2.

**AS-Level Chemistry**

*This is covered in Unit 1 in this book.*

**Exam Tip**
Both of the written exams (units F321 and F322) will have a mixture of short answer and long answer questions. Short answer questions are broken down into lots of parts but they can still be worth loads of marks overall.

| Unit F321 Atoms, Bonds and Groups | Unit F322 Chains, Energy and Resources | Unit F323 Practical Skills in Chemistry |
|---|---|---|

*This is covered in Unit 2 in this book.*

| Exam Length: 1 hour Marks: 60 Worth: 30% | Exam Length: 1 hour 45 mins Marks: 100 Worth: 50% | Practical skills assessment Marks: 40 Worth: 20% |
|---|---|---|

### Unit F323 — Practical skills in Chemistry 1

You'll do this unit in school with your teacher. It'll test your understanding of chemistry and your ability to plan, carry out and evaluate experiments in the lab. It's worth 20% of your total AS-Level.

The assessments in Unit F323 test that you can demonstrate safe and skilful practical techniques, make and record suitable observations, take measurements with precision and accuracy, correctly record data and analyse, interpret and evaluate your experiment. This may sound a bit menacing but there's some stuff on pages 221-225 to help you out.

***Figure 1:*** *Chemistry lesson — that guy at the back is totally checking out that girl.*

## Quality of written communication (QWC)

All of the units you take for AS-Level Chemistry will have a quality of written communication element — this means that the examiner will assess your ability to write properly.

This may seem like a bit of a drag but you will lose marks if you don't do it. You need to make sure that:

- your scribble, sorry, writing is legible,
- your spelling, punctuation and grammar are accurate,
- your writing style is appropriate,
- you organise your answer clearly and coherently,
- you use specialist scientific vocabulary where it's appropriate.

In your F321 and F322 exams certain questions will be designated as QWC questions — they'll be the ones with a nice picture of a pencil (see Figure 2) next to them. On these questions make sure you write in full sentences and check your spelling — you don't want to lose marks for something as simple as spelling 'electrons' incorrectly.

*Figure 2: A picture of a pencil next to a question means that you'll be assessed on the quality of your written communication in your answer.*

## Time management

This is one of the most important exam skills to have. How long you spend on each question is really important in an exam — it could make all the difference to your grade. Some questions will require lots of work for only a few marks but other questions will be much quicker. Don't spend ages struggling with questions that are only worth a couple of marks — move on. You can come back to them later when you've bagged loads of other marks elsewhere.

> ### Example
>
> The questions below are both worth the same number of marks but require different amounts of work.
>
> **1 (a)** Define the term 'standard enthalpy change of combustion'.
>
> *(2 marks)*
>
> **2 (a)** Draw a structural isomer of molecule **B** and state the type of structural isomerism it shows.
>
> *(2 marks)*
>
> Question 1 (a) only requires you to write down a definition — if you can remember it this shouldn't take you too long.
>
> Question 2 (a) requires you to draw an isomer and then work out what type of isomer it is — this may take you a lot longer than writing down a definition, especially if you have to draw out a few structures before getting it right.
>
> So, if you're running out of time it makes sense to do questions like 1(a) first and come back to 2 (a) if you've got time at the end.

**Exam Tip**
Everyone has their own method of getting through the exam. Some people find it easier to go through the paper question by question and some people like to do the questions they find easiest first. The most important thing is to find out the way that suits you best <u>before</u> the exam — that means doing all the practice exams you can before the big day.

**Exam Tip**
Don't forget to go back and do any questions that you left the first time round — you don't want to miss out on marks because you forgot to do the question.

## Calculations

There's no getting away from those pesky calculation questions — they come up a lot in AS-Level Chemistry. The most important thing to remember is to show your working. You've probably heard it a million times before but it makes perfect sense — it only takes a few seconds more to write down what's in your head and it'll stop you from making silly errors and losing out on easy marks. You won't get a mark for a wrong answer but you could get marks for the method you used to work out the answer.

**Exam Tip**
It's so easy to mis-type numbers into a calculator when you're under pressure in an exam. Always double check your calculations and make sure the answer looks sensible.

## Units

Make sure you always give the correct units for your answer (see pages 232-233 for more on units).

**Exam Tip**
You'll need to know what units your figures need to be in for different formulas — see page 231 for the units used in different formulas and pages 232-233 for how to convert between units.

> **Example**
>
> Here's an example of a question where you need to change the units so they match the answer the examiner wants.
>
> **1**    A student measures the enthalpy change of reaction **A**. The temperature of the water increased by 2 °C during the reaction.
>
>     **(a)** Calculate the heat given out in the reaction in kJ.
>
> *(2 marks)*
>
> When you use $q = mc\Delta T$ to calculate the heat given out you'll get an answer in joules. Make sure you convert the units to kilojoules by dividing by 1000.

## Significant figures

Use the number of significant figures given in the question as a guide for how many to give in the answer. You should always give your answer to the lowest number of significant figures (s.f.) given in the question — if you're really unsure, write down the full answer and then round it to 3 s.f.. It always helps to write down the number of significant figures you've rounded to after your answer — it shows the examiner you really know what you're talking about.

> **Examples**
>
> In this question the data given to you is a good indication of how many significant figures you should give your answer to.
>
> **1**  **(b)** Calculate the enthalpy change measured by the student in kJ mol$^{-1}$. (The specific heat capacity of water is 4.18 J g$^{-1}$ K$^{-1}$).
>
> *(2 marks)*
>
> The data in the question is given to 3 s.f. so it makes sense to give your answer to 3 s.f. too. But sometimes it isn't as clear as that.
>
> **3**  **(b)** 13.5 cm$^3$ of a 0.51 M solution of sodium hydroxide reacts with 1.5 M hydrochloric acid. Calculate the volume of hydrochloric acid required to neutralise the sodium hydroxide.
>
> *(2 marks)*
>
> There are two types of data in this question, volume data and concentration data. The volume data is given to 3 s.f. and the concentration data is given to 2 s.f.. You should always give your answer to the lowest number of significant figures given — in this case that's to 2 s.f.. The answer in full is 4.59 cm$^3$ so the answer rounded correctly would be 4.6 cm$^3$ (2 s.f.).

## Standard form

You might be asked to give your answer in standard form. Standard form is used for writing very big or very small numbers in a more convenient way. Standard form must always look like this:

*This number must always be between 1 and 10.* ⟶ $A \times 10^n$ ⟵ *This number is the number of places the decimal point moves.*

## Examples

Here's how to write 3 500 000 in standard form.

- First write the non-zero digits with a decimal point after the first number and a '× 10' after it:

$$3.5 \times 10$$

- Then count how many places the decimal point has moved to the left. This number sits to the top right of the 10.

$$3\,500\,000 = 3.5 \times 10^6$$

- Et voilà... that's 3 500 000 written in standard form.

Here are some more examples.

- You can write 450 000 as $4.5 \times 10^5$.

- The number 0.000056 is $5.6 \times 10^{-5}$ in standard form — the n is negative because the decimal point has moved to the right instead of the left.

**Tip:** Your calculator might give you your answer in standard form already — result.

**Tip:** These examples give the answer to 2 s.f. In the exam, if you're asked to give your answer to 3 s.f. then you'll need to include an extra digit after the decimal point. For example 3 500 000 would become $3.50 \times 10^6$.

# Diagrams

When you're asked to draw diagrams or mechanisms in an exam it's important that you draw everything correctly.

## Examples

### Drawing organic reaction mechanisms

When you're drawing organic reaction mechanisms the curly arrows must come from either a lone pair of electrons or from a bond, like this:

The mechanisms below are incorrect — you wouldn't get marks for them:

*You won't get marks if the curly arrows come from atoms, like this...*  or this...

You show the movement of an electron pair with a full curly arrow — don't use half arrows, it's just plain wrong...

**Tip:** It's important that the curly arrows come from a lone pair or a bond because that's where the electrons are found. Remember, curly arrows are supposed to show the movement of electrons.

**Exam Tip**
Make sure that you draw carbocations with a full positive charge (+) and dipoles clearly as dipoles ($\delta+$) — you will lose marks in the exam if it's not clear which you mean.

### Drawing displayed formulas

If a question asks you for a displayed formula you have to show all of the bonds and all of the atoms in the molecule. That means you have to draw displayed formulas like this:

And not like this:

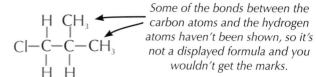

*Some of the bonds between the carbon atoms and the hydrogen atoms haven't been shown, so it's not a displayed formula and you wouldn't get the marks.*

If you're not asked specifically for a displayed formula then either of the diagrams above will do. Just make sure that the bonds are always drawn between the right atoms. For example, ethanol should be drawn like this:

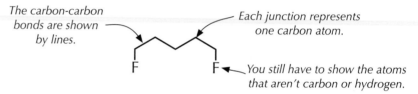

And not like this:

*It's the oxygen atom that's bonded to the carbon, not the hydrogen, so drawing it like this is just plain wrong.*

### Drawing skeletal formulas

There's a pretty good chance that you'll have to draw skeletal formulas in your exam so you need to be able to draw them properly. Bonds between carbon atoms are shown by a line and carbon atoms are found at each end. Atoms that aren't carbon or hydrogen have to be drawn on:

*The carbon-carbon bonds are shown by lines.*

*Each junction represents one carbon atom.*

*You still have to show the atoms that aren't carbon or hydrogen.*

You don't draw any carbon or hydrogen atoms from the main carbon chain when you're drawing skeletal formulas, so the diagrams below are both wrong.

*You don't show the carbon atoms or the hydrogen atoms.*

### Drawing hydrogen bonding

Drawing hydrogen bonds is a common exam question. You need to know how to draw them properly to pick up all the marks you can.

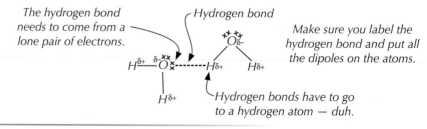

*The hydrogen bond needs to come from a lone pair of electrons.*

*Hydrogen bond*

*Make sure you label the hydrogen bond and put all the dipoles on the atoms.*

*Hydrogen bonds have to go to a hydrogen atom — duh.*

When you're drawing any diagram make sure it's really clear what you're drawing. A small scribble in the bottom corner of a page isn't going to show enough detail to get you the marks. Draw the diagrams nice and big, but make sure that you stay within the space given for that answer.

# 2. Formulas and Equations

*There's quite a lot of mathsy type stuff in the exams, and a whole load of formulas that you need to learn to make sure that you get it all right. Luckily, here's a nice page with them all neatly summarised for you. Enjoy.*

## Unit 1 Formulas

First up is a really important equation that it's easy to forget about:

$$\text{Number of moles} = \frac{\text{Number of particles you have}}{\text{Number of particles in a mole}}$$

Here is perhaps the most useful equation of all...

$$\text{Number of moles} = \frac{\text{Mass of substance}}{\text{Molar mass}} \qquad \text{also written as... } n = \frac{m}{M_r}$$

**Tip:** $M_r$ is relative molecular mass (or relative formula mass). You work it out by adding up all the $A_r$s (atomic masses) of all the atoms in the compound.

You'll need these ones when you're dealing with solutions...

$$\text{Number of moles} = \frac{\text{Concentration} \times \text{Volume (in cm}^3)}{1000}$$

$$\text{Number of moles} = \text{Concentration} \times \text{Volume (in dm}^3)$$

...and these when you've got gases at room temperature and pressure.

$$\text{Number of moles} = \frac{\text{Volume (in dm}^3)}{24} \qquad \text{Number of moles} = \frac{\text{Volume (in cm}^3)}{24\,000}$$

**Tip:** In the formula for working out the number of moles of a gas, the "24" comes from the fact that at room temperature and pressure one mole of any gas occupies 24 dm³. See page 18 for more on this.

## Unit 2 Formulas

Here are some equations that will help you out with practical chemistry...

$$\%\text{ yield} = \frac{\text{Actual yield}}{\text{Theoretical yield}} \times 100\%$$

$$\text{atom economy} = \frac{\text{Molecular mass of desired product}}{\text{Sum of molecular masses of all products}} \times 100\%$$

**Exam Tip**
You'll have to learn all the Unit 1 formulas for your Unit 2 exam too.

There are two formulas you need to calculate enthalpy changes of a reaction. Here's one:

$$q = mc\Delta T$$
(g) (K or °C) (J) (J g⁻¹K⁻¹)

*It doesn't matter whether the temperature is in K or °C — it's the change in temperature that goes into the formula, and that will be the same no matter what the units are.*

And the slightly easier:

$$\text{Enthalpy change of reaction} = \text{Total energy absorbed} - \text{Total energy released}$$

**Exam Tip**
All these formulas are really important — you have to learn them because they won't be given to you in the exam. Make sure you can rearrange them all and give the units of each formula too.

# 3. Units

*Units can trip you up if you're not sure which ones to use or how to convert between them. Here are the ones you're likely to have to deal with.*

## Volume

Volume can be measured in $m^3$, $dm^3$ and $cm^3$.

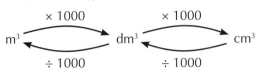

**Exam Tip**
You need to practice these conversions until you're sick of them. It'll save you loads of time in the exam if you're confident changing between units.

**Tip:** Standard form (that's showing numbers as, for example, $6 \times 10^{-3}$) is covered on pages 228-229.

--- Examples ---

**Write 6 $dm^3$ in $m^3$ and $cm^3$.**

First, to convert 6 $dm^3$ into $m^3$ you need to divide by 1000.
$$6 \text{ dm}^3 \div 1000 = 0.006 \text{ m}^3 = 6 \times 10^{-3} \text{ m}^3$$

Then, to convert 6 $dm^3$ into $cm^3$ you need to multiply by 1000.
$$6 \text{ dm}^3 \times 1000 = 6000 \text{ cm}^3 = 6 \times 10^3 \text{ m}^3$$

**Write 0.4 $cm^3$ in $dm^3$ and $m^3$.**

First, to convert 0.4 $cm^3$ into $dm^3$ you need to divide by 1000.
$$0.4 \text{ cm}^3 \div 1000 = 0.0004 \text{ dm}^3 = 4 \times 10^{-4} \text{ dm}^3$$

Then, to convert 0.0004 $dm^3$ into $m^3$ you need to divide by 1000.
$$0.0004 \text{ dm}^3 \div 1000 = 0.0000004 \text{ m}^3 = 4 \times 10^{-7} \text{ m}^3$$

## Temperature

Temperature can be measured in K and °C.

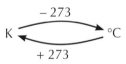

--- Examples ---

**Write 21 °C in Kelvin.**

To convert 21 °C into K you need to add 273:
$$21 \text{ °C} + 273 = 294 \text{ K}$$

**Write 298 K in °C.**

To convert 298 K into °C you need to subtract 273:
$$298 \text{ K} - 273 = 25 \text{ °C}$$

**Figure 1:** *A calculator. In an exam your brain can turn to mush and you can forget how to do the most simple maths. Don't be afraid to put every calculation into the calculator (even if it's just $2 \times 10$). If it stops you making mistakes then it's worth it.*

## Mass

Mass can be measured in kg and g.

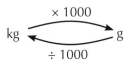

**Write 4.6 kg in g.**

To convert 4.6 kg into g you need to multiply by 1000.

$$4.6 \text{ kg} \times 1000 = 4600 \text{ g}$$

**Write 320 g in kg.**

To convert 320 g into kg you need to divide by 1000.

$$320 \text{ g} \div 1000 = 0.32 \text{ kg}$$

# Energy

Energy can be measured in kJ and J.

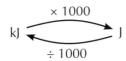

┌─ Examples ─────────────────

**Write 56 kJ in J.**

To convert 56 kJ into J you need to multiply by 1000.

$$56 \text{ kJ} \times 1000 = 56\,000 \text{ J} = 5.6 \times 10^4 \text{ J}$$

**Write 48 000 J in kJ.**

To convert 48 000 J into kJ you need to divide by 1000.

$$48\,000 \text{ J} \div 1000 = 48 \text{ kJ}$$

# Concentration

Concentration can be measured in mol dm$^{-3}$ (M) and mol cm$^{-3}$.

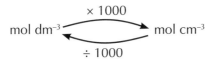

┌─ Examples ─────────────────

**Write 0.2 mol dm$^{-3}$ in mol cm$^{-3}$.**

To convert 0.2 mol dm$^{-3}$ into mol cm$^{-3}$ you need to multiply by 1000.

$$0.2 \text{ mol dm}^{-3} \times 1000 = 200 \text{ mol cm}^{-3}$$

**Write 34 mol cm$^{-3}$ in mol dm$^{-3}$.**

To convert 34 mol cm$^{-3}$ into mol dm$^{-3}$ you need to divide by 1000.

$$34 \text{ mol cm}^{-3} \div 1000 = 0.034 \text{ mol dm}^{-3}$$

Life gets a bit confusing if you have to do lots of calculations one after the other — sometimes it can be difficult to keep track of your units.
To avoid this, always write down the units you're using with each line of the calculation. Then when you get to the end you know what units to give with your answer.

# 4. The Periodic Table — Facts and Trends

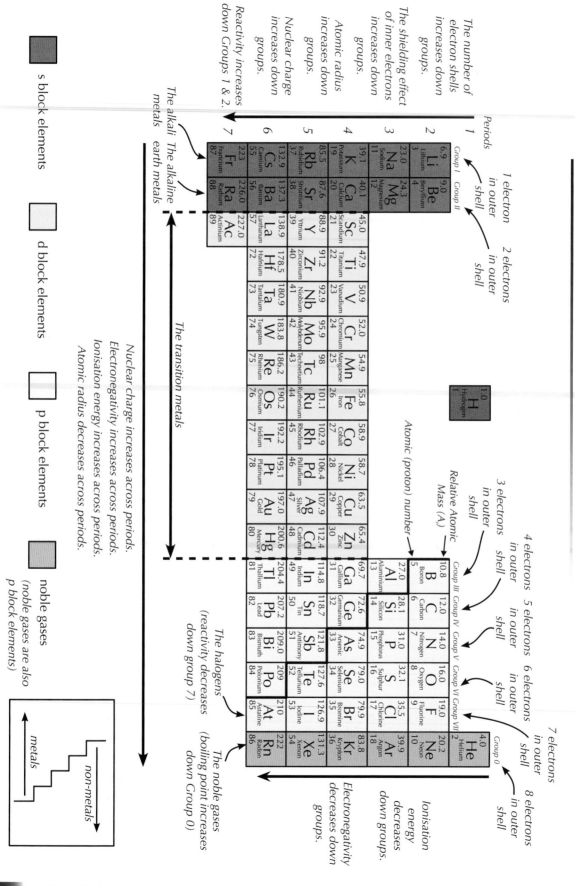

# Answers

## Module 1: Atoms and Reactions

### 1. The Atom
#### Page 7 — Application Questions
Q1  a)  13
    b)  13
    c)  27 – 13 = **14**
Q2  a)  19
    b)  19 + 20 = **39**
    c)  $^{39}_{19}\text{K}$
    d)  19 – 1 = **18**
Q3  a)  20 – 2 = **18**
    b)  40 – 20 = **20**
Q4  a)  $^{93}_{41}\text{A}$
        (mass number = 41 + 52 = 93)
    b)  E.g. $^{94}_{41}\text{A}$

The atomic number must be the same, the mass number must be different as an isotope will have a different number of neutrons.

Q5  a)  A and C both have 10 electrons.
    b)  A and D both have 8 protons.
    c)  B and C both have 10 neutrons.
        (17 – 7 = 10 and 20 – 10 = 10)
    d)  B and D both have 10 neutrons.
        (17 – 7 = 10 and 18 – 8 = 10)
    e)  A and D are isotopes of each other because they have the same number of protons (8) but different numbers of neutrons.
        (A has 16 – 8 = 8 and D has 18 – 8 = 10)

#### Page 7 — Fact Recall Questions
Q1  proton, neutron, electron
Q2  proton: 1, neutron: 1, electron: 1/2000
Q3  Protons and neutrons are found in the nucleus. Electrons are found in orbitals around the nucleus.
Q4  The total number of protons and neutrons in the nucleus of an atom.
Q5  The number of protons in the nucleus of an atom.
Q6  By subtracting the atomic number from the mass number.
Q7  Atoms with the same number of protons but different numbers of neutrons.
Q8  Chemical properties of an element are decided by the number and arrangement of electrons. Isotopes have the same configuration of electrons so have the same chemical properties.
Q9  Physical properties depend on the mass of an atom. Isotopes have different masses so can have different physical properties.

### 2. Atomic Models
#### Page 10 — Fact Recall Questions
Q1  Dalton described atoms as solid spheres.
    J J Thomson suggested that atoms were not solid spheres — he thought they contained small negatively charged particles (electrons) in a positively charged "pudding".
Q2  the plum pudding model
Q3  Ernest Rutherford, Hans Geiger and Ernest Marsden.
Q4  If Dalton's model was correct the alpha particles fired at the sheet of gold should have been deflected very slightly by the positive "pudding" that made up most of the atom. Instead, most of the alpha particles passed straight through the gold atoms, and a very small number were deflected backwards. So the plum pudding model couldn't be right.
Q5  Rutherford's model has a tiny positively charged nucleus at the centre surrounded by a "cloud" of negative electrons. Most of the atom is empty space.
Q6  In Bohr's model the electrons only exist in fixed shells and not anywhere in between. Each shell has a fixed energy. When an electron moves between shells electromagnetic radiation is emitted or absorbed. Because the energy of the shells is fixed, the radiation will have a fixed frequency.
Q7  No

### 3. Relative Mass
#### Pages 13-14 — Application Questions
Q1  a)  85.5
    b)  200.6
    c)  65.4
    You can just read these $A_r$s off the periodic table. There's one in this book on page 274.
Q2  $A_r = ((0.1 \times 180) + (26.5 \times 182) + (14.3 \times 183) + (30.7 \times 184) + (28.4 \times 186)) \div 100 = 183.891 \approx$ **183.9**
Q3  $A_r = ((51.5 \times 90) + (11.2 \times 91) + (17.1 \times 92) + (17.4 \times 94) + (2.8 \times 96)) \div 100 = 91.318 \approx$ **91.3**
Q4  a)  $A_r = ((79 \times 60.8) + (81 \times 59.2)) \div 120 = 79.986 \approx$ **80.0**
    b)  $A_r = ((6 \times 11.1) + (7 \times 138.9)) \div 150 = 6.926 \approx$ **6.9**
    c)  $A_r = ((39 \times 130.6) + (41 \times 9.4)) \div 140 = 39.134 \approx$ **39.1**
Q5  a)  14 + (3 × 1) = **17**
    b)  12 + (16 × 2) = **44**
    c)  (12 × 2) + (1 × 4) + (16 × 6) + (14 × 2) = **152**
Q6  a)  40.1 + (35.5 × 2) = **111.1**
    b)  24.3 + 32.1 + (16 × 4) = **120.4**
    c)  23 + 16 + 1 = **40**

#### Page 14 — Fact Recall Questions
Q1  The average mass of an atom of an element on a scale where an atom of carbon–12 is exactly 12.
Q2  The mass of an isotope of an element on a scale where an atom of carbon–12 is exactly 12.
Q3  a)  Spreadsheets can now be used to perform the calculations automatically.
    b)  This is particularly useful when a large amount of data is being used.
Q4  The average mass of a molecule on a scale where an atom of carbon-12 is exactly 12.
Q5  The average mass of a formula unit on a scale where an atom of carbon-12 is exactly 12.

## 4. The Mole
### Page 16 — Application Questions
Q1   4 moles of Na react with 1 mole of $O_2$ to give 2 moles of $Na_2O$. So 6 moles of Na must react with 1.5 moles of oxygen to give **3 moles** of $Na_2O$.

Q2   a)  $M_r = 19 + 19 = 38$
        $M = \textbf{38 g mol}^{-1}$
    b)  $M_r = 40.1 + (35.5 \times 2) = 111.1$
        $M = \textbf{111.1 g mol}^{-1}$
    c)  $M_r = 24.3 + 32.1 + (4 \times 16) = 120.4$
        $M = \textbf{120.4 g mol}^{-1}$

Q3   $M = 23 + 14 + (16 \times 3) = 85$ g mol$^{-1}$
    number of moles = $212.5 \div 85 = \textbf{2.5 moles}$

Q4   $M = 65.4 + (35.5 \times 2) = 136.4$ g mol$^{-1}$
    number of moles = $15.5 \div 136.4 = \textbf{0.114 moles}$

Q5   $M = 23 + 35.5 = 58.5$ g mol$^{-1}$
    Mass = $58.5 \times 2 = \textbf{117 g}$

Q6   $M = 24.3 + 12 + (3 \times 16) = 84.3$ g mol$^{-1}$
    Mass = $84.3 \times 0.25 = \textbf{21.1 g}$

Q7   $M = 66 \div 1.5 = \textbf{44 g mol}^{-1}$

### Page 16 — Fact Recall Questions
Q1   a)  $6 \times 10^{23}$
    b)  The Avogadro constant.

Q2   The mass of one mole of the chemical.

Q3   Number of moles = mass of substance ÷ molar mass

## 5. Concentration Calculations
### Pages 18-19 — Application Questions
Q1   Number of moles = $(2 \times 50) \div 1000 = \textbf{0.1 moles}$

Q2   Number of moles = $0.08 \times 0.5 = \textbf{0.04 moles}$

Q3   Number of moles = $(0.7 \times 30) \div 1000 = \textbf{0.021 moles}$

Q4   Concentration = $0.25 \div 0.5 = \textbf{0.5 mol dm}^{-3}$

Q5   Concentration = $0.08 \div 0.75 = \textbf{0.11 mol dm}^{-3}$

Q6   Concentration = $0.1 \div (36 \div 1000) = \textbf{2.8 mol dm}^{-3}$
    *Dividing a volume in cm³ by 1000 converts it to dm³. Then you can stick it into the equation concentration = number of moles ÷ volume (dm³).*

Q7   Volume = $0.46 \div 1.8 = \textbf{0.26 dm}^3$

Q8   Volume = $0.01 \div 0.55 = \textbf{0.02 dm}^3$

Q9   Number of moles = concentration × volume (dm³)
                    = $0.8 \times (75 \div 1000) = 0.06$
    M of $Na_2O = (23 \times 2) + 16 = 62$ g mol$^{-1}$
    Mass = moles × molar mass = $0.06 \times 62 = \textbf{3.72 g}$

Q10  Number of moles = concentration × volume (dm³)
                    = $0.5 \times (30 \div 1000) = 0.015$
    M of $CoBr_2 = 58.9 + (79.9 \times 2) = 218.7$ g mol$^{-1}$
    Mass = number of moles × molar mass
           = $0.015 \times 218.7 = \textbf{3.3 g}$

Q11  Number of moles = concentration × volume (dm³)
                    = $1.2 \times (100 \div 1000) = 0.12$
    molar mass = mass ÷ number of moles
           = $4.08 \div 0.12 = \textbf{34 g mol}^{-1}$

Q12  Number of moles = $2.4 \div 24 = \textbf{0.1 moles}$

Q13  Number of moles = $0.65 \div 24 = \textbf{0.027 moles}$

Q14  Number of moles = $3120 \div 24\,000 = \textbf{0.13 moles}$

Q15  Volume = $0.21 \times 24 = \textbf{5.04 dm}^3$

Q16  Volume = $1.1 \times 24 = \textbf{26.4 dm}^3$

Q17  Volume = $0.028 \times 24000 = \textbf{672 cm}^3$

Q18  Volume = $0.072 \times 24000 = \textbf{1728 cm}^3$

### Page 19 — Fact Recall Questions
Q1   E.g. mol dm$^{-3}$ / M

Q2   Solution A is more dilute.

Q3   Number of moles = $\dfrac{\text{concentration} \times \text{volume (in cm}^3)}{1000}$
    Number of moles = concentration × volume (dm³)

Q4   1000

## 6. Formulas
### Page 21 — Application Questions
Q1   CH

Q2   Molecular formula: $C_2H_6O_4$, empirical formula: $CH_3O_2$.

Q3   a)  $C_4H_8Br_2$
    b)  $C_2H_4Br$

Q4   empirical mass = $(4 \times 12) + (9 \times 1) = 57$
    molecular mass = 114, so there are
    $(114 \div 57) = 2$ empirical units in the molecule.
    molecular formula = $\textbf{C}_8\textbf{H}_{18}$

Q5   empirical mass = $(3 \times 12) + (5 \times 1) + (2 \times 16) = 73$
    $M_r = 146$, so there are $(146 \div 73) = 2$ empirical units in the molecule.
    molecular formula = $\textbf{C}_6\textbf{H}_{10}\textbf{O}_4$

Q6   empirical mass = $(4 \times 12) + (6 \times 1) + (2 \times 35.5) + (1 \times 16) = 141$
    $M_r = 423$, so there are $(423 \div 141) = 3$ empirical units in the molecule.
    molecular formula = $\textbf{C}_{12}\textbf{H}_{18}\textbf{Cl}_6\textbf{O}_3$

### Page 21 — Fact Recall Questions
Q1   The empirical formula gives the smallest whole number ratio of atoms in a compound.

Q2   The molecular formula gives the actual numbers of atoms in a molecule.

## 7. Calculating Formulas
### Page 23 — Application Questions
Q1   mols $CO_2$ = mass ÷ $M_r = 17.6 \div 44 = 0.4$ mols
    mols $H_2O$ = mass ÷ $M_r = 10.8 \div 18 = 0.6$ mols
    There is 1 mol of C in 1 mol of $CO_2$ so you must have started with 0.4 moles of C.
    There are 2 mols of H in 1 mol of $H_2O$ so you must have started with $2 \times 0.6 = 1.2$ moles of H.
    So, the ratio of C : H = 0.4 : 1.2 = 1 : 3 and the empirical formula is $\textbf{CH}_3$.

Q2   mols $CO_2$ = mass ÷ $M_r = 3.52 \div 44 = 0.08$ mols
    mols $H_2O$ = mass ÷ $M_r = 2.88 \div 18 = 0.16$ mols
    There is 1 mol of C in 1 mol of $CO_2$ so you must have started with 0.08 moles of C.
    There are 2 mols of H in 1 mol of $H_2O$ so you must have started with $2 \times 0.16 = 0.32$ moles of H.
    So, the ratio of C : H = 0.08 : 0.32 = 1 : 4 and the empirical formula is $\textbf{CH}_4$.

Q3   If 5.52 g of sodium burns to give 7.44 g of sodium oxide then $7.44 - 5.52 = 1.92$ g of oxygen must be added.
    mols Na = mass ÷ $M_r = 5.52 \div 23 = 0.24$ mols
    mols O = mass ÷ $M_r = 1.92 \div 16 = 0.12$ mols
    So, the ratio of Na : O = 0.24 : 0.12 = 2 : 1 and the empirical formula is $\textbf{Na}_2\textbf{O}$.

Q4   If 50.2 g of iron burns to give 69.4 g or iron oxide then $69.4 - 50.2 = 19.2$ g of oxygen must be added.
    mols Fe = mass ÷ $M_r = 50.2 \div 55.8 = 0.9$ mols
    mols O = mass ÷ $M_r = 19.2 \div 16 = 1.2$ mols
    So, the ratio of Fe : O = 0.9 : 1.2 = 3 : 4 and the empirical formula is $\textbf{Fe}_3\textbf{O}_4$.
    *In this question the highest number of moles isn't divisible by the lowest number of moles. So to get the whole number ratio you have to divide by a common factor. In this case 0.3.*

## Page 24 — Application Questions

**Q1** Mass of each element:
H = 5.9 g     O = 94.1 g
Moles of each element:
H = (5.9 ÷ 1) = 5.9 moles
O = (94.1 ÷ 16) = 5.9 moles
Divide each by 5.9:
H = (5.9 ÷ 5.9) = 1     O = (5.9 ÷ 5.9) = 1
The ratio of H : O is 1 : 1.
So the empirical formula is **HO**.

**Q2** Mass of each element:
Al = 20.2 g     Cl = 79.8 g
Moles of each element:
Al = (20.2 ÷ 27) = 0.75 moles
Cl = (79.8 ÷ 35.5) = 2.25 moles
Divide each by 0.75:
Al = (0.75 ÷ 0.75) = 1     Cl = (2.25 ÷ 0.75) = 3
The ratio of Al : Cl is 1 : 3.
So the empirical formula is **$AlCl_3$**.

**Q3** Mass of each element:
C = 8.5 g     H = 1.4 g     I = 90.1 g
Moles of each element:
C = (8.5 ÷ 12) = 0.7 moles
H = (1.4 ÷ 1) = 1.4 moles
I = (90.1 ÷ 126.9) = 0.7 moles
Divide each by 0.7:
C = (0.7 ÷ 0.7) = 1
H = (1.4 ÷ 0.7) = 2
I = (0.7 ÷ 0.7) = 1
The ratio of C : H : I is 1 : 2 : 1.
So the empirical formula is **$CH_2I$**.

**Q4** % V = 32.3     % Cl = 100 − 32.3 = 67.7
Mass of each element:
V = 32.3 g     Cl = 67.7 g
Moles of each element:
V = (32.3 ÷ 50.9) = 0.63 moles
Cl = (67.7 ÷ 35.5) = 1.91 moles
Divide each by 0.63:
V = (0.63 ÷ 0.63) = 1     Cl = (1.91 ÷ 0.63) = 3
The ratio of V : Cl is 1 : 3.
So the empirical formula is **$VCl_3$**.

**Q5** % O = 31.58     % Cr = 100 − 31.58 = 68.42
Mass of each element:
O = 31.58 g     Cr = 68.42 g
Moles of each element:
O = (31.58 ÷ 16) = 1.97 moles
Cr = (68.42 ÷ 52) = 1.32 moles
Divide each by 1.32:
O = (1.97 ÷ 1.32) = 1.5     Cr = (1.32 ÷ 1.32) = 1
The ratio of Cr : O is 1 : 1.5.
Multiply by 2... 2 × (1 : 1.5) = 2 : 3.
So the empirical formula is **$Cr_2O_3$**.

## Page 25 — Application Questions

**Q1** mass O in oxide = 7.1 − 3.1 = 4.0 g
mols O = mass ÷ $M_r$ = 4.0 ÷ 16 = 0.25 mols
mols P = mass ÷ $M_r$ = 3.1 ÷ 31 = 0.1 mols
So, the ratio of P : O = 0.1 : 0.25 = 2 : 5 and the empirical formula is $P_2O_5$.
mass of empirical formula is (31 × 2) + (5 × 16) = 142 g mol$^{-1}$. 284 ÷ 142 = 2 so the empirical formula is scaled up by a factor of 2 and the molecular formula is **$P_4O_{10}$**.

**Q2** Mass of each element:
C = 85.7 g     H = 14.3 g
Moles of each element:
C = (85.7 ÷ 12) = 7.14 moles
H = (14.3 ÷ 1) = 14.30 moles
Divide each by 7.14:
C = (7.14 ÷ 7.14) = 1.00  O = (14.3 ÷ 7.14) = 2.00
The ratio of C : H is 1 : 2. So the empirical formula is $CH_2$.
mass of empirical formula is 12 + (2 × 1) = 14 g mol$^{-1}$.
56 ÷ 14 = 4 so the empirical formula is scaled up by a factor of 4 and the molecular formula is **$C_4H_8$**.

**Q3** Mass of each element:
Cl = 42.5 g     O = 100 − 42.5 = 57.5 g
Moles of each element:
Cl = (42.5 ÷ 35.5) = 1.20 moles
O = (57.5 ÷ 16) = 3.60 moles
Divide each by 1.20:
Cl = (1.20 ÷ 1.20) = 1     O = (3.60 ÷ 1.20) = 3
The ratio of Cl : O is 1 : 3. So the empirical formula is $ClO_3$.
mass of empirical formula is 35.5 + (3 × 16) = 83.5 g mol$^{-1}$.
167 ÷ 83.5 = 2 so the empirical formula is scaled up by a factor of 2 and the molecular formula is **$Cl_2O_6$**.

**Q4** mols $CO_2$ = mass ÷ $M_r$ = 17.6 ÷ 44 = 0.4 mols
mols $H_2O$ = mass ÷ $M_r$ = 14.4 ÷ 18 = 0.8 mols
There is 1 mol of C in 1 mol of $CO_2$ so you must have started with 0.4 moles of C.
There are 2 mols of H in 1 mol of $H_2O$ so you must have started with 2 × 0.8 = 1.6 moles of H.
mass of C in alcohol = mols × $M_r$ = 0.4 × 12 = 4.8 g
mass of H in alcohol = mols × $M_r$ = 1.6 × 1 = 1.6 g
mass of O in alcohol = 12.8 − (4.8 + 1.6) = 6.4 g
mols O = mass ÷ $M_r$ = 6.4 ÷ 16 = 0.4 mols
So, the ratio of C : H : O = 0.4 : 1.6 : 0.4 = 1 : 4 : 1 and the empirical formula is $CH_4O$.
mass of empirical formula is 12 + (4 × 1) + 16 = 32 g mol$^{-1}$
32 ÷ 32 = 1 so the empirical formula is not scaled up and the molecular formula is **$CH_4O$**.

**Q5** mols $CO_2$ = mass ÷ $M_r$ = 5.28 ÷ 44 = 0.12 mols
mols $H_2O$ = mass ÷ $M_r$ = 2.16 ÷ 18 = 0.12 mols
There is 1 mol of C in 1 mol of $CO_2$ so you must have started with 0.12 moles of C.
There are 2 mols of H in 1 mol of $H_2O$ so you must have started with 2 × 0.12 = 0.24 moles of H.
mass of C in alcohol = mols × $M_r$ = 0.12 × 12 = 1.44 g
mass of H in alcohol = mols × $M_r$ = 0.24 × 1 = 0.24 g
mass of O in alcohol = 2.64 − (1.44 + 0.24) = 0.96 g
mols O = mass ÷ $M_r$ = 0.96 ÷ 16 = 0.06 mols
So, the ratio of C : H : O = 0.12 : 0.24 : 0.06 = 2 : 4 : 1 and the empirical formula is $C_2H_4O$.
mass of empirical formula is (12 × 2) + (4 × 1) + 16 = 44 g mol$^{-1}$. 88 ÷ 44 = 2 so the empirical formula is scaled up by a factor of 2 and the molecular formula is **$C_4H_8O_2$**.

# 8. Balancing Equations

## Page 27 — Application Questions

**Q1**
a) $Mg + \textbf{2}HCl \rightarrow MgCl_2 + H_2$
b) $S_8 + \textbf{24}F_2 \rightarrow \textbf{8}SF_6$
c) $Ca(OH)_2 + H_2SO_4 \rightarrow CaSO_4 + \textbf{2}H_2O$
d) $Na_2CO_3 + \textbf{2}HCl \rightarrow \textbf{2}NaCl + CO_2 + H_2O$
e) $C_4H_{10} + \textbf{6½}O_2 \rightarrow \textbf{4}CO_2 + \textbf{5}H_2O$
*If you wanted to double the numbers to get rid of the half in this equation that would be fine too (making it $2C_4H_{10} + 13O_2 \rightarrow 8CO_2 + 10H_2O$).*

Q2 a) $Ag \rightarrow Ag^{2+} + 2e^-$
b) $Br_2 + 2e^- \rightarrow 2Br^-$
c) $CrO_4^{2-} + 2H_2O + 3e^- \rightarrow CrO_2^- + 4OH^-$
d) $MnO_4^- + 8H^+ + 5e^- \rightarrow Mn^{2+} + 4H_2O$

## 9. Equations and Calculations
### Page 29 — Application Questions
Q1 a) $Zn + 2HCl \rightarrow ZnCl_2 + H_2$
b) $M_r$ of $Zn = 65.4$
number of moles = mass ÷ $M_r$ = 3.3 ÷ 65.4
= **0.05 moles**
c) The molar ratio of $Zn : ZnCl_2$ is 1 : 1. So 0.0504 moles of Zn will give **0.05 moles** of $ZnCl_2$.
d) $M_r$ of $ZnCl_2 = 65.4 + (2 \times 35.5) = 136.4$
mass = number of moles × $M_r$ = 0.05 × 136.4 = **6.82 g**
Q2 a) $C_2H_4 + 3O_2 \rightarrow 2CO_2 + 2H_2O$
b) $M_r$ of $H_2O = (2 \times 1) + 16 = 18$
number of moles = mass ÷ $M_r$ = 15 ÷ 18 = **0.83 moles**
c) The molar ratio of $H_2O : C_2H_4$ is 2 : 1.
So 0.83 moles of $H_2O$ must be made from
(0.83 ÷ 2) = **0.42 moles** of $C_2H_4$.
d) $M_r$ of $C_2H_4 = (2 \times 12) + (4 \times 1) = 28$
mass = number of moles × $M_r$ = 0.42 × 28 = **11.7 g**
Q3 $Na_2CO_3 + BaCl_2 \rightarrow 2NaCl + BaCO_3$
$M_r$ of $BaCl_2 = 137.3 + (2 \times 35.5) = 208.3$
number of moles = mass ÷ $M_r$ = 4.68 ÷ 208.3 = 0.022 moles
The molar ratio of $BaCl_2 : BaCO_3$ is 1 : 1.
So 0.022 moles of $BaCO_3$ must be made from 0.022 moles of $BaCl_2$.
$M_r$ of $BaCO_3 = 137.3 + 12 + (16 \times 3) = 197.3$
mass = number of moles × $M_r$ = 0.022 × 197.3 = **4.34 g**

### Page 30 — Application Questions
Q1 a) aq
b) s
c) l
d) aq
e) g
f) s
Q2 a) $2H_2O_{(l)} \rightarrow 2H_{2(g)} + O_{2(g)}$
b) $M_r$ of $H_2O = (2 \times 1) + 16 = 18$
number of moles = mass ÷ $M_r$ = 9 ÷ 18 = **0.5 moles**
c) The molar ratio of $H_2O$ to $O_2$ is 2 : 1.
So 0.5 moles of $H_2O$ will produce
(0.5 ÷ 2) = **0.25 moles** of $O_2$.
d) At room temperature and pressure 1 mole of gas takes up 24 dm³.
Volume in dm³ = number of moles × 24
Volume of $O_2$ = 0.25 × 24 = **6 dm³**
Q3 a) $ZnS_{(s)} + 1½O_{2(g)} \rightarrow ZnO_{(s)} + SO_{2(g)}$
b) $M_r$ of $ZnS = 65.4 + 32.1 = 97.5$
number of moles = mass ÷ $M_r$ = 7 ÷ 97.5 = **0.0718 moles**
c) The molar ratio of $ZnS$ to $SO_2$ is 1 : 1.
So 0.0718 moles of $ZnS$ will give **0.0718 moles** of $SO_2$.
d) At room temperature and pressure 1 mole of gas takes up 24 dm³.
Volume in dm³ = number of moles × 24
Volume of $SO_2$ = 0.0718 × 24 = **1.72 dm³**
Q4 a) $C_6H_{14(g)} \rightarrow C_4H_{10(g)} + C_2H_{4(g)}$
b) $M_r$ of $C_4H_{10} = (4 \times 12) + (10 \times 1) = 58$
number of moles = mass ÷ $M_r$ = 3 ÷ 58 = **0.0517 moles**
c) The molar ratio of $C_4H_{10}$ to $C_6H_{14}$ is 1 : 1.
So 0.0517 moles of $C_4H_{10}$ must be made from
**0.0517 moles** of $C_6H_{14}$.

d) At room temperature and pressure 1 mole of gas takes up 24 dm³.
Volume in dm³ = number of moles × 24
Volume of $C_6H_{14}$ = 0.0517 × 24 = **1.24 dm³**
Q5 $Mg_{(s)} + H_2O_{(g)} \rightarrow MgO_{(s)} + H_{2(g)}$
$M_r$ of $MgO = 24.3 + 16.0 = 40.3$
number of moles = mass ÷ $M_r$ = 10 ÷ 40.3 = 0.25 moles
The molar ratio of $MgO : H_2O$ is 1 : 1.
So 0.25 moles of $MgO$ is made from 0.25 moles of $H_2O$.
At room temperature and pressure 1 mole of gas takes up 24 dm³.
Volume in dm³ = number of moles × 24
Volume of $H_2O$ = 0.25 × 24 = **6 dm³**

## 10. Acids, Bases and Salts
### Page 33 — Application Questions
Q1 a) $CuO_{(s)} + 2HCl_{(aq)} \rightarrow CuCl_{2(aq)} + H_2O_{(l)}$
b) $NaOH_{(aq)} + HCl_{(aq)} \rightarrow NaCl_{(aq)} + H_2O_{(l)}$
c) $MgCO_{3(s)} + 2HCl_{(aq)} \rightarrow MgCl_{2(aq)} + CO_{2(g)} + H_2O_{(l)}$
*Don't forget to balance your equations. You'll lose marks in the exam if you don't.*
Q2 a) $ZnO_{(s)} + H_2SO_{4(aq)} \rightarrow ZnSO_{4(aq)} + H_2O_{(l)}$
b) $2Fe_{(s)} + 3H_2SO_{4(aq)} \rightarrow Fe_2(SO_4)_{3(aq)} + 3H_{2(g)}$
c) $CaCO_{3(s)} + H_2SO_{4(aq)} \rightarrow CaSO_{4(aq)} + CO_{2(g)} + H_2O_{(l)}$
Q3 a) $Al_2O_{3(s)} + 6HNO_{3(aq)} \rightarrow 2Al(NO_3)_{3(aq)} + 3H_2O_{(l)}$
b) $KOH_{(aq)} + HNO_{3(aq)} \rightarrow KNO_{3(aq)} + H_2O_{(l)}$
c) $MgCO_{3(s)} + 2HNO_{3(aq)} \rightarrow Mg(NO_3)_{2(aq)} + H_2O_{(l)} + CO_{2(g)}$

### Page 33 — Fact Recall Questions
Q1 a) A substance that releases $H^+$ ions in aqueous solution (a proton donor).
b) A substance that removes $H^+$ ions from an aqueous solution (a proton acceptor).
Q2 a) HCl
b) $H_2SO_4$
c) $HNO_3$
d) NaOH
e) KOH
f) $NH_3$
Q3 a) chloride
b) sulfate
c) nitrate
Q4 a) A salt and water.
b) A salt and hydrogen.
c) A salt, carbon dioxide and water.

## 11. Anhydrous and Hydrated Salts
### Page 35 — Application Questions
Q1 mass $H_2O$ in hydrated salt = 57.5 − 32.3 = 25.2 g
*This is the mass of the hydrated salt minus the mass of the anhydrous salt.*
mols $ZnSO_4$ = mass ÷ M = 32.3 ÷ 161.5 = 0.2 mols
mols $H_2O$ = mass ÷ M = 25.2 ÷ 18 = 1.4 mols
So, the ratio of $ZnSO_4 : H_2O$ in the hydrated salt =
0.2 : 1.4 = 1 : 7 so **X = 7** and the formula of the hydrated salt is $ZnSO_4.7H_2O$.
Q2 mass $CoCl_2$ in hydrated salt = 35.685 − 16.200 = 19.485 g
*This is the mass of the hydrated salt minus the mass of the water in the hydrated salt.*
mols $CoCl_2$ = mass ÷ M = 19.485 ÷ 129.9 = 0.15 mols
mols $H_2O$ = mass ÷ M = 16.200 ÷ 18 = 0.9 mols
So, the ratio of $CoCl_2 : H_2O$ in the hydrated salt =
0.15 : 0.9 = 1 : 6 so **X = 6** and the formula of the hydrated salt is $CoCl_2.6H_2O$.

Q3 % mass $BaCl_2$ = 100 − 14.74 = 85.26%.
Assuming you have 100 g of hydrated salt it would contain 85.26 g of $BaCl_2$ and 14.74 g of water.
mols $BaCl_2$ = mass ÷ M = 85.26 ÷ 208.3 = 0.41 mols
mols $H_2O$ = mass ÷ M = 14.74 ÷ 18 = 0.82 mols
So, the ratio of $BaCl_2$ : $H_2O$ in the hydrated salt = 0.41 : 0.82 = 1 : 2 so the formula of the hydrated salt is **$BaCl_2.2H_2O$**.

Q4 % mass $Fe(NO_3)_3$ = 100 − 30.87 = 69.13%.
Assuming you have 100 g of hydrated salt it would contain 69.13 g of $Fe(NO_3)_3$ and 30.87 g of water.
mols $Fe(NO_3)_3$ = mass ÷ M = 69.13 ÷ 241.8 = 0.29 mols
mols $H_2O$ = mass ÷ M = 30.87 ÷ 18 = 1.72 mols
So, the ratio of $Fe(NO_3)_3$ : $H_2O$ in the hydrated salt = 0.29 : 1.72 = 1 : 6 and so the formula of the hydrated salt is **$Fe(NO_3)_3.6H_2O$**.

## Page 35 — Fact Recall Questions
Q1 Water of crystallisation.
Q2 Anhydrous means that a substance doesn't contain water of crystallisation.
Q3 By heating — hydrated salts lose their water of crystallisation and become anhydrous when they are heated.

## 12. Titrations
### Page 38 — Application Questions
Q1 a) $HCl_{(aq)}$ + $KOH_{(aq)}$ → $KCl_{(aq)}$ + $H_2O_{(l)}$
b) moles HCl = (conc. × volume ($cm^3$)) ÷ 1000
= (0.75 × 28) ÷ 1000 = **0.021 moles**
c) 1 mole of HCl reacts with 1 mole of KOH.
So 0.021 moles of HCl must react with **0.021 moles** of KOH.
d) concentration = (moles KOH × 1000) ÷ vol. ($cm^3$)
= (0.021 × 1000) ÷ 40 = **0.525 mol $dm^{-3}$**

Q2 a) $NaOH_{(aq)}$ + $HNO_{3\,(aq)}$ → $NaNO_{3\,(aq)}$ + $H_2O_{(l)}$
b) moles NaOH = (conc. × volume ($cm^3$)) ÷ 1000
= (1.5 × 15.3) ÷ 1000 = **0.023 moles**
c) 1 mole of NaOH reacts with 1 mole of $HNO_3$.
So 0.023 moles of NaOH must react with **0.023 moles** of $HNO_3$.
d) concentration = (moles $HNO_3$ × 1000) ÷ vol. ($cm^3$)
= (0.023 × 1000) ÷ 35 = **0.66 mol $dm^{-3}$**

Q3 $LiOH_{(aq)}$ + $HCl_{(aq)}$ → $LiCl_{(aq)}$ + $H_2O_{(l)}$
moles HCl = (conc. × volume ($cm^3$)) ÷ 1000
= (0.5 × 12) ÷ 1000 = 0.006 moles
1 mole of HCl reacts with 1 mole of LiOH, so 0.006 moles of HCl must react with 0.006 moles of LiOH.
concentration = (moles LiOH × 1000) ÷ vol. ($cm^3$)
= (0.006 × 1000) ÷ 24 = **0.25 mol $dm^{-3}$**

### Page 39 — Application Questions
Q1 a) $HNO_3$ + LiOH → $LiNO_3$ + $H_2O$
b) moles $HNO_3$ = (conc. × volume ($cm^3$)) ÷ 1000
= (0.2 × 18.8) ÷ 1000 = **0.0038 moles**
c) 1 mole of $HNO_3$ reacts with 1 mole of LiOH.
So 0.0038 moles of $HNO_3$ must react with **0.0038 moles** of LiOH.
d) volume = (moles LiOH × 1000) ÷ concentration
= (0.0038 × 1000) ÷ 0.45 = **8.4 $cm^3$**

Q2 a) KOH + $CH_3COOH$ → $CH_3COOK$ + $H_2O$
b) moles KOH = (conc. × volume ($cm^3$)) ÷ 1000
= (0.42 × 37.3) ÷ 1000 = **0.016 moles**
c) 1 mole of KOH reacts with 1 mole of $CH_3COOH$.
So 0.016 moles of KOH must react with **0.016 moles** of $CH_3COOH$.
d) volume = (moles $CH_3COOH$ × 1000) ÷ conc.
= (0.016 × 1000) ÷ 1.1 = **14.5 $cm^3$**

Q3 NaOH + HCl → NaCl + $H_2O$
moles of NaOH = (conc. × volume ($cm^3$)) ÷ 1000
= (14 × 1) ÷ 1000 = 0.014 moles
1 mole of NaCl reacts with 1 mole of HCl. So, 0.014 moles of NaOH must react with 0.014 moles of HCl.
volume = (moles HCl × 1000) ÷ conc. = (0.014 × 1000) ÷ 0.5
= **28 $cm^3$**

## Page 39 — Fact Recall Questions
Q1 pipette
Q2 To make sure that the acid and the alkali are properly mixed.
Q3 The exact point at which the indicator changes colour (at this point the amount of acid added is just enough to neutralise the alkali).
Q4 yellow to red

## 13. Oxidation States
### Page 43 — Application Questions
Q1 a) +1
b) −1
c) +2

Q2 a) −1
b) −2
c) −1

Q3 a) H: +1, Cl: −1
b) C: +4, O: −2
c) Cl: +7, O: −2
d) H: +1, S: +6, O: −2
*Oxygen has an oxidation state of −2. There are 4 oxygen atoms here so the total is −8. The overall oxidation state of the ion is −1. Hydrogen has an oxidation state of +1. So, sulfur must have an oxidation state of +6 (as −8 + 1 + 6 = −1).*

Q4 a) +2
b) +4
c) +4
*Calcium forms $Ca^{2+}$ ions so has an oxidation state of +2. Oxygen has an oxidation state of −2. There are 3 oxygen atoms here so the total is −6. The overall oxidation state of the compound is 0. So, carbon must have an oxidation state of +4 (as −6 + 4 = −2).*
d) −2
*Hydrogen has an oxidation state of +1. So, in $C_3H_6$, carbon must have an oxidation state of −2 (as (6 × +1) + (3 × −2) = 0).*

Q5 a) 0
b) −3
c) +6
d) +2
*Fluorine is the most electronegative element so its oxidation state is equal to its ionic charge, −1. There are 4 fluorine atoms here so the total is −4. So, phosphorus must have an oxidation state of +2 (as (4 × −1) + (2 × +2) = 0).*

Q6 a) +3
b) +7

Q7 a) iron(II) sulfate
b) manganese(II) carbonate
c) copper(II) oxide

Q8 a) $CuSO_4$
b) FeO
c) $NO_2^-$
d) $CrO_4^{2-}$

Q1 0
Q2 0
Q3 −1
Q4 −1

## 14. Redox Reactions

### Page 45 — Application Questions
Q1 a) The oxidation state of magnesium increases from 0 to +2. The oxidation state of hydrogen decreases from +1 to 0.
b) The oxidations state of vanadium increases from 0 to +3. The oxidation state of hydrogen decreases from +1 to 0.
c) The oxidation state of iron increases from 0 to +3. The oxidation state of hydrogen decreases from +1 to 0.
Q2 a) The oxidation state of manganese decreases from +4 to +2. The oxidation state of chlorine increases from −1 to 0.
*Only two of the chlorine atoms show an increase in oxidation state. The other two stay with an oxidation state of −1.*
b) $MnO_2$ is the oxidising agent. It accepts electrons and gets reduced. HCl is the reducing agent. It donates electrons and gets oxidised.

### Page 45 — Fact Recall Questions
Q1 Oxidation is a loss of electrons.
Q2 Reduction is a gain of electrons.
Q3 An oxidising agent accepts electrons from another reactant and is reduced.
Q4 A reducing agent donates electrons to another reactant and is oxidised.
Q5 It increases by 1.
Q6 It decreases by 1.

## Exam-style Questions — pages 47–49

1 a) (i) Isotopes are atoms of the same element which have the same number of protons / same atomic number *(1 mark)* but different numbers of neutrons / different mass numbers *(1 mark)*.
(ii)

| | Protons | Neutrons | Electrons |
|---|---|---|---|
| $^{28}Si$ | 14 | 14 | 14 |
| $^{29}Si$ | 14 | 15 | 14 |
| $^{30}Si$ | 14 | 16 | 14 |

*(1 mark for protons and electrons correct, 1 mark for all neutrons correct)*.
(b) (i) The average mass of an atom of an element *(1 mark)* measured on a scale where an atom of carbon-12 *(1 mark)* is exactly 12 *(1 mark)*.
*Make sure you talk about atoms here and not just elements or isotopes. If you say 'the mean mass of an element' or 'the mean mass of an isotope' you won't get the marks.*
(ii) $A_r = [(28 \times 92.23) + (29 \times 4.67) + (30 \times 3.1)] \div 100$
$= 28.1$ *(1 mark)*.
(c) (i) +4 *(1 mark)*
(ii) silicon(IV) oxide *(1 mark)*
(d) (i) This is not a redox reaction *(1 mark)*. There are no changes in oxidation state during this reaction *(1 mark)*.
(ii) $M_r = (2 \times 23) + 28.1 + (3 \times 16)$
$= 122.1$ *(1 mark)*

2 (a)

| | Mass | Charge |
|---|---|---|
| Proton | 1 | +1 |
| Neutron | 1 | 0 |
| Electron | 1/2000 | −1 |

*(1 mark for all entries correct)*
(b) (i) Most alpha particles went straight through the gold sheet *(1 mark)*. This shows that atoms are mostly empty space *(1 mark)*.
(ii) Some alpha particles were deflected backwards *(1 mark)*. This shows that the positively charged protons in the atom must be concentrated in one place *(1 mark)*.
(c) moles of gold = mass ÷ $M_r$ = 5 ÷ 197 = 0.0254 moles *(1 mark)*.
Number of atoms = moles × Avogadro's constant
= 0.0254 × (6 × 10²³) = 1.52 × 10²² atoms *(1 mark)*

3 (a) The empirical formula is a formula giving the simplest whole number ratio of atoms of each element present in a compound *(1 mark)*.
(b) (i) moles $CO_2$ = mass ÷ $M_r$ = 17.6 ÷ 44 = **0.4 moles**
moles $H_2O$ = mass ÷ $M_r$ = 9.0 ÷ 18 = **0.5 moles**
*(1 mark for each correct number of moles)*.
(ii) There is 1 mole of C in 1 mole of $CO_2$ so must have started with 0.4 moles of C.
mass C = moles × $M_r$ = 0.4 × 12 = **4.8 g**
There are 2 moles of H in 1 mole of $H_2O$ so must have started with 0.5 × 2 = 1.0 moles of H.
mass H = 1.0 × 1 = **1 g**
mass O = total mass − (mass of C + mass of H)
= 9 − (4.8 + 1.0) = **3.2 g**
*(1 mark for each correct mass)*.
(iii) moles O = mass ÷ $M_r$ = 3.2 ÷ 16 = 0.2 moles *(1 mark)*. So the ratio of C : H : O = 0.4 : 1.0 : 0.2
= 2 : 5 : 1 so the empirical formula is **$C_2H_5O$** *(1 mark)*.
(c) (i) The molecular formula is a formula giving the actual number of atoms of each element present in a molecule *(1 mark)*.
(ii) The formula mass of the empirical formula is $(12 \times 2) + (5 \times 1) + 16 = 45$ *(1 mark)*.
90 ÷ 45 = 2 so the empirical formula is scaled up by a factor of 2 and the molecular formula is **$C_4H_{10}O_2$** *(1 mark)*.

4 (a) (i) $HCl_{(aq)} + NaOH_{(aq)} \rightarrow NaCl_{(aq)} + H_2O_{(l)}$ *(1 mark)*
(ii) moles HCl = (concentration × volume) ÷ 1000 = (0.6 × 26) ÷ 1000 = **0.0156 moles**.
*(2 marks for correct answer, 1 mark for correct method if answer incorrect)*.
(iii) From the equation you know that 1 mole of HCl reacts with 1 mole of NaOH. So 0.0156 moles of HCl must react with 0.0156 moles of NaOH.
concentration of NaOH = (moles ÷ volume) × 1000
= (0.0156 ÷ 20) × 1000 = **0.78 mol dm⁻³**
*(2 marks for correct answer, 1 mark for correct method if answer incorrect)*.
*If you get a question like this where you need your answer to the previous part of a question to answer it, you'll get the marks if everything you've done is right, even if you don't get the right answer because you made an error in the earlier part of the question.*

(b) (i) +3 *(1 mark)*.
    (ii) $AlCl_3$
Cl forms $Cl^-$ ions so has an oxidation state of −1. The overall oxidation state of aluminium chloride is 0 and aluminium has an oxidation state of +3 so there must be 3 $Cl^-$ ions and the formula must be $AlCl_3$.
    (iii) The aluminium would dissolve *(1 mark)* and bubbles of hydrogen gas would be produced *(1 mark)*.
(c) (i) The oxidation state of sodium increases from 0 to +1 *(1 mark)*.
    (ii) It is a reducing agent *(1 mark)*.
(d) (i) Anhydrous means that a substance doesn't contain any water of crystallisation *(1 mark)*.
    (ii) Assuming there was 100 g of hydrated calcium nitrate, 30.5 g would be water and 100 − 30.5 = 69.5 g would be calcium nitrate *(1 mark)*. moles water = mass ÷ M = 30.5 ÷ 18 = 1.694 mol *(1 mark)*.
M of $Ca(NO_3)_2$ = 40.1 + [2 × (14 + (3 × 16))] = 164.1.
moles $Ca(NO_3)_2$ = mass ÷ M = 69.5 ÷ 164.1 = 0.424 mol *(1 mark)*.
$Ca(NO_3)_2 : H_2O$ = 0.424 : 1.694 = 1 : 4 so the value of **X = 4** *(1 mark)*.

# Module 2 — Electrons, Bonding and Structure

## 1. Electronic Structure

### Page 53 — Application Questions
Q1   a)   $1s^2\ 2s^1$
     b)   $1s^2\ 2s^2\ 2p^6\ 3s^2\ 3p^6\ 3d^2\ 4s^2$
     c)   $1s^2\ 2s^2\ 2p^6\ 3s^2\ 3p^6\ 3d^{10}\ 4s^2\ 4p^1$
     d)   $1s^2\ 2s^2\ 2p^3$
Q2   a)

Remember — the 4s sub-shell has a lower energy level than the 3d sub-shell even though its principal quantum number is bigger. This means the 4s sub-shell fills up first.

b)

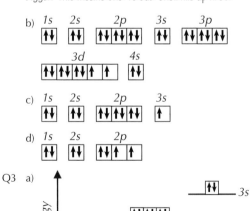

Q3   a)

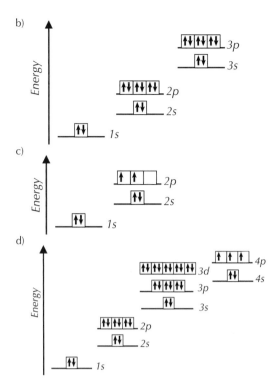

Q4   a)   $1s^2\ 2s^2\ 2p^6$
     b)   $1s^2\ 2s^2\ 2p^6$
     c)   $1s^2\ 2s^2\ 2p^6$
     d)   $1s^2\ 2s^2\ 2p^6\ 3s^2\ 3p^6$
Q5   a)   bromine
     b)   phosphorus
     c)   vanadium

### Page 53 — Fact Recall Questions
Q1   3
Q2   6 (it can hold two electrons in each orbital)
Q3   18
Q4   a)   spherical
     b)   dumbbell-shaped
Q5   The number of electrons that an atom or ion has and how they are arranged.
Q6   The shells with the lowest energy (e.g. 1s then 2s then 2p etc.).
Q7   Electrons fill orbitals singly before they start sharing, so the two electrons in the 2p sub-shell should be in separate orbitals.
Q8   They form negative ions with an inert gas configuration.

## 2. Ionisation Energies

### Page 56 — Application Questions
Q1   a)   $Cl_{(g)} \rightarrow Cl^+_{(g)} + e^-$
     b)   $Cl^+_{(g)} \rightarrow Cl^{2+}_{(g)} + e^-$
Q2   a)   Group 6
     b)   2 electrons in the first shell and 6 electrons in the second shell.
     c)   Oxygen

Q3 a)

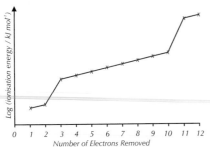

b) Within each shell, successive ionisation energies increase. This is because electrons are being removed from an increasingly positive ion — there's less repulsion amongst the remaining electrons, so they're held more strongly by the nucleus. The big jumps in ionisation energy happen when a new shell that's closer to the nucleus is broken into — the first shell has 2 electrons in it, the second shell has 8 electrons and the third shell has 2 electrons.

Q4 Beryllium's outer electron is in a 2s orbital. Boron's outer electron is in a 2p orbital, which means it has a higher energy and is located further from the nucleus. The 2p orbital also has more shielding (provided by the 2s electrons). These two factors override the effect of the increased nuclear charge of the boron atom, so the first ionisation energy of beryllium is higher than the first ionisation energy of boron.

Q5 The outer electron being removed is in the same sub-shell and the shielding is identical in the two atoms. But the silicon atom has one more proton than the aluminium atom so its nuclear charge is greater. This means that the attraction between the outer electron and the nucleus is greater in silicon, and it takes more energy to remove it.

Q6 The first electron is removed from the 2s orbital, whereas the second and third electrons are removed from the 1s orbital. The 2s orbital is further from the nucleus and is shielded by the inner electrons so it takes much less energy to remove the first electron than the second. The second and third electrons have no shielding and are the same distance from the nucleus so there's less difference between their ionisation energies.

## Page 56 — Fact Recall Questions

Q1 The first ionisation energy is the energy needed to remove 1 electron from each atom in 1 mole of gaseous atoms to form one mole of gaseous 1+ ions.

Q2 The more protons there are, the more positively charged the nucleus is, the stronger the attraction for the electrons and the higher the ionisation energy.

Q3 The distance between the outer electron and the nucleus, and the shielding effect of inner electrons.

Q4 The second ionisation energy is the energy needed to remove 1 electron from each ion in 1 mole of gaseous 1+ ions to form one mole of gaseous 2+ ions.

Q5 Within each shell, successive ionisation energies increase because electrons are being removed from an increasingly positive ion — there's less repulsion amongst the remaining electrons, so they're held more strongly by the nucleus.

## 3. Ionic Bonding
### Page 60 — Application Questions

Q1 a) 1–
   b) 1+
   c) 2+

Q2 a) E.g. $S + 2e^- \rightarrow S^{2-}$
   b) E.g.

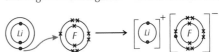

Q3 a) 2+
   b) 1–
   c) $CaI_2$

Q4 a) $LiF$
   b) A lithium atom (Li) loses 1 electron to form a lithium ion ($Li^+$). The fluorine atom (F) gains 1 electron to form a fluoride ion ($F^-$). Electrostatic attraction holds the positive and negative ions together — this is an ionic bond.
   c)

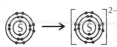

## Page 60 — Fact Recall Questions

Q1 It holds positive and negative ions together.
Q2 A regular structure made up of ions.
Q3

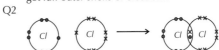

Q4 The ions in a molten ionic compound are free to move (and they carry a charge).
Q5 It will have a high melting point and a high boiling point. It will dissolve in water.

## 4. Covalent Bonding
### Page 64 — Fact Recall Questions

Q1 It forms when two atoms share electrons so that they've both got full outer shells of electrons.
Q2

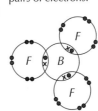

Q3 It is a covalent bond formed when two atoms share three pairs of electrons.
Q4

Q5 A covalent bond formed between two atoms where one of the atoms provides both of the shared electrons.
Q6 Co-ordinate bonding.
Q7 The arrow the dative bond. The direction of the arrow shows which atom is the donor atom.

Q8 a) The weak forces between the molecules are easily broken.
  b) No — chlorine wouldn't conduct electricity because there are no free ions or electrons to carry the charge.
Q9 Diamond is a giant covalent structure made up of carbon atoms. Each carbon atom is covalently bonded to four other carbon atoms and the atoms arrange themselves in a tetrahedral shape.

## 5. Shapes of Molecules
### Page 68 — Application Questions
Q1 a) Sulfur has 6 outer electrons and 2 hydrogen atoms donate one electron each. So there are 8 electrons on the S atom, which is **4** electron pairs.
  b) 2 electron pairs are involved in bonding, so there are **2** lone pairs.
  c)

  non-linear
  d) 104.5°
Q2 a)

  The shape is trigonal pyramidal.
  *Arsenic has 5 outer electrons and 3 hydrogen atoms donate one electron each. So there are 8 electrons on the As atom, which is 4 electron pairs. 3 electron pairs are involved in bonding, so there is 1 lone pair.*
  b) 107°
Q3

  The shape is tetrahedral.
  *Carbon has 4 outer electrons and 2 chlorine and 2 fluorine atoms donate one electron each. So there are 8 electrons on the C atom, which is 4 electron pairs. All the electron pairs are involved in bonding.*

### Page 68 — Fact Recall Questions
Q1 120°
Q2 four
Q3 octahedral

## 6. Polarisation
### Page 69 — Fact Recall Questions
Q1 Electronegativity is the ability to attract the bonding electrons in a covalent bond. So a chlorine atom is better able to attract the electrons than a hydrogen atom.
Q2 Fluorine is more electronegative than hydrogen so attracts the electrons in the H—F covalent bond more than hydrogen. The bonding electrons are pulled towards the fluorine atom. This makes the bond polar.
Q3 A dipole is a difference in charge between two atoms caused by a shift in the electron density in the bond between them.

## 7. Intermolecular Forces
### Page 73 — Application Questions
Q1 van der Waals forces / induced dipole-dipole forces
Q2 a) Oxygen is more electronegative than chlorine so it has a greater ability to pull the bonding electrons away from hydrogen atoms. So the bonds are more polarised in $H_2O$ than in HCl, which means that hydrogen bonds form in $H_2O$ but not in HCl.
  b) fluorine/F
  c) permanent dipole-dipole forces
  d) carbon/C
Q3 a) $NH_3$ has hydrogen bonds between molecules whereas $PH_3$ only has van der Waals forces, as the electronegativity values of P and H are very similar. It takes less energy to break van der Waals forces than hydrogen bonds so the boiling point of $PH_3$ is lower.
  b) lower

### Page 73 — Fact Recall Questions
Q1 van der Waals forces / induced dipole interactions / temporary dipole-temporary dipole
Q2 There are covalent bonds within iodine molecules and van der Waals forces between iodine molecules. The intermolecular forces mean that iodine forms a simple molecular lattice.
Q3 Permanent dipole-dipole forces are weak electrostatic forces of attraction between polar molecules.
Q4 a) hydrogen bonding
  b)

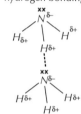

Q5 hydrogen bonding
Q6 Ice has more hydrogen bonds than liquid water, and hydrogen bonds are relatively long. So the $H_2O$ molecules in ice are further apart on average, making ice less dense than liquid water.

## 8. Metallic Bonding
### Page 74 — Fact Recall Questions
Q1 Magnesium exists as a giant metallic lattice structure. The outermost shell of electrons of a magnesium atom is delocalised — the electrons are free to move about the metal. This leaves positive metal ions, $Mg^{2+}$, which are attracted to the delocalised negative electrons. They form a lattice of closely packed positive ions in a sea of delocalised electrons.
Q2 metallic bonding
Q3 a) As there are no bonds holding specific ions together, the copper ions can slide over each other when the structure is pulled, so it can be drawn into a wire.
  b) Copper has delocalised electrons which can pass kinetic energy to each other, making copper a good thermal conductor.

# Exam-style Questions — pages 76-78

1 a) The p block *(1 mark)*.
   b) (i) As you go down Group 5 the atoms have more electrons in them *(1 mark)* so the van der Waals forces between the molecules increase *(1 mark)*. It takes more energy to break stronger van der Waals forces so the boiling points increase from $PH_3$ to $SbH_3$ *(1 mark)*.
      (ii) The melting point would increase from $PH_3$ to $AsH_3$ to $SbH_3$ *(1 mark)*.
   c) hydrogen bonding *(1 mark)*
2 a) (i) Giant covalent/macromolecular *(1 mark)*
      (ii) Graphite consists of flat sheets of carbon atoms *(1 mark)* covalently bonded to three other carbon atoms and arranged in hexagons *(1 mark — covalent must be spelled correctly at least once to get this mark)*. The sheets of hexagons are bonded together by weak van der Waals forces *(1 mark)*. Each carbon atom in diamond is covalently bonded to four other carbon atoms *(1 mark)*. The atoms arrange themselves in a tetrahedral shape *(1 mark)*.
      (iii) The delocalised electrons in graphite are free to move along the sheets, so an electric current can flow *(1 mark)*. Diamond doesn't have any free electrons *(1 mark)*.
   b) (i) van der Waals forces / induced dipole interactions / temporary dipole-temporary dipole *(1 mark)*
      (ii) For diamond to boil the covalent bonds between carbon atoms have to be broken *(1 mark)*. This would need a lot more energy than breaking the van der Waals forces between methane molecules *(1 mark)*.
3 a) (i) The first ionisation energy is the energy needed to remove 1 electron from each atom *(1 mark)* in 1 mole of gaseous atoms *(1 mark)* to form 1 mole of gaseous 1+ ions *(1 mark)*.
      (ii) $F^{2+}_{(g)} \rightarrow F^{3+}_{(g)} + e^-$ *(1 mark)*
      (iii) For the first 7 electrons, the successive ionisation energies gradually increase as they're all removed from the same shell *(1 mark)*. However, there's a big jump in ionisation energies between the 7th and the 8th electrons *(1 mark)*. This is because a new shell has been broken into and the 8th and 9th electrons are removed from a shell closer to the nucleus *(1 mark)*.
      (iv) Chlorine is below fluorine in Group 7 *(1 mark)*. This means the outer electron is in a shell further from the nucleus so there is less attraction between the electrons and the nucleus *(1 mark)*. Shielding is also increased in chlorine, because there are more electrons between the outer electron and the nucleus *(1 mark)*.
   b) (i) $S_8 + 24F_2 \rightarrow 8SF_6$ *(1 mark)*
      (ii)

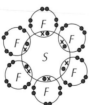

*(1 mark)*
The molecule has 6 bonding pairs of electrons on the central atom *(1 mark)* and these repel each other equally *(1 mark)*. This means that all the angles between the bonding pairs are 90° *(1 mark)* and the shape is octahedral *(1 mark)*.

c) (i) 120° *(1 mark)*
   (ii) A covalent bond formed between two atoms where one of the atoms provides both of the shared electrons *(1 mark)*.
   (iii) The shape will be tetrahedral *(1 mark)*. This is because the ion has four bonding pairs on its central atom which will repel each other equally *(1 mark)*, giving bond angles of 109.5° *(1 mark)*.
4 a) (i) Electronegativity is the ability of an atom to attract the bonding electrons *(1 mark)* in a covalent bond *(1 mark)*.
      (ii) If there's a difference in the electronegativities of two covalently bonded atoms *(1 mark)* there's a shift in the electron density towards the more electronegative atom, making the bond polar *(1 mark)*. This creates a dipole and causes weak electrostatic forces of attraction between molecules *(1 mark)*.
   b) (i) HCl: permanent dipole-dipole forces *(1 mark)*
      $CH_4$: van der Waals forces / induced dipole interactions / temporary dipole-temporary dipole *(1 mark)*
      HF: hydrogen bonds *(1 mark)*
      (ii)

*(3 marks, otherwise 1 mark for showing all lone pairs, 1 mark for showing the partial charges and 1 mark for showing the hydrogen bond going from a lone pair on an F atom to an H atom.)*
      (iii) The Cl atoms in $Cl_2$ have equal electronegativities so the covalent bond is non-polar *(1 mark)*.
5 a)

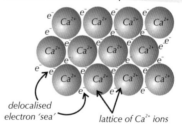

delocalised electron 'sea'        lattice of $Ca^{2+}$ ions

*(2 marks, otherwise 1 mark for showing the positive calcium ions, 1 mark for showing the delocalised electrons surrounding the ions.)*
The delocalised electrons are free to move within the structure so are able to carry the charge and allow current to flow *(1 mark)*.
   b) (i) A compound containing ions held together by ionic bonding *(1 mark)*. An ionic bond is an electrostatic attraction between two oppositely charged ions *(1 mark)*.
      (ii) $1s^2\ 2s^2\ 2p^6\ 3s^2\ 3p^6$ *(1 mark)*
      (iii)

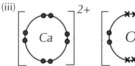

*(2 marks, otherwise 1 mark for showing the correct number of outer electrons, 1 mark for showing the correct charges.)*
   c) (i) $CO_3^{2-}$ *(1 mark)*
      (ii) Carbon dioxide is linear *(1 mark)* with a bond angle of 180° *(1 mark)*. The molecule has two double bonds and no lone pairs on the central atom *(1 mark)* and the bonding pairs repel each other as much as possible *(1 mark)*.

# Module 3 — The Periodic Table

## 1. The Periodic Table

### Page 82 — Application Questions
Q1 a) 3
   b) 4
   c) 5
Q2 a) 6
   b) 3
   c) 1
Q3 a) $1s^2\,2s^2\,2p^6\,3s^1$
   b) $1s^2\,2s^2\,2p^6\,3s^2\,3p^6\,4s^2$
   c) $1s^2\,2s^2\,2p^6\,3s^2\,3p^5$
   d) $1s^2\,2s^2\,2p^6\,3s^2\,3p^6\,3d^{10}\,4s^2\,4p^3$
   e) $1s^2\,2s^2\,2p^6\,3s^2\,3p^6\,3d^3\,4s^2$
   f) $1s^2\,2s^2\,2p^6\,3s^2\,3p^6\,3d^1\,4s^2$

### Page 82 — Fact Recall Questions
Q1 a) Mendeleev arranged the elements by atomic mass but left gaps where the next element didn't seem to fit so that he could keep elements with similar chemical properties in the same group.
   b) In the modern periodic table the elements are arranged by atomic number.
Q2 a) A period is a row in the periodic table.
   b) A group is a column in the periodic table.
Q3 Elements in a group have similar chemical properties because they all have the same number of electrons in their outer shell.

## 2. Periodic Trends

### Pages 86-87 — Application Questions
Q1 a) Lithium is a metal so it has strong metallic bonds holding all the atoms together. Nitrogen is a molecular substance with only van der Waals forces between the molecules. It takes much less energy to break van der Waals forces than metallic bonds, so the boiling point of lithium is much higher than the boiling point of nitrogen.
   b) Beryllium and lithium are both metals so both have strong metallic bonds holding the atoms together. But a beryllium ion has a charge of 2+ so there are 2 delocalised electrons per ion, while a lithium ion only has a charge of 1+ and 1 delocalised electron per ion. As a result, beryllium ions have a greater charge density so the metallic bonds in beryllium are stronger and it has a higher boiling point.
Q2 a) Magnesium forms 2+ ions so there are two delocalised electrons for each ion. Sodium only forms 1+ ions so there is only one delocalised electron for each ion. Because magnesium contains more delocalised electrons than sodium, magnesium has a higher charge density so the metallic bonds in magnesium are stronger than the metallic bonds in sodium. As a result, more energy is required to break the bonds and the melting temperature of magnesium is higher.
   b) Sulfur forms $S_8$ molecules while phosphorus forms $P_4$ molecules. Because sulfur molecules are larger than phosphorus molecules, the van der Waals forces which hold the molecules together are stronger. This means more heat energy is required to break the van der Waals forces and the melting point of sulfur is higher.
Q3 a) Silicon is macromolecular so has strong covalent bonds linking all its atoms together. Phosphorus is a molecular substance with van der Waals forces between its molecules. It takes much less energy to break van der Waals forces than covalent bonds so the melting point of phosphorus is much lower than the melting point of silicon.

b) chlorine / argon
Q4 a) Aluminium has 13 protons and sulfur has 16 protons. So the positive charge of the nucleus of sulfur is greater. This means electrons are pulled closer to the nucleus, making the atomic radius of sulfur smaller than the atomic radius of aluminium.
   b) sodium/magnesium
Q5 a) Boron has 5 protons, beryllium only has 4 protons. So the positive charge of the nucleus of boron is greater. This means electrons are pulled closer to the nucleus, making the atomic radius of boron smaller than the atomic radius of beryllium.
   b) lithium
Q6 a) Calcium would have a higher boiling point than potassium. The boiling point of metals increases across a period and calcium is after potassium in Period 4.
   b) Strontium would have a smaller atomic radius than rubidium. Atomic radius generally decreases across a period and strontium is after rubidium in Period 5.
   c) Bromine would have a higher first ionisation energy than selenium. Ionisation energy generally increases across a period and bromine is after selenium in Period 4.

### Page 87 — Fact Recall Questions
Q1 Periodicity means the repeating trends in the physical and chemical properties of the elements as you go across a period.
Q2 The melting and boiling points generally increase from lithium to carbon, but then decrease from carbon to neon.
Q3 a) The atomic radius decreases across the period.
   b) As you move across the period the amount of shielding remains constant but the number of protons increases, so the positive charge of the nucleus increases. As a result, electrons are pulled closer to the nucleus, making the atomic radius smaller.
Q4 a) There's a general increase in the first ionisation energy as you go across a period.
   b) As you move across the period the amount of shielding remains constant but the number of protons increases and the amount of nuclear attraction increases. As a result the electrons become more difficult to remove, increasing the first ionisation energy.
Q5 As you go down a group the number of electron shells increases. This means that the outer electron is further from the nucleus and there are more inner electron shells shielding the outer electron from the nucleus. As a result, the attraction between the nucleus and the outer electron is reduced so the outer electron is easier to lose and the first ionisation energy is lower.

## 3. Group 2 — The Alkaline Earth Metals

### Pages 90-91 — Application Questions
Q1 a) $Ca_{(s)} + 2H_2O_{(l)} \rightarrow Ca(OH)_{2(aq)} + H_{2(g)}$
   b) The oxidation state of calcium increases from 0 to +2.
   c) The solution would fizz as bubbles of hydrogen gas are given off.
   d) The reaction would be more vigorous/happen faster.
   *You know the reaction would be faster/more vigorous because reactivity increases down the group.*
Q2 a) $2Sr_{(s)} + O_{2(g)} \rightarrow 2SrO_{(s)}$
   b) Strontium oxide is a white solid.
   c) $SrO_{(s)} + H_2O_{(l)} \rightarrow Sr^{2+}_{(aq)} + 2OH^-_{(aq)}$
   d) pH 12 – 13
   *The solution is strongly alkaline due to the OH⁻ ions that are released when the strontium hydroxide dissolves in the water.*

Q3 a) $MgCO_{3(s)} \rightarrow MgO_{(s)} + CO_{2(g)}$
b) Higher — thermal stability increases down the group.

## Page 91 — Fact Recall Questions
Q1 As you go down the group ionisation energy decreases. The lower the ionisation energy the easier it is to lose electrons and the more reactive the element is. So reactivity increases down the group.
Q2 a) 2+
b) Group 2 elements have two electrons in their outer shell. When they lose these two electrons to form 2+ ions they end up with a full outer electron shell (the same as the noble gases). This is very stable so Group 2 elements usually form 2+ ions.
Q3 An increase in oxidation state from 0 to +2.
Q4 pH 12 – 13
Q5 Thermal stability of the Group 2 carbonates increases down the group.
Q6 Calcium hydroxide is used in agriculture to neutralise acid soils. Magnesium hydroxide is used in some indigestion tablets as an antacid.

## 4. Group 7 — The Halogens
## Page 95 — Application Questions
Q1 Bromine atoms have fewer electrons than iodine atoms. As a result the van der Waals forces in bromine are weaker than those in iodine. So less energy is required to break the intermolecular forces and the boiling point is lower.
Q2 Atoms of the other halogens are larger than fluorine atoms. This means their outer electrons are further from the nucleus and there are more electron shells shielding the outer electrons from the nucleus. So the nuclear attraction is less and it is more difficult for the other halogens to gain an electron. So they are less reactive than fluorine.
Q3 a) There are iodide ions in the unknown solution.
b) $Br_{2(aq)} + 2I^-_{(aq)} \rightarrow 2Br^-_{(aq)} + I_{2(aq)}$
Q4 a) iodide ions
b) fluoride ions
c) bromide ions

## Page 95 — Fact Recall Questions
Q1 The boiling points of the halogens increase down the group. This is due to the increasing strength of the van der Waals forces as the size and relative mass of the atoms increases.
Q2 As you go down the group, the atoms become larger so the outer electrons are further from the nucleus. The outer electrons are also shielded more from the attraction of the positive nucleus, because there are more inner electrons. This makes it harder for larger atoms to attract the electron needed to form an ion (despite the increased charge on the nucleus), so larger atoms are less reactive.
Q3 Bromide ions and iodide ions.
Q4 a) Pale yellow/green
b) Orange/red
c) Violet/pink
Q5 The silver nitrate test. Add dilute nitric acid to remove any ions that might interfere with the reaction. Then add silver nitrate and a precipitate will be formed. The colour of the precipitate identifies the halide (chloride gives a white precipitate, bromide gives a cream precipitate and iodide gives a yellow precipitate). If no precipitate forms it must be fluoride ions.

## 5. Disproportionation and Water Treatment
## Page 98 — Application Questions
Q1 a) $I_{2(s)} + 2KOH_{(aq)} \rightarrow KIO_{(aq)} + KI_{(aq)} + H_2O_{(l)}$
b) The oxidation number of iodine increases from 0 in $I_2$ to +1 in KIO and decreases from 0 to –1 in KI. So iodine is simultaneously oxidised and reduced and it is a disproportionation reaction.
Q2 The oxidation state of O in $H_2O_2$ is –1. When $H_2O$ is formed, the oxidation state of O decreases from –1 to –2. This is a reduction reaction. When $O_2$ is formed the oxidation state of O increases from –1 to 0. This is an oxidation reaction. So O is being simultaneously oxidised and reduced and it is a disproportionation reaction.
Q3 a) $HClO_{(aq)} + H_2O_{(l)} \rightarrow ClO^-_{(aq)} + H_3O^+_{(aq)}$
b) Chlorate(I) ions kill bacteria so adding them to water can make it safe to drink or swim in.

## Page 98 — Fact Recall Questions
Q1 Disproportionation is when a single element is simultaneously oxidised and reduced during a reaction.
Q2 a) sodium chlorate(I), sodium chloride, water
b) $2NaOH_{(aq)} + Cl_{2(g)} \rightarrow NaClO_{(aq)} + NaCl_{(aq)} + H_2O_{(l)}$
Q3 When you mix chlorine with water, it undergoes disproportionation. It makes a mixture of hydrochloric acid and chloric(I) acid. The aqueous chloric(I) acid then ionises to make chlorate(I) ions.
Q4 a) Chlorine kills disease-causing microorganisms. It also prevents the growth of algae, eliminating bad tastes and smells, and removes discolouration caused by organic compounds.
b) Chlorine gas is very harmful if it's breathed in — it irritates the respiratory system. Liquid chlorine on the skin or eyes causes severe chemical burns. Accidents involving chlorine could be really serious, or fatal. Water contains a variety of organic compounds, e.g. from the decomposition of plants. Chlorine reacts with these compounds to form chlorinated hydrocarbons, e.g. chloromethane ($CH_3Cl$) — and many of these chlorinated hydrocarbons are carcinogenic (cancer-causing).
Q5 a) Fluoride ions are also added to water.
b) There is evidence showing that fluoride ions prevent tooth decay.
c) There is some evidence linking fluoridated water to some bone cancers / most toothpaste is fluoridated so some people think adding fluoride ions to water is unnecessary.

## Exam-style Questions — pages 100-102
1 a) (i) Arsenic, p-block (*1 mark*)
(ii) $1s^2 2s^2 2p^6 3s^2 3p^6 3d^{10} 4s^2 4p^3$ (*1 mark*)
b) (i) $2Sr_{(s)} + O_{2(g)} \rightarrow 2SrO_{(s)}$
$2Ba_{(s)} + O_{2(g)} \rightarrow 2BaO_{(s)}$
(*1 mark for correct equations, 1 mark for state symbols*).
(ii) Strontium and barium are in the same group of the periodic table so have similar electron configurations/have the same number of electrons in their outer shell (*1 mark*). This means they have similar chemical properties so they react with oxygen in similar ways (*1 mark*).
2 a) (i) As you move from Na to Al the metal ions have an increasing number of delocalised electrons (*1 mark*). This means that the metallic bonds are stronger (*1 mark*) so more energy is required to break the bonds and boil the metal (*1 mark*).

(ii) Si has a giant, macromolecular structure *(1 mark)* with strong covalent bonds holding the atoms together *(1 mark)*. Lots of energy is required to break these bonds so the boiling point of Si is extremely high *(1 mark)*.

(iii) Sulfur forms larger molecules than chlorine ($S_8$ compared to $Cl_2$) so its molecules have more electrons *(1 mark)*. So the van der Waals forces holding the sulfur molecules together are stronger *(1 mark)*. So more energy is required to break the bonds and the boiling point is higher *(1 mark)*.

b) (i) Aluminium has more protons than magnesium *(1 mark)*. This means there is greater attraction between the nucleus and the outer electron shell *(1 mark)*. So the outer electron shell is pulled closer to the nucleus and the atomic radius decreases *(1 mark)*.

(ii) E.g. silicon/phosphorus/sulfur/chlorine/argon *(1 mark)*.

c) First ionisation energy increases across Period 2 *(1 mark)*. The number of protons increases across the period so nuclear attraction also increases *(1 mark — nuclear must be spelled correctly at least once to get this mark)*. All of the electrons are at roughly the same energy level *(1 mark)* so there is little extra shielding or extra distance to lessen the attraction *(1 mark)*. The stronger attraction means that more energy is required to remove the outer electron so the ionisation energy is higher *(1 mark)*.

3 a) (i) $Ca_{(s)} + 2H_2O_{(l)} \rightarrow Ca(OH)_{2\,(aq)} + H_{2\,(g)}$ *(1 mark)*.

(ii) The calcium would disappear/dissolve *(1 mark)* and the solution would fizz/bubbles would be produced *(1 mark)*.

*Make sure you describe what you actually see here. If you just say hydrogen gas is given off you won't get the mark because you can't actually see the hydrogen gas. What you can see is the bubbles that are produced.*

(iii) pH 12-13 *(1 mark)*.

b) (i) Calcium hydroxide is used in agriculture to neutralise acidic soils *(1 mark)*.

(ii) $H^+_{(aq)} + OH^-_{(aq)} \rightarrow H_2O_{(l)}$ *(1 mark)*

c) (i) Ionisation energy decreases as you move down the group *(1 mark)*. Elements further down the group have more electron shells *(1 mark)*. This means the outer electron is further from the nucleus *(1 mark)* and there are more inner shells shielding the outer electrons from the nucleus *(1 mark)*. As a result, nuclear attraction is reduced *(1 mark)*. So less energy is needed to remove the outer electron and the ionisation energy is lower *(1 mark)*.

(ii) Calcium is below magnesium in the group, so it has a lower first (and second) ionisation energy *(1 mark)*. Because its outer electrons are more easily removed, it reacts more vigorously *(1 mark)*.

(iii) E.g. It is used as an antacid in some indigestion tablets *(1 mark)*.

4 a) A chlorine atom is smaller than a bromine atom *(1 mark)* so its outer electron shell is less shielded/closer to the nucleus *(1 mark)*. This means nuclear attraction is greater so chlorine is able to gain an electron more easily and is a stronger oxidising agent *(1 mark)*.

b) (i) $Cl_{2(aq)} + 2Br^-_{(aq)} \rightarrow 2Cl^-_{(aq)} + Br_{2(aq)}$ *(1 mark)*.

(ii) Potassium bromide solution would give an orange/red colour *(1 mark)*, whereas potassium iodide solution would give a violet/pink colour *(1 mark)*.

c) (i) Add dilute nitric acid to the unknown solution to remove any ions that might interfere with the test *(1 mark)*. Add silver nitrate and a precipitate will form *(1 mark)*. The precipitate will be cream coloured if $Br^-$ ions are present *(1 mark)*.

(ii) $Ag^+_{(aq)} + Br^-_{(aq)} \rightarrow AgBr_{(s)}$ *(1 mark for equation, 1 mark for state symbols)*.

*You know the AgBr has to be a solid because this is the precipitate that forms.*

(iii) He could add ammonia solution and look at the solubility of the precipitate *(1 mark)*. AgBr will dissolve in concentrated ammonia but not dilute ammonia *(1 mark)*.

5 a) $2NaOH_{(aq)} + Cl_{2\,(g)} \rightarrow NaClO_{(aq)} + NaCl_{(aq)} + H_2O_{(l)}$ *(1 mark)*.
NaClO is used as bleach *(1 mark)*.
Uses of bleach: any two from, e.g. bleaching paper / bleaching textiles / water treatment / cleaning products *(1 mark for each)*.
The oxidation state of chlorine increases from 0 to +1 in NaClO and decreases from 0 to –1 in NaCl *(1 mark)*. Because chlorine is simultaneously oxidised and reduced it is a disproportionation reaction *(1 mark)*.

b) $Cl_{2(g)} + H_2O_{(l)} \rightleftharpoons HCl_{(aq)} + HClO_{(aq)}$ *(1 mark)*.
$HClO_{(aq)} + H_2O_{(l)} \rightleftharpoons ClO^-_{(aq)} + H_3O^+_{(aq)}$ *(1 mark)*.
Advantages: any two from, e.g. it kills disease-causing microorganisms / it stays in the water and prevents reinfection further down the supply / it prevents growth of algae / it eliminates bad tastes and odours / it removes discolouration caused by organic compounds *(1 mark for each)*.
Disadvantages: any two from: chlorine gas is toxic / liquid chlorine causes severe chemical burns / chlorine reacts with organic compounds to form chlorinated hydrocarbons which are carcinogenic / it could be considered unethical that people aren't given a choice *(1 mark for each)*.

*If you're asked to discuss the advantages and disadvantages, make sure you talk about both. If you just talk about advantages or just talk about disadvantages you'll lose marks for sure.*

# Unit 2

## Module 1 — Basic Concepts and Hydrocarbons

### 2. Formulas

#### Pages 106-107 — Application Questions

Q1

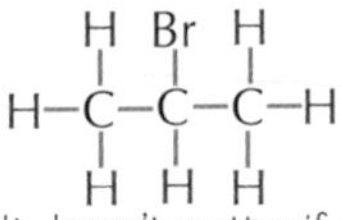

It doesn't matter if you draw the bromine atom above or below the carbon atom — it means the same thing.

Q2 $C_8H_{18}$

Q3 a) $CH_2$
b) $C_4H_7Br$
c) $C_9H_{17}Cl_3$

Q4 a) $C_4H_8$
b) Heptene contains 14 H atoms.

Q5 a) $C_3H_6Br_2$
b)

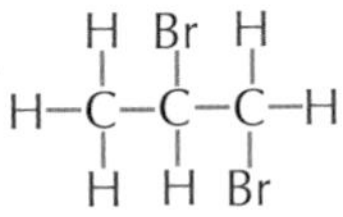

c) $C_3H_6Br_2$
For this molecule the empirical formula is the same as the molecular formula because you can't cancel the atoms down and still have whole numbers.

Q6 a) $C_5H_{10}$
b) $CH_3CH_2CH_2CHCH_2$
c) $CH_2$

Q7 a)

Skeletal formulas have a carbon atom at each end and at each junction.

b)

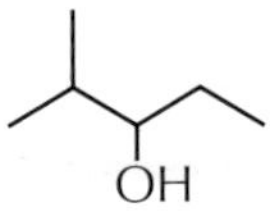

c)

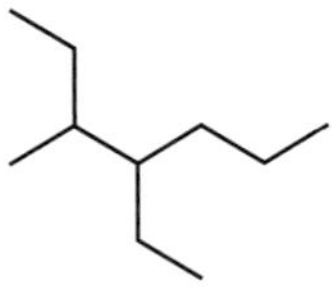

d)

Q8 a) $CH_3CH(CH_3)CH(CH_3)CH_2CH_2CH_3$
b) $CH_3CH_2C(CH_2)CH_2CH_2CH_3$
c) $CH_3CH_2CClCHCH_2CH_3$
d) $CH_3CHBrCH(OH)CH_2CHCH_2$

#### Page 107 — Fact Recall Questions

Q1 A molecular formula is a formula which gives the actual number of atoms of each element in a molecule.

Q2 A displayed formula shows how all the atoms are arranged, and all the bonds between them.

Q3 To find the empirical formula you have to divide the molecular formula by the smallest number of atoms for a given element in the molecule.

Q4 A homologous series is a family of organic compounds which have the same general formula and similar chemical properties.

### 3. Structural Isomers

#### Page 110 — Application Questions

Q1

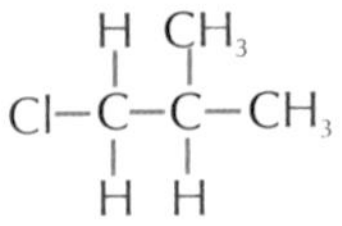

You could draw the chlorine atom attached to any other carbon atom apart from the one it was on originally.

Q2 There are three chain isomers of $C_5H_{12}$.

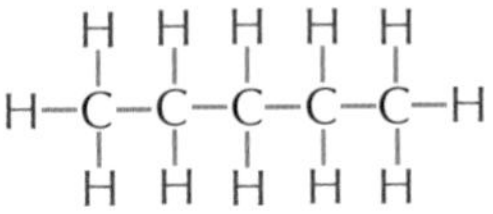

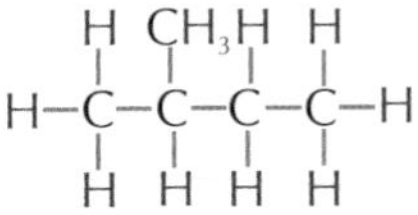

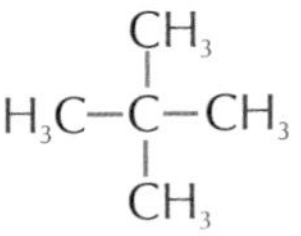

Q3

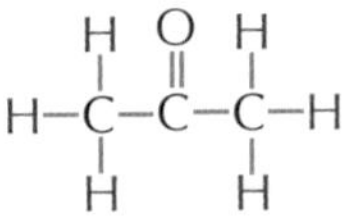

Q4 a) A and B
b) chain isomerism

#### Page 110 — Fact Recall Questions

Q1 A chain isomer is a molecule that has the same molecular formula but a different arrangement of the carbon skeleton to another molecule. Some are straight chains and others branched in different ways.

Q2 A positional isomer has the same skeleton and the same atoms or groups of atoms attached as another molecule. The difference is that the atom or group of atoms is attached to a different carbon atom.

Q3 A functional group isomer has the same atoms as another molecule but the atoms are arranged into different functional groups.

### 4. Stereoisomers

#### Page 112 — Application Questions

Q1 a) i) Z-isomer
ii) E-isomer
b) i) cis-isomer
ii) trans-isomer

Q2

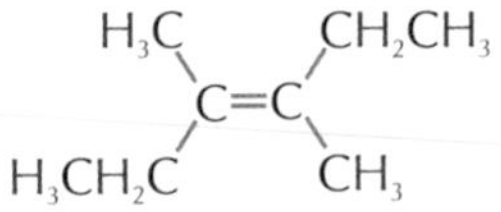

E-isomer

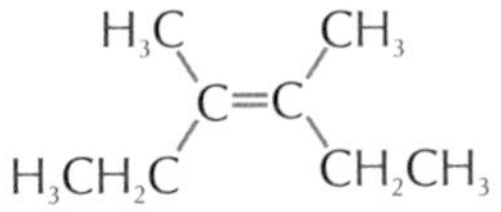

Z-isomer

## 5. Chemical Yield

### Page 114 — Application Questions
Q1 % yield = (actual yield ÷ theoretical yield) × 100
 = (1.76 ÷ 3.24) × 100 = **54.3%**
Q2 % yield = (actual yield ÷ theoretical yield) × 100
 = (3.70 ÷ 6.10) × 100 = **60.7%**
Q3 a) Molar mass of $(CH_3CO)_2O$ = 2 × ((12 + (3 × 1) + 12 + 16)) + 16 = 102 g mol$^{-1}$
 Number of moles $(CH_3CO)_2O$ = mass ÷ molar mass
 = 3.00 ÷ 102 = **0.0294 moles**
 b) From the equation: 1 mole of $(CH_3CO)_2O$ produces 2 moles of $CH_3COOH$, so 0.0294 moles of $(CH_3CO)_2O$ will produce (0.0294 × 2) = 0.0588 moles of $CH_3COOH$.
 Molar mass of $CH_3COOH$ = 12 + (3 × 1) + 12 + 16 + 16 + 1 = 60 g mol$^{-1}$
 Theoretical yield = moles $CH_3COOH$ × molar mass
 = 0.0588 × 60 = **3.53 g**
 c) % yield = (actual yield ÷ theoretical yield) × 100
 = (2.80 ÷ 3.53) × 100 = **79.3%**
Q4 a) Molar mass of $CH_3CHCH_2$ = 12 + (3 × 1) + 12 + 1 + 12 + (2 × 1) = 42 g mol$^{-1}$
 Number of moles $CH_3CHCH_2$ = mass ÷ molar mass
 = 50 ÷ 42 = 1.19 moles
 From the equation: 1 mole of $CH_3CHCH_2$ produces 1 mole of $CH_3CH_2CH_2Cl$, so 1.19 moles of $CH_3CHCH_2$ will produce 1.19 moles of $CH_3CH_2CH_2Cl$.
 Molar mass of $CH_3CH_2CH_2Cl$ = 12 + (3 × 1) + 12 + (2 × 1) + 12 + (2 × 1) + 35.5 = 78.5 g mol$^{-1}$
 Theoretical yield = moles $CH_3CH_2CH_2Cl$ × molar mass
 = 1.19 × 78.5 = **93.4 g**
 b) % yield = (actual yield ÷ theoretical yield) × 100
 = (54 ÷ 93.4) × 100 = **57.8%**
Q5 Molar mass of HCOOH = 1 + 12 + 16 + 16 + 1 = 46 g mol$^{-1}$
 Number of moles HCOOH = mass ÷ molar mass
 = 4.70 ÷ 46 = 0.102 moles
 From the equation: 2 moles of HCOOH produce 1 mole of $(CHO)_2O$, so 0.102 moles of NaOH will produce (0.102 ÷ 2) = 0.051 moles of $(CHO)_2O$.
 Molar mass of $(CHO)_2O$ = (2 × (12 + 1 + 16)) + 16 = 74 gmol$^{-1}$
 Theoretical yield = moles $(CHO)_2O$ × molar mass
 = 0.051 × 74 = 3.77 g
 % yield = (actual yield ÷ theoretical yield) × 100
 = (3.60 ÷ 3.77) × 100 = **95.5%**

### Page 114 — Fact Recall Questions
Q1 The theoretical yield is the mass of product that should be formed in a chemical reaction, assuming no chemicals are 'lost' in the process.

Q2 percentage yield = $\dfrac{\text{actual yield}}{\text{theoretical yield}}$ × 100

## 6. Atom Economy

### Page 117 — Application Questions
Q1 a) mass of products = (12 + (3 × 1) + 35.5) + (1 + 35.5) = **87**
 b) mass of $CH_3Cl$ = 12 + (3 × 1) + 35.5 = **50.5**

 c) % atom economy = $\dfrac{M_r \text{ of desired product}}{\text{Total mass of all products}}$ × 100
 = (50.5 ÷ 87) × 100 = **58.0%**
 d) E.g. sell the HCl so it can be used in other chemical reactions / use the HCl as a reactant in another reaction.

Q2 mass of product = (2 × 12) + (5 × 1) + 16 + 1 = 46
 mass of $C_2H_5OH$ = (2 × 12) + (5 × 1) + 16 + 1 = 46

 % atom economy = $\dfrac{M_r \text{ of desired product}}{\text{Total mass of all products}}$ × 100
 = (46 ÷ 46) × 100 = **100%**

 *Award yourself an extra chocolate biscuit if you spotted that this reaction has 100% atom economy before you did the calculations — any reaction where there's only one product will have 100% atom economy.*
Q3 mass of $C_2H_4$ = (2 × 12) + (4 × 1) = 28
 mass of $H_2O$ = (2 × 1) + 16 = 18
 total mass of products = 28 + 18 = 46
 mass of $C_2H_4$ produced = 2 × (12 + (2 × 1)) = 28

 % atom economy = $\dfrac{M_r \text{ of desired product}}{\text{Total mass of all products}}$ × 100
 = (28 ÷ 46) × 100 = **60.9%**
Q4 a) Reaction 1:
 mass of products = 2 × (14 + (3 × 1)) = 34
 mass of $2NH_3$ = 2 × (14 + (3 × 1)) = 34

 % atom economy = $\dfrac{M_r \text{ of desired product}}{\text{Total mass of all products}}$ × 100
 = (34 ÷ 34) × 100 = **100%**

 Reaction 2:
 mass of $CaCl_2$ = 40.1 + (35.5 × 2) = 111.1
 mass of $2NH_3$ = 2 × (14 + (3 × 1)) = 34
 mass of $2H_2O$ = 2 × ((2 × 1) + 16) = 36
 total mass of products = 181.1
 mass of $2NH_3$ = 2 × (14 + (3 × 1)) = 34

 % atom economy = $\dfrac{M_r \text{ of desired product}}{\text{Total mass of all products}}$ × 100
 = (34 ÷ 181.1) × 100 = **18.8%**
 b) E.g. reaction 1 has a much higher atom economy / produces no waste.

### Page 117 — Fact Recall Questions
Q1 Atom economy is the proportion of reactant atoms that become part of the desired product (rather than by-products) in the balanced chemical equation.

Q2 % atom economy = $\dfrac{M_r \text{ of desired product}}{\text{Total mass of all products}}$ × 100

Q3 Any two from: e.g. for low atom economy reactions there's lots of waste produced / it costs money to separate the desired product from waste / it costs money to dispose of waste products safely / reactant chemicals are expensive so it wastes money if a high proportion of them end up as useless products / high atom economy reactions are more sustainable.

## 7. Alkanes and Nomenclature

### Page 120 — Application Questions
Q1 a) butane
 b) ethane
 c) methane
 d) nonane
 e) heptane
 f) decane
Q2 a) 3-methylpentane
 b) 3-ethyl-3-methylpentane
 c) 3,3-diethylhexane
 d) 3,3-diethyl-2-methylhexane

### Page 120 — Fact Recall Questions
Q1 $C_nH_{2n+2}$
Q2 A cycloalkane is a ring of carbon atoms with two hydrogens attached to each carbon.

## 8. Properties of Alkanes

### Page 123 — Application Questions

Q1  a)  Octane molecules are larger than propane molecules, so there is more surface contact between the octane molecules than the propane molecules. As a result the van der Waals forces between octane molecules are stronger than those between propane molecules. So more energy is required to break the forces and the boiling point is higher.

*In questions like this, make sure you give your answer as a comparison. If you just say octane molecules are big so it has a high boiling point you won't get the marks. You have to say that octane molecules are bigger than propane molecules so octane has a higher boiling point than propane.*

b)  When alkanes burn, some energy is used in breaking the covalent bonds but more energy is released by forming the new bonds in the products ($CO_2$ and $H_2O$). Octane releases more energy per mole than propane, because more $CO_2$ and $H_2O$ are formed from 1 mole of octane than 1 mole of propane.

c)  Complete combustion:
$2C_8H_{18} + 25O_2 \rightarrow 16CO_2 + 18H_2O$
Incomplete combustion:
$2C_8H_{18} + 17O_2 \rightarrow 16CO + 18H_2O$

Q2  Pentane has a higher boiling point. 2,2-dimethylpropane is branched, so the molecules don't pack together closely and there is less surface contact between molecules than in pentane, which is a straight-chain molecule. As a result there are more van der Waals forces between molecules of pentane than between 2,2-dimethylpropane molecules and so more energy is required to break them. So pentane has the higher boiling point.

### Page 123 — Fact Recall Questions

Q1  The molecules form tetrahedral shapes around each carbon.

Q2  The length of the carbon–carbon chain and the amount of branching in the molecule.

Q3  The products of complete combustion are carbon dioxide and water. The products of incomplete combustion are carbon monoxide and water (and sometimes particulate carbon and carbon dioxide).

Q4  E.g. propane is used as a central heating and cooking fuel / butane is used for camping gas / petrol and diesel are made up of mixtures of alkanes and are used as fuels for transport.

Q5  Carbon monoxide binds to haemoglobin in the blood. This prevents the haemoglobin binding to oxygen. As a result less oxygen can be transported around the body and symptoms of oxygen deprivation occur.

## 9. Petroleum

### Page 127 — Application Questions

Q1  Any three from: methane ($CH_4$), ethane ($C_2H_6$), propane ($C_3H_8$) or butane ($C_4H_{10}$).

Q2  a)  It easily auto-ignites in a petrol engine and doesn't combust very efficiently.

b)  By adding in hydrocarbons with higher octane ratings, e.g. shorter branched-chain alkanes, cycloalkanes or arenes.

Q3  a)  High octane fuels can be burnt more efficiently than low octane fuels because they are less likely to auto-ignite.

b)  Shorter branched-chain alkanes like 2,2,4-trimethylpentane or cycloalkanes like cyclohexane.

Q4  a)

b)  Pass the mixture through a molecular sieve (zeolite). Straight-chain molecules go through the sieve, branched molecules are filtered out.

Q5  a)

b)  A catalyst made of platinum and another metal, bound to inert aluminium oxide.

### Page 127 — Fact Recall Questions

Q1  A mixture that consists mainly of alkane hydrocarbons.

Q2  They are separated by their boiling points.

Q3  a)  Cracking is breaking long-chain alkanes into smaller hydrocarbons.

b)  A catalyst, high temperature and moderate pressure.

Q4  There is more demand for lighter petroleum fractions so, to meet the demand, the heavier fractions are cracked into lighter fractions.

Q5  The reaction can be done at a lower temperature and pressure.

Q6  a)  Octane ratings tell you how likely a fuel is to auto-ignite and how efficiently it can be burnt.

b)  Petrols with high octane ratings can be burnt more efficiently than petrols with low octane ratings.

Q7  By isomerisation. Straight-chain alkanes are heated with a catalyst stuck on inert aluminium oxide. The alkanes break up and join back together as branched isomers.

Q8  By reforming. Straight-chain alkanes are mixed with a catalyst made of platinum and another metal, stuck on inert aluminium oxide. The straight-chain alkanes break up and reform into cyclic alkanes.

## 10. Fossil Fuels

### Page 129 — Fact Recall Questions

Q1  Fossil fuels are used as an energy source and as raw materials in the production of plastics and petrochemicals.

Q2  Any two from: e.g. burning fossil fuels produces $CO_2$ which is a greenhouse gas and contributes to global warming / fossil fuels are non-renewable and will eventually run out.

Q3  a)  Bioethanol is made by the fermentation of sugar from crops such as maize.

b)  Biodiesel is made by refining renewable fats and oils, such as vegetable oils.

Q4  Biodiesel and bioethanol are thought of as carbon-neutral because all the $CO_2$ that is released when these fuels are burnt was removed by the crop as it grew.

Q5  Biodiesel and bioethanol aren't 100% carbon-neutral because making fertilisers and powering agricultural machinery to harvest/process the crops will probably involve using fossil fuels which release $CO_2$.

Q6  Advantages: e.g. they are nearly carbon-neutral / they are a renewable source of energy / they avoid the need to use fossil fuels which release $CO_2$.
Disadvantages: e.g. if poorer countries convert a lot of their land to grow crops for fuel they may not be able to grow enough food to eat / forests are being cleared to make room for biofuels and these would absorb more $CO_2$ than the crop / growing crops for fuel may reduce soil fertility.

## 11. Bond Fission

### Page 130 — Fact Recall Questions
Q1   The breaking of a covalent bond.
Q2   a)  Heterolytic fission and homolytic fission.
     b)  In heterolytic fission two different substances are formed — a positively charged cation and a negatively charged anion. In homolytic fission, two electrically uncharged radicals are formed.
Q3   A free radical is a particle with an unpaired electron.
Q4   a)  The movement of a pair of electrons.
     b)  The movement of a single electron.

## 12. Substitution Reactions

### Page 132 — Application Questions
Q1   a)  Initiation, propagation and termination.
     b)  Initiation:
         $Br_2 \rightarrow 2Br\cdot$
         Propagation:
         $Br\cdot + CH_4 \rightarrow CH_3\cdot + HBr$
         $CH_3\cdot + Br_2 \rightarrow CH_3Br + Br\cdot$
         Termination:
         E.g. $CH_3\cdot + Br\cdot \rightarrow CH_3Br$ / $CH_3\cdot + CH_3\cdot \rightarrow C_2H_6$
     c)  E.g. $CH_2Br_2$ / $CHBr_3$ / $CBr_4$
Q2   a)  Free-radical substitution.
     b)  Initiation: UV light provides enough energy to split the Cl–Cl bond (homolytic fission), this produces two radicals.
         $Cl_2 \rightarrow 2Cl\cdot$
         Propagation: free radicals are created and used up in a chain reaction.
         E.g. $Cl\cdot + C_2H_6 \rightarrow C_2H_5\cdot + HCl$
         E.g. $C_2H_5\cdot + Cl_2 \rightarrow C_2H_5Cl + Cl\cdot$
         Termination: the free radicals are mopped up — two radicals react together to form a stable molecule.
         E.g. $C_2H_5\cdot + Cl\cdot \rightarrow C_2H_5Cl$ / $C_2H_5\cdot + C_2H_5\cdot \rightarrow C_4H_{10}$
     c)  Make sure the ethane is in excess.

### Page 132 — Fact Recall Questions
Q1   $Cl_2 + CH_4 \rightarrow CH_3Cl + HCl$
Q2   UV light
Q3   homolytic fission
Q4   Some or all of the hydrogen atoms found on halogenoalkane molecules can be swapped for halogen atoms, creating multi-substituted products like $CH_2Cl_2$, $CHCl_3$ and $CCl_4$.

## 13. Alkenes and Their Properties

### Page 136 — Application Questions
Q1   a)  propene
     b)  but-2-ene
     c)  hexa-1,3-diene / 1,3-hexadiene
     d)  methylpropene
Q2   Propene is an alkene so it contains a double bond. Because there are two electron pairs in the bond the C=C double bond has a really high electron density. Plus, the π bond sticks out above and below the rest of the molecule. These two factors mean that propene is susceptible to attack by electrophiles. Propane doesn't contain a double bond so isn't susceptible to attack by electrophiles. So propene is more reactive.
Q3   Double bonds are formed from a sigma bond and a pi bond. Single bonds are just sigma bonds. The pi bond is weaker than the sigma bond so the double bond is not twice as strong as a single bond.

### Page 136 — Fact Recall Questions
Q1   $C_nH_{2n}$
Q2   a)

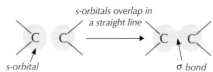

This is how you need to draw your diagram in the exam (though it doesn't have to be coloured in). Make sure you label the s-orbitals and the sigma bond and make sure you say how the orbitals are overlapping. Otherwise you might lose out on valuable marks.
     b)

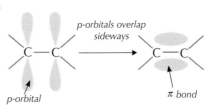

Q3   electrophiles
Q4   a)  Trigonal planar means that all of the atoms lie in the same plane and are at the corners of an imaginary equilateral triangle with bond angles of 120° between them, like the atoms attached to a double-bonded carbon atom.
     b)  The atoms attached to each carbon in the C=C double bond of alkenes have a trigonal planar shape.
Q5   The carbons atoms in the C=C bond can't rotate because the p-orbitals have to stay in the same position to overlap and form a π bond. The restricted rotation around the C=C double bond is what causes E/Z isomerism.

## 14. Polymers

### Page 138 — Application Questions
Q1   a)

F   CH₃
— C — C —
Br   H

If you're asked to draw more than one repeating unit in the exam, make sure you draw them all linked together. You won't get the marks if you draw them separately.
     b)

H₃C   H
— C — C —
H₃C   CH₃

     c)

H   H
— C — C —
    H
(benzene ring)

Q2   a)

H₃C        H
   C = C
H        CH₃

     b)

Br       H
   C = C
Br       H

     c)

H₃C        CH₃
   C = C
H₃C        CH₃

## Page 138 — Fact Recall Questions

Q1 Addition polymers

Q2 The double bond of the alkene opens up and the alkenes join together to form a polymer.

Q3 a) E.g. making water pipes / insulation for electric wires / building material.

b) E.g. non-stick coatings on pans.

# 15. Disposing of Polymers

## Page 141 — Fact Recall Questions

Q1 a) It means they won't react when they are being used (e.g. food doesn't react with PTFE coating on pans, plastic windows don't rot etc.).

b) Because they are unreactive, most plastics are non-biodegradable, so disposing of them is a problem.

Q2 Any two from: e.g. the plastic is too difficult to separate from other waste / it's not produced in sufficient quantities to make separating financially worthwhile / it's too technically difficult to recycle.

Q3 a) E.g. by melting and remoulding / by cracking into monomers which can be used to make more plastic or other chemicals.

b) Plastic products are marked with numbers which show what type of plastic they are made from.

Q4 a) HCl

b) By passing the waste gases through a scrubber which can neutralise the HCl by allowing it to react with a base.

Q5 From materials such as starch or from the hydrocarbon isoprene (2-methyl-1,3-butadiene).

Q6 E.g. renewable raw materials aren't going to run out like oil will / if the polymer is plant-based the $CO_2$ released as it decomposes is the same $CO_2$ absorbed by the plant when it grew, so it is more carbon-neutral than using non-renewable raw materials / over their lifetime some plant-based polymers save energy compared to oil-based plastics.

Q7 E.g. they require specific conditions to decompose so can't just be placed in a landfill — they still have to be separated from other waste / they are more expensive than oil-based equivalents.

# 16. Reactions of Alkenes

## Page 145 — Application Questions

Q1 a) $CH_3CHCH_2 + Br_2 \rightarrow CH_3CHBrCH_2Br$

b) electrophilic substitution

*If you're asked to name and outline a mechanism, make sure you do just that. It's really easy to forget the name and dive straight in to the mechanism — but don't forget or you'll lose a valuable mark in the exam.*

c) It doesn't contain a C=C double bond.

Q2

*It doesn't matter which carbon you add the bromine to as you'll always end up with the same product (2-bromobutane).*

Q3

Q4 If only one HBr adds onto the molecule you could get any of these products:

If two HBr add onto the molecule you could get any of these molecules:

*Give yourself a pat on the back if you managed to get all of these molecules.*

## Page 145 — Fact Recall Questions

Q1 An electrophile is an electron-pair acceptor.

Q2 Any two from: e.g. $NO_2^+$ / $H^+$ / HBr / $H_2O$ / $H_2$ / $Br_2$ / $CH_3CH_2Br$.

Q3 Carbon-carbon double bonds/unsaturation/alkenes.

Q4 hydrogen bromide

Q5

$$H_2C=CH_{2(g)} + H_2O_{(g)} \underset{\substack{300\ °C \\ 60\ atm}}{\overset{H_3PO_4}{\rightleftharpoons}} CH_3CH_2OH_{(g)}$$

Q6 You can recycle the unreacted ethene gas.

## Exam-style Questions — pages 147-150

1 (a) (i) A homologous series is a group of compounds with the same functional group and the same general formula *(1 mark)*.

    (ii) $C_3H_5OCl$ *(1 mark)*

*The stem prop- means three so propanoyl chloride must contain 3 carbons.*

(b) (i) molar mass of $CH_3COCl = 12 + (3 \times 1) + 12 + 16 + 35.5 = 78.5$ g mol$^{-1}$
number of moles $CH_3COCl$ = mass ÷ molar mass
$= 10 ÷ 78.5 = 0.127$ moles *(1 mark)*.
From the equation: 1 mole of $CH_3COCl$ produces 1 mole of $CH_3COOCH_3$, so 0.127 moles of $CH_3COCl$ will produce 0.127 moles of $CH_3COOCH_3$.
molar mass of $CH_3COOCH_3 = 12 + (3 \times 1) + 12 + 16 + 16 + 12 + (3 \times 1) = 74$ g mol$^{-1}$
theoretical yield = moles $CH_3COOCH_3$ × molar mass
$= 0.127 \times 74 = $ **9.40 g** *(1 mark)*.

    (ii) % yield = (actual yield ÷ theoretical yield) × 100
$= (7.20 ÷ 9.40) \times 100 = $ **76.6%** *(1 mark)*.

    (iii) E.g. reactions with high atom economies are less wasteful / reactions with high atom economies are more sustainable / reactions with high atom economies are more profitable *(1 mark)*.

(c) (i) molar mass of $CH_3COOH = 12 + (3 \times 1) + 12 + 16 + 16 + 1 = 60$ g mol$^{-1}$
molar mass of $CH_3OH = 12 + (3 \times 1) + 16 + 1 = 32$ g mol$^{-1}$
total molar mass of reactants $= 60 + 32 = 92$ g mol$^{-1}$ *(1 mark)*.
molar mass of $CH_3COOCH_3 = 12 + (3 \times 1) + 12 + 16 + 16 + 12 + (3 \times 1) = 74$ g mol$^{-1}$
% atom economy $= \dfrac{M_r \text{ of desired product}}{\text{Total mass of all products}} \times 100$
$= (74 ÷ 92) \times 100 = $ **80.4%** *(1 mark)*.

    (ii) Structural isomers are compounds with the same molecular formula but different structural formulas *(1 mark)*.

    (iii) Functional group isomer:
E.g.

*(1 mark)*

Positional isomer:
E.g.

*(1 mark)*

2 (a) (i)

*(1 mark)*

(ii) Octane would have a higher boiling point *(1 mark)*. Octane is a straight-chain molecule. As a result there is more surface contact between octane molecules than between branched 2,2,4-trimethylpentane molecules *(1 mark)*. This means the van der Waals forces between the octane molecules are stronger / there are more van der Waals forces between the molecules *(1 mark)*. So more energy is required to overcome the van der Waals forces and the boiling point is higher *(1 mark)*.

(iii) E.g. 2,2,4-trimethylpentane is branched and branched alkanes can be burnt more efficiently / 2,2,4-trimethylpentane will have a higher octane rating and so can be burnt more efficiently *(1 mark)*.

(b) (i) $2C_8H_{18} + 25O_2 \rightarrow 16CO_2 + 18H_2O$
*(1 mark for correct reactants and products, 1 mark for correctly balanced equation)*.

(ii) Energy is released when bonds are formed in $CO_2$ and $H_2O$ *(1 mark)*. 2,2,4-trimethylpentane is larger than pentane and more $CO_2/H_2O$ is formed from it per mole, so it releases more energy per mole when it is burnt *(1 mark)*.

(c) With insufficient oxygen, incomplete combustion occurs *(1 mark)*. Incomplete combustion of alkanes produces carbon monoxide (CO) *(1 mark)*. Carbon monoxide binds to haemoglobin in the blood instead of oxygen so is toxic to humans *(1 mark)*.

3 (a) (i) Radicals are particles that have an unpaired electron *(1 mark)*.

    (ii) homolytic fission *(1 mark)*

(b) (i) $CH_3CH_3 + Br_2 \rightarrow CH_3CH_2Br + HBr$ *(1 mark)*.

    (ii) Initiation *(1 mark)*
$Br_2 \rightarrow 2Br\cdot$ *(1 mark)*
Propagation *(1 mark)*
$Br\cdot + CH_3CH_3 \rightarrow \cdot CH_2CH_3 + HBr$ *(1 mark)*
$\cdot CH_2CH_3 + Br_2 \rightarrow CH_3CH_2Br + Br\cdot$ *(1 mark)*
Termination *(1 mark)*
$\cdot CH_2CH_3 + Br\cdot \rightarrow CH_3CH_2Br$
or $\cdot CH_2CH_3 + \cdot CH_2CH_3 \rightarrow C_4H_{10}$ *(1 mark)*

(c) (i) Any two from: e.g. $CH_3CHBr_2$ / $CH_3CBr_3$ / $CH_2BrCBr_3$ / $CHBr_2CBr_3$ / $CBr_3CBr_3$ / $CH_2BrCH_2Br$ / $CHBr_2CHBr_2$ *(1 mark for each)*.

    (ii) By increasing the concentration of ethane *(1 mark)*.

4 (a) (i) cracking *(1 mark)*

    (ii) High temperature, moderate pressure and a catalyst *(1 mark)*.

    (iii) Shorter-chain alkanes and alkenes are found in things like petrol, diesel and jet fuel *(1 mark)*. These are in very high demand so companies can make more money if they crack longer-chain alkanes to shorter-chain alkanes to meet this demand *(1 mark)*.

(b) (i)

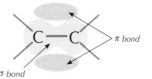

*(1 mark for diagram, 1 mark for labels)*

*Always make sure you label any diagram you draw in the exam. You could lose marks if you don't because it's the labels that show you really know what you're talking about.*

    (ii) The double bond contains two pairs of electrons, so has a really high electron density / the pi bond sticks out above and below the rest of the molecule *(1 mark)*. Electrophiles are attracted to these electron dense regions *(1 mark)*.

**(1 mark for correct curly arrows in step 1, 1 mark for correct curly arrow in step 2, 1 one mark for correct dipole shown on Br₂, 1 mark for correct carbocation)**

*Make sure your curly arrows are all top-notch — they must be going from a pair of electrons/bond to the electron acceptor. Also make sure you've included the dipoles and all the charges. You'll lose marks if these are missing too.*

(ii) The solution would go from orange to colourless **(1 mark)**.

(d)

5 (a) (i) Stereoisomerism occurs when molecules have the same structural formula **(1 mark)** but a different arrangement of atoms in space **(1 mark)**.

(ii)

(iii)

This is the E-isomer **(1 mark)**.

(b) (i) An addition polymer **(1 mark)**.

(ii)

(c) (i) Burying in landfill, recycling, burning **(1 mark)**.

(ii) Advantages: e.g. they won't permanently take up space in landfill / they avoid the need to burn plastics which produces toxic gases / they can be made from renewable materials which decreases our dependency on oil **(1 mark for each, maximum 2 marks)**.

Disadvantages: e.g. they need specific conditions to decompose so need to be sorted from other waste / they're more expensive than oil-based equivalents **(1 mark for each, maximum 2 marks)**.

*If you're asked to discuss advantages and disadvantages, make sure you talk about both. If you only mention advantages or only talk about disadvantages you'll lose marks.*

6 E.g. it's important for us to find alternatives to fossil fuels because they are non-renewable and will eventually run out **(1 mark)**. When they are burnt they release $CO_2$ which is contributing to global warming **(1 mark)**.
Plant-based alternatives to fossil fuels include bioethanol **(1 mark)** which is made by fermenting sugar from crops like maize **(1 mark)**, and biodiesel **(1 mark)** which is made by refining renewable fats and oils such as vegetable oils **(1 mark)**.
Advantages: e.g. they are renewable and will never run out / they are carbon-neutral because the $CO_2$ released when they are burnt is absorbed by the plants as they grow / they decrease the need to use fossil fuels **(1 mark for each, maximum 2 marks)**.
Disadvantages: e.g. if land is used for growing crops for fuel there may not be enough land to grow food to eat / forests may be cleared to grow crops for fuel and crops usually absorb less $CO_2$ than forests / it may reduce soil fertility **(1 mark for each, maximum 2 marks)**.

# Module 2 — Alcohols, Halogenoalkanes and Analysis

## 1. Alcohols and their Uses

### Page 153 — Application Questions

Q1 a) pentan-2-ol
b) 2-methylbutan-2-ol
c) 2,3-dimethylbutan-1-ol
d) 3-ethyl-2-methylpentane-1,5-diol
*That last one is a tricky one... Make sure you have the side chains in alphabetical order and the name has the lowest possible numbers in it.*

Q2 a) secondary
b) tertiary
c) primary

Q3 Propan-1-ol, as its hydrogen bonding allows it to mix freely with water. Octan-1-ol has a larger non-polar carbon chain, so it won't mix as easily with water molecules.

Q4 Butan-1-ol will have a higher boiling point than butane. Hydrogen bonding between the molecules in butan-1-ol means that the intermolecular forces are stronger than those in butane (which only has van der Waals forces holding its molecules together). So it will take more energy to break the molecules apart in butan-1-ol.

### Page 153 — Fact Recall Questions

Q1 -ol

Q2 A secondary alcohol is an alcohol with the –OH group attached to a carbon with two alkyl groups attached.

Q3 The hydrogen bonds between water and the hydroxyl (–OH) group in the alcohol molecules allow the alcohol molecules to mix evenly with the water.

Q4 Any three from: e.g. ethanol is the alcohol found in alcoholic drinks. / Methylated spirits is used as an industrial solvent. / Ethanol can be used as a fuel. / Unleaded petrol contains 5% methanol and 15% MTBE (an ether made from methanol) to improve combustion. / Methanol is important as a feedstock (starting point) for manufacturing organic chemicals, e.g. plastics and dyes.

## 2. Reactions of Alcohols
### Page 155 — Fact Recall Questions
Q1 300 °C, 60 atm, phosphoric acid catalyst.
Q2 a) $C_6H_{12}O_{6(aq)} \longrightarrow 2C_2H_5OH_{(aq)} + 2CO_{2(g)}$
   b) If it's too cold, the reaction is slow. If it's too hot, the enzyme is denatured.
Q3 a) When the solution reaches about 15% ethanol, the yeast dies.
   b) Fractional distillation can be used to increase the concentration of ethanol.
Q4 a) $CH_2CHOH \rightarrow CH_2CH_2 + H_2O$
   b) ethene and water
   c) E.g. concentrated sulfuric acid / concentrated phosphoric acid.

## 3. Oxidising Alcohols
### Page 159 — Application Questions
Q1 a) butanal
   b) methanoic acid
   c) pentan-3-one
   d) hexan-2-one
Q2 a)

b)

c)

*You could also draw the skeletal structures of these molecules.*

### Page 159 — Fact Recall Questions
Q1 $C_2H_5OH_{(l)} + 3O_{2(g)} \rightarrow 2CO_{2(g)} + 3H_2O_{(g)}$
Q2 Aldehydes have the functional group C=O and have one hydrogen atom and one R group attached to the carbon atom. Ketones have the functional group C=O and have two R groups attached either side of the carbon atom. Carboxylic acids have the functional group COOH.
   *As long as you've got the basic answer right, any way that you've chosen to describe the functional groups is fine — you might have written out their formulas, or even drawn them...*
Q3

## 4. Esterification and Esters
### Page 160 — Application Question
Q1 a) (i) propyl methanoate
   (ii) methyl propanoate
   b) (i) $HCOOH + CH_3CH_2CH_2OH \rightarrow$
       $HCOOCH_2CH_2CH_3 + H_2O$
   (ii) $CH_3CH_2COOH + CH_3OH \rightarrow$
       $CH_3CH_2COOCH_3 + H_2O$

## 5. Halogenoalkanes
### Page 162 — Application Question
Q1 a)

b)

c)

d)

### Page 162 — Fact Recall Questions
Q1 A halogenoalkane that contains only chlorine, fluorine and carbon atoms.
Q2 Because they're very stable, volatile and non-toxic which makes them useful for lots of applications.
Q3 E.g. HCFCs / HFCs / hydrocarbons.

## 6. More Halogenoalkanes
### Page 166 — Application Questions
Q1

Q2 Reaction C would happen the quickest because the C–I bond has the lowest bond enthalpy of all the carbon-halogen bonds. This means that the C–I bond is the easiest to break and therefore the reaction will happen the quickest.

Q3

Q4

*After this step in the mechanism the extra hydrogen atom attached to the nitrogen atom would break away and form HI with the I⁻ ion — but you wouldn't have to show this in the exam to get the marks.*

### Page 166 — Fact Recall Questions
Q1 Nucleophilic substitution reactions are reactions in which a nucleophile attacks a polar molecule and replaces a functional group.
Q2 E.g. sodium hydroxide / potassium hydroxide / water.
Q3 For a hydrolysis reaction to occur the carbon-halogen bond needs to break. The C–F bond is the strongest — it has the highest bond enthalpy. So fluoroalkanes are hydrolysed more slowly than other halogenoalkanes.
Q4 $CH_3CH_2Br + OH^- \rightarrow CH_3CH_2OH + Br^-$

E.g. set up two flasks containing the different halogenoalkanes, ethanol (as a solvent) and dilute silver nitrate solution. You can measure the rates of the reactions by timing how quickly a silver halide is precipitated. The flask which goes cloudy first contains the halogenoalkane that has the fastest rate of hydrolysis.

## 7. Infrared Spectroscopy
### Page 169 — Application Questions
Q1  a)  A (~3000 cm⁻¹) — O–H (carboxylic acid)
    B (~1700 cm⁻¹) — C=O

    b)

The mass of the carboxylic acid group (COOH) is 45 (12 + 16 + 16 + 1). The $M_r$ of the molecule is 74, so the rest of the molecule has a mass of 74 – 45 = 29. This corresponds to an ethyl group ($CH_3CH_2$), so the molecule must be propanoic acid.

Q2  There is a strong, sharp peak at about 1700 cm⁻¹, this indicates that a C=O bond is present in the molecule.

Q3  Spectrum A is the infrared spectrum for propanol.
    O–H bonds in an alcohol create a strong broad absorption at around 3200-3550 cm⁻¹. Spectrum A has this absorption and Spectrum B doesn't — so Spectrum A must be propan-2-ol.

### Page 169 — Fact Recall Questions
Q1  A beam of IR radiation is passed through a sample of a chemical. The IR radiation is absorbed by the covalent bonds in the molecules, increasing their vibrational energy. Bonds between different atoms absorb different frequencies of IR radiation. Bonds in different places in a molecule absorb different frequencies too. The frequencies where they absorb IR radiation are plotted to give an IR spectrum.

Q2  If a person's suspected of drink driving, they're breathalysed by the roadside. If it says that the driver's over the limit, they're taken into a police station for a more accurate test using infrared spectroscopy. The amount of ethanol vapour in the driver's breath is found by measuring the intensity of the peak corresponding to the C–H bond in the IR spectrum.

## 8. Mass Spectrometry
### Page 173 — Application Questions
Q1  E.g. $CH_3^+ / CH_3CH_2^+ / CH_2^+ / CH_3CH_2CH_2^+ / OH^+$.

Q2  The molecule is propene.

This table shows some of the m/z peaks from the mass spectrum and the fragment ions they can be assigned to:

| m/z | fragment ion |
|-----|--------------|
| 15 | $CH_3^+$ |
| 27 | $CH_2CH^+$ |
| 41 | $CH_3CCH_2^+$ |
| 42 | $CH_3CHCH_2^+$ (Molecular ion) |

Don't forget that you don't have to assign all of these peaks — just as long as you've done enough to be able to prove that it's propene...

Q3  E.g. $CH_3CH_2CHOH^+ / CH_3CHOH^+$.
### Page 173 — Fact Recall Questions
Q1  The one with the highest mass/charge ratio.
    This isn't strictly true — in real-life it's really just the big peak that's almost got the highest mass/charge ratio. But for all the spectra that you see in this book, and in the exam, it will be the one with the highest mass/charge ratio.

Q2  The molecular mass of the compound.
Q3  $CH_3^+$
Q4  Any two from: e.g. probes to Mars have carried small mass spectrometers to study the composition of the surface of Mars and to look for elements and compounds that might suggest that life existed on the planet. / Mass spectrometry can be used to measure the levels of pollutants present in the environment. / Mass spectrometry can be used to measure the amount of lead/pesticides entering the food chain.

## Exam-style Questions — pages 175-177
Q1  a)  (i)   $CH_3CH_2Br + OH^- \rightarrow CH_3CH_2OH + Br^-$ *(1 mark)*
        You'd also get the mark if you included the $Na^+$ ions in the equation, like this: $CH_3CH_2Br + NaOH \rightarrow CH_3CH_2OH + NaBr$
        (ii)

        ***(3 marks, 1 mark for each correct curly arrow and 1 mark for the C–Br dipole correctly shown.)***
        (iii) The reaction of water with iodoethane would be quicker than the reaction of bromoethane with water *(1 mark)*. This is because the C–I bond is weaker than the C–Br bond *(1 mark)*, which means it is more easily broken *(1 mark)*.
    b)  (i)   The hydration of ethene by steam is carried out at 300 °C and at a pressure of 60 atm *(1 mark)*. It also needs a phosphoric acid catalyst *(1 mark)*.
        (ii)  $C_6H_{12}O_{6(aq)} \rightarrow 2C_2H_5OH_{(aq)} + 2CO_{2(g)}$ *(1 mark)*
        The reaction needs to be carried out in the presence of yeast and at 30–40 °C *(1 mark)*.
        (iii) Ethene is produced from crude oil *(1 mark)*. Fermentation uses renewable resources/sugar and so may become more important as the amount of crude oil decreases *(1 mark)*.
    c)  (i)   The hydroxyl groups can form hydrogen bonds with the water molecules *(1 mark)*.
        (ii)  In butan-1-ol more of the molecule is a non-polar carbon chain, which won't mix easily with water molecules *(1 mark)*.
    d)  (i)   $CH_3CH_2OH + CH_3CH_2COOH \rightarrow$ $CH_3CH_2COOCH_2CH_3 + H_2O$ *(1 mark)* ethyl propanoate *(1 mark)*
        (ii)  A strong acid catalyst/concentrated $H_2SO_4$ and heat *(1 mark)*.
    You'd be allowed any other named strong acid catalyst too, e.g. 'concentrated HCl' or 'concentrated hydrochloric acid'.
Q2  a)  (i)   Molecule A is:

                                                    *(1 mark)*
        (ii)  Molecule A is propan-1-ol *(1 mark)*.
    b)  Acidified potassium dichromate(VI)/$K_2Cr_2O_7$ and $H_2SO_4$ *(1 mark)*. Heat under reflux *(1 mark)*.

c) Spectrum Y belongs to molecule A *(1 mark)*. Spectrum Y contains a broad peak at ~3400 cm$^{-1}$ which corresponds to the vibration of an O–H bond *(1 mark)*. Spectrum X doesn't contain a peak associated with an O–H bond and so can't be the spectrum of molecule A *(1 mark)*.

*Make sure you show how the structure of molecule A links to the spectrum — you won't get marks for written communication unless you do this.*

Q3 a) If a person's suspected of drink driving, they're breathalysed at a police station using infrared spectroscopy *(1 mark)*. The amount of ethanol vapour in the driver's breath is found by measuring the intensity of the peak corresponding to the C–H bond in the IR spectrum *(1 mark)*.

b) (i) You can tell similar molecules apart using mass spectrometry because they won't produce exactly the same set of fragments *(1 mark)*.

(ii) E.g. probes to Mars have carried small mass spectrometers to study the composition of the surface of Mars and to look for molecules that might suggest that life existed on the planet. / Mass spectrometry can be used to measure the levels of pollutants/lead/pesticides present in the environment *(1 mark)*.

c) The molecular ion peak has a m/z of 58 and so the M$_r$ of the compound is 58 *(1 mark)*.
The peak at 15 m/z could be caused by a CH$_3^+$ fragment ion. The peak at 29 m/z could be caused by a CH$_3$CH$_2^+$ fragment ion. The peak at 43 m/z could be caused by a CH$_3$CH$_2$CH$_2^+$ fragment ion. *(1 mark for each correctly assigned fragment up to a maximum of 2 marks)*
The molecule is butane.

$$\text{H--C--C--C--C--H}$$

*(1 mark)*

*There are only two hydrocarbons with an M$_r$ of 58 — butane and 2-methylpropane. Molecule J has a mass spectrum peak at m/z = 29, so it can't be 2-methylpropane because that doesn't have a peak there.*

d) The infrared spectrum shows a strong broad peak at about 3300 cm$^{-1}$ which corresponds to an O–H group on an alcohol *(1 mark)*. Acidified potassium dichromate(VI) will oxidise secondary alcohols under reflux to ketones — so molecule **K** must be a secondary alcohol *(1 mark)*. The only secondary alcohol with an M$_r$ of 74 is butan-2-ol *(1 mark)*.
So molecule **K** is butan-2-ol:

$$\text{H--C--C--C--C--H}$$ *(1 mark)*

# Module 3: Energy
## 1. Enthalpy Changes
### Page 179 — Fact Recall Questions
Q1 $\Delta H^{\ominus}$

Q2 Standard enthalpy change of reaction, $\Delta H_r^{\ominus}$, is the enthalpy change when a reaction occurs in the molar quantities shown in the chemical equation, under standard conditions with all reactants and products in their standard states.

Q3 Exothermic reactions give out energy, and endothermic reactions absorb energy. For exothermic reactions, the enthalpy change ($\Delta H$) is negative. For endothermic reactions it is positive.

Q4 a)

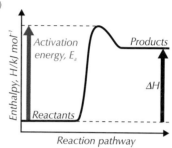

b) (See above for arrow.) The activation energy, $E_a$, is the minimum amount of energy needed to begin breaking reactant bonds and start a chemical reaction.

## 2. Bond Enthalpies
### Page 182 — Application Questions
Q1 a) Bonds broken = (1 × C=C) + (1 × H–H)
So total energy absorbed = 612 + 436
= 1048 kJ mol$^{-1}$.
Bonds formed = (2 × C–H) + (1 × C–C)
So total energy released = (2 × 413) + 347
= 1173 kJ mol$^{-1}$.
Enthalpy change of reaction
= total energy absorbed – total energy released
= 1048 – 1173 = **–125 kJ mol$^{-1}$**.

*You can ignore any bonds that don't change when you're calculating the enthalpy change of a reaction.*

b) Bonds broken = (1 × C–O) + (1 × H–Cl)
So total energy absorbed = 358 + 432
= 790 kJ mol$^{-1}$.
Bonds formed = (1 × C–Cl) + (1 × O–H)
So total energy released = 346 + 460
= 806 kJ mol$^{-1}$.
Enthalpy change of reaction
= total energy absorbed – total energy released
= 790 – 806 = **–16 kJ mol$^{-1}$**.

c) Bonds broken =
(2 × C–C) + (8 × C–H) + (5 × O=O)
So total energy absorbed =
(2 × 347) + (8 × 413) + (5 × 498) = 6488 kJ mol$^{-1}$.
Bonds formed = (6 × C=O) + (8 × O–H)
So total energy released = (6 × 805) + (8 × 460)
= 8510 kJ mol$^{-1}$.
Enthalpy change of reaction/combustion
= total energy absorbed – total energy released
= 6488 – 8510 = **–2022 kJ mol$^{-1}$**.

*It really helps if you draw out a sketch for this question.*

d) Bonds broken = $(1 \times C–Cl) + (1 \times N–H)$
So total energy absorbed = $346 + 391$
= 737 kJ mol$^{-1}$.
Bonds formed = $(1 \times C–N) + (1 \times H–Cl)$
So total energy released = $286 + 432$
= 718 kJ mol$^{-1}$.
Enthalpy change of reaction
= total energy absorbed – total energy released
= $737 – 718 = $ **+19 kJ mol$^{-1}$**.

Q2 The balanced equation for the combustion of ethene is:
$C_2H_4 + 3O_2 \rightarrow 2CO_2 + 2H_2O$.
Bonds broken =
$(1 \times C=C) + (4 \times C–H) + (3 \times O=O)$
So total energy absorbed =
$(1 \times 612) + (4 \times 413) + (3 \times 498) = 3758$ kJ mol$^{-1}$.
Bonds formed = $(4 \times C=O) + (4 \times O–H)$
So total energy released = $(4 \times 805) + (4 \times 460)$
= 5060 kJ mol$^{-1}$.
Enthalpy change of combustion
= total energy absorbed – total energy released
= $3758 – 5060 = $ **–1302 kJ mol$^{-1}$**.

Q3 The balanced equation for the formation of HCl is:
$H_2 + Cl_2 \rightarrow 2HCl$.
Bonds broken = $(1 \times H–H) + (1 \times Cl–Cl)$
So total energy absorbed = $436 + 243.4$
= 679.4 kJ mol$^{-1}$.
Bonds formed = $2 \times H–Cl$
So total energy released = $2 \times 432 = 864$ kJ mol$^{-1}$.
Enthalpy change of formation
= total energy absorbed – total energy released
= $679.4 – 864 = $ **–184.6 kJ mol$^{-1}$**.

Q4 Call the unknown bond enthalpy between
N and O '$X$'.
Bonds broken = $2 \times X$
So total energy absorbed = $2X$ kJ mol$^{-1}$.
Bonds formed = $(1 \times N≡N) + (1 \times O=O)$
So total energy released = $945 + 498$
= 1443 kJ mol$^{-1}$.
Enthalpy change of reaction = $-181$ kJ mol$^{-1}$
= total energy absorbed – total energy released.
So: $-181 = 2X – 1443$
$2X = -181 + 1443 = 1262$
$X = 1262 \div 2 = $ **+631 kJ mol$^{-1}$**.

## Page 182 — Fact Recall Questions
Q1 endothermic
Q2 The energy required to make bonds.
Q3 Average bond enthalpy is the energy needed to break one mole of bonds in the gas phase, averaged over many different compounds.
Q4 Enthalpy change of reaction =
Total energy absorbed – Total energy released

## 3. Measuring Enthalpy Changes
## Page 185 — Application Questions
Q1 $q = mc\Delta T = 220 \times 4.18 \times (301 – 298) = 2758.8$ J
= 2.7588 kJ

$\Delta H = \dfrac{q}{n} = -\dfrac{2.7588 \text{ kJ}}{0.05 \text{ mol}} = $ **–55.2 kJ mol$^{-1}$** (to 3 s.f.).

*Don't forget — the enthalpy change must be negative because it's an exothermic reaction (you can tell because the temperature increased).*

Q2 a) $q = mc\Delta T = 200 \times 4.18 \times 29 = 24244$ J
= 24.244 kJ

$n = \dfrac{\text{mass}}{M} = \dfrac{0.5 \text{ g}}{72 \text{ g mol}^{-1}} = 0.00694$ moles of fuel

$\Delta H = \dfrac{q}{n} = -\dfrac{24.244 \text{ kJ}}{0.00694 \text{ mol}}$

= **–3490 kJ mol$^{-1}$** (to 3 s.f.).

b) E.g. some heat from the combustion will be transferred to the surroundings and not the water. / The combustion may not be complete combustion. / The combustion may not have taken place under standard conditions. / There could be inaccuracies due to the measuring equipment.

Q3 $q = mc\Delta T = 300 \times 4.18 \times 55 = 68\,970$ J
= 68.97 kJ

$\Delta H_c^{\ominus}$ octane = $-5512$ kJ mol$^{-1}$ = $\dfrac{q}{n}$

$n = \dfrac{q}{\Delta H} = \dfrac{68.97 \text{ kJ}}{5512 \text{ kJ mol}^{-1}} = 0.0125...$ mol.

$n = \dfrac{\text{mass}}{M}$, so mass = $n \times M = 0.0125... \times 114$

= **1.43 g** of octane (to 3 s.f.).

## Page 185 — Fact Recall Questions
Q1 The mass of reactant, the volume of the solution, and the initial and final temperature.
Q2 E.g.

Q3 $q$ is the heat lost or gained during a reaction. It's measured in joules (J).
Q4 The reaction needs to be performed at a constant pressure of 100 kPa, with all reactants and products in their standard states.
Q5 Find the number of moles of that reactant that reacts in the balanced chemical equation, then calculate $\Delta H_r^{\ominus}$ using:
$\Delta H_r^{\ominus} = \dfrac{q}{n} \times$ number of moles reacting in balanced chemical equation

## 4. Hess's Law
## Page 188 — Application Questions

Q1 $\Delta H_{f \text{ (reactants)}}^{\ominus} = \Delta H_{f \text{ [Mg]}}^{\ominus} + (2 \times \Delta H_{f \text{ [H}_2\text{O]}}^{\ominus})$
$\Delta H_{f \text{ (reactants)}}^{\ominus} = 0 + (2 \times -286) = -572$ kJ mol$^{-1}$.
$\Delta H_{f \text{ (products)}}^{\ominus} = \Delta H_{f \text{ [Mg(OH)}_2\text{]}}^{\ominus} + \Delta H_{f \text{ [H}_2\text{]}}^{\ominus}$
$\Delta H_{f \text{ (products)}}^{\ominus} = -925 + 0 = -925$ kJ mol$^{-1}$.
Using Hess's Law: Route 1 = Route 2, so:
$\Delta H_{f \text{ (reactants)}}^{\ominus} + \Delta H_r^{\ominus} = \Delta H_{f \text{ (products)}}^{\ominus}$
$-572 + \Delta H_r^{\ominus} = -925$
$\Delta H_r^{\ominus} = -925 + 572 = $ **–353 kJ mol$^{-1}$**.

**Q2** a) First draw out a reaction scheme with an alternative reaction route that includes balanced equations for the formation of each compound:

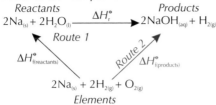

$\Delta H^{\circ}_{f \text{ (reactants)}} = (2 \times \Delta H^{\circ}_{f \text{ [Na]}}) + (2 \times \Delta H^{\circ}_{f \text{ [H}_2\text{O]}})$

$\Delta H^{\circ}_{f \text{ (reactants)}} = (2 \times 0) + (2 \times -286) = -572 \text{ kJ mol}^{-1}$.

$\Delta H^{\circ}_{f \text{ (products)}} = (2 \times \Delta H^{\circ}_{f \text{ [NaOH]}}) + \Delta H^{\circ}_{f \text{ [H}_2\text{]}}$

$\Delta H^{\circ}_{f \text{ (products)}} = (2 \times -469) + 0 = -938 \text{ kJ mol}^{-1}$.

Remember that the enthalpy change of formation of Na and $H_2$ is zero because they're elements.

Using Hess's Law: Route 1 = Route 2, so:

$\Delta H^{\circ}_{f \text{ (reactants)}} + \Delta H^{\circ}_{r} = \Delta H^{\circ}_{f \text{ (products)}}$

$-572 + \Delta H^{\circ}_{r} = -938$

$\Delta H^{\circ}_{r} = -938 + 572 = \textbf{-366 kJ mol}^{-1}$.

b)

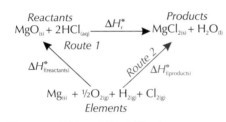

$\Delta H^{\circ}_{f \text{ (reactants)}} = \Delta H^{\circ}_{f \text{ [MgO]}} + (2 \times \Delta H^{\circ}_{f \text{ [HCl]}})$

$\Delta H^{\circ}_{f \text{ (reactants)}} = -602 + (2 \times -167) = -936 \text{ kJ mol}^{-1}$.

$\Delta H^{\circ}_{f \text{ (products)}} = \Delta H^{\circ}_{f \text{ [MgCl]}} + \Delta H^{\circ}_{f \text{ [H}_2\text{O]}}$

$\Delta H^{\circ}_{f \text{ (products)}} = -641 + (-286) = -927 \text{ kJ mol}^{-1}$.

Using Hess's Law: Route 1 = Route 2, so:

$\Delta H^{\circ}_{f \text{ (reactants)}} + \Delta H^{\circ}_{r} = \Delta H^{\circ}_{f \text{ (products)}}$

$-936 + \Delta H^{\circ}_{r} = -927$

$\Delta H^{\circ}_{r} = -927 + 936 = \textbf{+9 kJ mol}^{-1}$.

c)

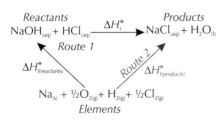

$\Delta H^{\circ}_{f \text{ (reactants)}} = \Delta H^{\circ}_{f \text{ [NaOH]}} + \Delta H^{\circ}_{f \text{ [HCl]}}$

$\Delta H^{\circ}_{f \text{ (reactants)}} = -469 + (-167) = -636 \text{ kJ mol}^{-1}$.

$\Delta H^{\circ}_{f \text{ (products)}} = \Delta H^{\circ}_{f \text{ [NaCl]}} + \Delta H^{\circ}_{f \text{ [H}_2\text{O]}}$

$\Delta H^{\circ}_{f \text{ (products)}} = -407 + (-286) = -693 \text{ kJ mol}^{-1}$.

Using Hess's Law: Route 1 = Route 2, so:

$\Delta H^{\circ}_{f \text{ (reactants)}} + \Delta H^{\circ}_{r} = \Delta H^{\circ}_{f \text{ (products)}}$

$-636 + \Delta H^{\circ}_{r} = -693$

$\Delta H^{\circ}_{r} = -693 + 636 = \textbf{-57 kJ mol}^{-1}$.

## Page 190 — Application Questions

**Q1** a) First draw out balanced reactions for the formation of the compound, and the combustion of the reactants and product:

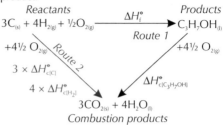

Using Hess's Law: Route 1 = Route 2, so:

$\Delta H^{\circ}_{f} + \Delta H^{\circ}_{c \text{ [C}_3\text{H}_7\text{OH]}} = (3 \times \Delta H^{\circ}_{c \text{ [C]}}) + (4 \times \Delta H^{\circ}_{c \text{ [H}_2\text{]}})$

$\Delta H^{\circ}_{f} + (-2021) = (3 \times -394) + (4 \times -286)$

$\Delta H^{\circ}_{f} = -1182 - 1144 + 2021 = \textbf{-305 kJ mol}^{-1}$.

b)

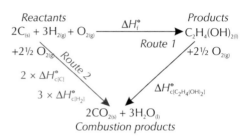

Using Hess's Law: Route 1 = Route 2, so:

$\Delta H^{\circ}_{f} + \Delta H^{\circ}_{c \text{ [C}_2\text{H}_4\text{(OH)}_2\text{]}} = (2 \times \Delta H^{\circ}_{c \text{ [C]}}) + (3 \times \Delta H^{\circ}_{c \text{ [H}_2\text{]}})$

$\Delta H^{\circ}_{f} + (-1180) = (2 \times -394) + (3 \times -286)$

$\Delta H^{\circ}_{f} = -788 - 858 + 1180 = \textbf{-466 kJ mol}^{-1}$.

c)

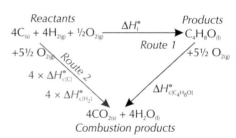

Using Hess's Law: Route 1 = Route 2, so:

$\Delta H^{\circ}_{f} + \Delta H^{\circ}_{c \text{ [C}_4\text{H}_8\text{O]}} = (4 \times \Delta H^{\circ}_{c \text{ [C]}}) + (4 \times \Delta H^{\circ}_{c \text{ [H}_2\text{]}})$

$\Delta H^{\circ}_{f} + (-2442) = (4 \times -394) + (4 \times -286)$

$\Delta H^{\circ}_{f} = -1576 - 1144 + 2442 = \textbf{-278 kJ mol}^{-1}$.

**Q2** First label the reaction scheme with the known enthalpy changes, and the chosen routes:

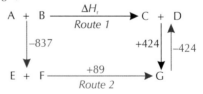

Using Hess's Law: Route 1 = Route 2, so:

$\Delta H_{r} = -837 + 89 + (-424) = \textbf{-1172 kJ mol}^{-1}$.

## 5. Reaction Rates
### Page 193 — Application Questions
Q1

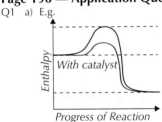

Enthalpy (kJ mol$^{-1}$): 456, 304, 112

Products, ΔH, Reactants

Progress of Reaction

The reaction is endothermic (ΔH is positive) because the products have a higher enthalpy than the reactants.

Q2 B is the curve for the gas at a higher temperature because it is shifted over to the right showing that more molecules have more energy.

### Page 193 — Fact Recall Questions
Q1 The particles must collide in the right direction (facing each other the right way) and with at least a certain minimum amount of kinetic energy.

Q2 The minimum amount of kinetic energy that particles need to have in order to react when they collide.

Q3 A small increase in temperature gives all molecules more energy, so a greater number of them have at least the minimum amount of energy to react when they collide. They will also collide more often because they will be moving about faster.

Q4 If you increase the concentration of reactants in a solution, the particles will be closer together in a given volume and so collide more often, increasing the reaction rate.

## 6. Catalysts
### Page 196 — Application Question
Q1 a) E.g.

Enthalpy

With catalyst

Progress of Reaction

You can draw the line anywhere as long as the peak is lower than it was before and the shape of the graph stays the same.

b) Adding a catalyst would lower the activation energy for the reaction so that it would not need such a high temperature in order to take place. Being able to carry out the reaction at a lower temperature would save energy and money.

### Page 196 — Fact Recall Questions
Q1 A substance that increases the rate of a reaction by providing an alternative reaction pathway with a lower activation energy. The catalyst is chemically unchanged at the end of the reaction.

Q2 Catalysts are used to speed up reactions in industrial processes that would be impossible or too slow to occur at practical temperatures and pressures. Using a catalyst means the temperature and pressure can be reduced, which saves energy and money.

Q3 A catalyst increases the rate of a reaction by providing an alternative reaction pathway with a lower activation energy. This means that more of the molecules collide with energies above the activation energy, and so can react.

Q4 Many enzymes operate in conditions close to room temperature and pressure, so they're useful in industry because they can reduce the need for high temperature, fuel-guzzling processes. Enzymes tend to be specific about what they catalyse so it means they can select one molecule from a mixture and cause that to react without affecting the others.

Q5 e.g. poly(ethene)
The properties of poly(ethene) change depending on whether a catalyst is used in its manufacture. Using a Ziegler-Natta catalyst gives denser and more rigid poly(ethene) that has a higher melting point.

## 7. Reversible Reactions
### Page 200 — Application Questions
Q1 a) Increasing the concentration of A will shift the equilibrium to the right (favouring the forwards reaction) in order to get rid of the excess A.

b) There are 3 moles on the left and only 2 on the right. Increasing the pressure will shift the equilibrium to the right (favouring the forwards reaction) in order to reduce the number of moles to reduce the pressure again.

c) The forwards reaction is exothermic, so the backwards reaction must be endothermic. Increasing the temperature will shift the equilibrium to the left (favouring the endothermic backwards reaction) in order to remove the extra heat energy.

d) The reaction should ideally be performed with a high concentration of A and B, at a high pressure and low temperature.

Q2 There are the same number of moles on either side of the reaction. Increasing the pressure favours the reaction producing the fewest moles, but since both reactions are equal in this respect, increasing the pressure will not shift the position of equilibrium.

### Page 200 — Fact Recall Questions
Q1 The concentrations of reactants and products are constant, and the forwards reaction and the backwards reaction are going at the same rate.

Q2 If there's a change in concentration, pressure or temperature, the equilibrium will move to help counteract the change.

Q3 The addition of a catalyst has no effect on the position of equilibrium in a reversible reaction.

Q4 A low temperature would reduce the rate of reaction. This means that although you'd get a high yield it would take so long that it wouldn't be worth it.

### Exam-style Questions — pages 202-204
1 a) In a reversible reaction, dynamic equilibrium is reached when the concentrations of reactants and products are constant *(1 mark)*, and the forwards reaction and the backwards reaction are going at the same rate *(1 mark)*.

b) If there's a change in concentration, pressure or temperature *(1 mark)*, the equilibrium will move to help counteract the change *(1 mark)*.

c) The higher the pressure, the faster the reaction rate *(1 mark)*. A high pressure also favours the forwards reaction, which produces fewer moles, so the higher the pressure, the greater the yield of ethanol *(1 mark)*. However, high pressures are very expensive/produce side reactions/require strong and expensive equipment, so the pressure used is limited by these factors *(1 mark)*.

d) Reducing the amount of $H_2O$ will shift the position of equilibrium to the left *(1 mark)* in order to increase the amount of $H_2O$ present *(1 mark)*. This shift will reduce the maximum yield of ethanol from the forwards reaction *(1 mark)*.

2  a) (i) The minimum amount of kinetic energy *(1 mark)* that particles need to have in order to react when they collide *(1 mark)*.

(ii)

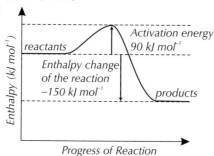

*(1 mark for products lower than reactants, 1 mark for correctly labelled activation energy, 1 mark for correctly labelled enthalpy change of reaction.)*

b) Heating the reactants gives the molecules more energy *(1 mark)*. This means that more molecules will have an energy higher than the activation energy *(1 mark)*, so more collisions between molecules will result in reaction, increasing the reaction rate *(1 mark)*.

c) Lowering the pressure will reduce the rate of reaction *(1 mark)*. This is because there will be fewer gas molecules in a given volume/the concentration will be reduced/the molecules will be further apart *(1 mark)*, so there will be fewer collisions between molecules that result in reaction *(1 mark)*.

d) (i) A catalyst is a substance that increases the rate of a reaction without being changed or used up by the reaction *(1 mark)*.

(ii)

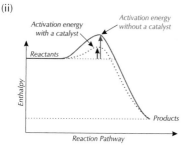

*(1 mark for diagram with correctly labelled activation energy)*

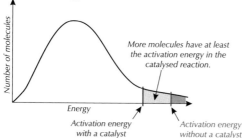

*(1 mark for diagram with correctly labelled axes)*
A catalyst increases the rate of a reaction by providing an alternative reaction pathway *(1 mark)* with a lower activation energy *(1 mark)*. With a catalyst present, the molecules still have the same amount of energy *(1 mark)*, so the Maxwell-Boltzmann distribution curve is unchanged. But because the catalyst lowers the activation energy, more of the molecules have energies above this threshold and are able to react *(1 mark)*.

(iii) The reactant molecules adsorb to the surface of the catalyst *(1 mark)*. This makes it easier to break the bonds, and so the activation energy of the reaction decreases *(1 mark)*. The broken reactant molecules then form product molecules *(1 mark)*, and desorb from the surface of the catalyst *(1 mark)*.

3  a) Hess's Law says that the total enthalpy change of a reaction is always the same, no matter which route is taken *(1 mark)*.

b) $C_8H_{18(l)} + 12\frac{1}{2}O_{2(g)} \rightarrow 8CO_{2(g)} + 9H_2O_{(l)}$ *(1 mark)*

c) (i)

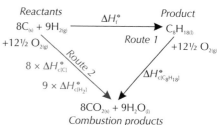

Using Hess's Law: Route 1 = Route 2, so:
$\Delta H_f^\circ + \Delta H_{c\,[C_8H_{18}]}^\circ = (8 \times \Delta H_{c\,[C]}^\circ) + (9 \times \Delta H_{c\,[H_2]}^\circ)$
$\Delta H_f^\circ + (-5470) = (8 \times -394) + (9 \times -286)$
$\Delta H_f^\circ = -3152 - 2574 + 5470 = \textbf{--256 kJ mol}^{-1}$.
*(3 marks for correct answer, otherwise 1 mark for correct equation using Hess's Law and 1 mark for correct molar quantities. Allow 1 mark only for an answer of +256 kJ mol$^{-1}$.)*

(ii) Exothermic *(1 mark)*. The enthalpy change for the formation of octane is negative *(1 mark)*.

4  a) (i) Standard enthalpy of combustion, $\Delta H_c^\circ$, is the enthalpy change when 1 mole of a substance *(1 mark)* is completely burned in oxygen *(1 mark)* under standard conditions with all reactants and products in their standard states *(1 mark)*.

(ii) The balanced equation for the combustion of but-1-ene is: $C_4H_8 + 6O_2 \rightarrow 4CO_2 + 4H_2O$.
Bonds broken =
$(1 \times C=C) + (2 \times C-C) + (8 \times C-H) + (6 \times O=O)$
So total energy absorbed =
$(1 \times 612) + (2 \times 347) + (8 \times 413) + (6 \times 498)$
$= 7598$ kJ mol$^{-1}$.
Bonds formed $= (8 \times C=O) + (8 \times O-H)$
So total energy released $= (8 \times 805) + (8 \times 460)$
$= 10\ 120$ kJ mol$^{-1}$.
Enthalpy change of combustion
= total energy absorbed – total energy released
$= 7598 - 10\ 120 = \textbf{--2522 kJ mol}^{-1}$.
*(3 marks for correct answer, otherwise 1 mark for 'total energy absorbed – total energy released', and 1 mark for correct value for either energy released or energy absorbed. Allow 1 mark only for an answer of +2522 kJ mol$^{-1}$).*

(iii) Some of the average bond enthalpies are average values for the bonds in many different compounds, so they are not accurate for the specific molecules involved in this combustion *(1 mark)*.

b) (i) $q = mc\Delta T = 200 \times 4.18 \times 32.8 = 27420.8$ J
$= \textbf{27.421 kJ}$
*(2 marks for correct answer, otherwise 1 mark for correct working.)*

(ii) $\Delta H_c^{\circ} = q \div n = 27.4208 \div 0.0215$
$= \mathbf{-1280\ kJ\ mol^{-1}}$ (to 3 s.f.).
***(1 marks for correct answer, 1 mark for minus sign)***

(iii) When the reaction happens, reactant bonds are broken and product bonds are formed ***(1 mark)***. The total energy needed to break the alkene bonds is less than the energy released when the product bonds are formed ***(1 mark)*** so the reaction is exothermic.

(iv) Any two from: e.g. some heat from the combustion will be transferred to the surroundings and not the water. / The combustion may not be complete combustion. / The combustion may not have taken place under standard conditions ***(1 mark each up to a maximum of 2 marks)***.

# Module 4: Resources

## 1. Green Chemistry
### Page 207 — Application Questions
Q1 Any three from: e.g. use a renewable energy source to generate electricity (e.g. plant based fuel/solar power/wind turbine) / use a biodegradable plastic to package food / use a plastic made from a renewable raw material to package food / take steps to reduce the number of plastic carrier bags used (e.g. charge for carrier bags/supply 'bags for life'/ give rewards for using your own bags) / sell more locally produced food rather than importing food from abroad.

Q2 Process B is more sustainable. It has a higher atom economy so it is more efficient and produces less waste.

Q3 Hexachlorobenzene was banned because it accumulates in the fatty tissues of living organisms. It is passed up the food chain and is toxic to humans and other animals.
*You know that hexachlorobenzene is toxic and accumulates in the fatty tissues of living organisms because it says in the question that it is a persistent organic compound (POP).*

### Page 207 — Fact Recall Questions
Q1 Sustainable chemistry means not using up all the Earth's resources or putting loads of damaging chemicals into the environment.

Q2 The raw materials used to make plastics often come from non-renewable crude oil and the products themselves are usually non-biodegradable or hard to recycle.

Q3 Any four from: e.g. ensure all the chemicals involved are as non-toxic as possible / use renewable raw materials / use renewable energy sources / ensure that any products and waste are biodegradable or recyclable / use reactions with high atom economies.

Q4 E.g. biofuels. Growing grain for biodiesel or sugar for bioethanol means less land is available to grow food so food gets more expensive. Large biofuel companies may buy up the most fertile land, forcing small farmers onto land with poorer crop yields. Alternatively, forests may be cleared to produce land. This means less $CO_2$ is absorbed and biodiversity is reduced.

Q5 a) International cooperation is needed because rivers flow from one country to the next, and the atmosphere and oceans are constantly mixing and moving. This means that eventually everyone suffers from pollution produced by other countries.
b) E.g. the Montreal Protocol/the Stockholm Treaty/the Rio Declaration.
c) Some countries are worried that signing up to the treaty will be bad for their economy.

## 2. Global Warming
### Page 210 — Application Question
Q1 $SF_6$ has a much higher 20 year GWP than $CO_2$. This means that $SF_6$ absorbs much more radiation. However, the atmospheric concentration of $SF_6$ is much lower than that of $CO_2$.

### Page 210 — Fact Recall Questions
Q1 Infrared radiation.

Q2 Any two from: e.g. how much radiation one molecule of the gas absorbs / how much of the gas there is in the atmosphere / how long the gas stays in the atmosphere for (the residence time).

Q3 Human activities have caused a rise in greenhouse gas concentrations. This has enhanced the greenhouse effect which means that more heat is being trapped and the Earth is getting warmer. This is global warming.

Q4 Any from: e.g. global warming may cause oceans to expand and ice sheets in polar regions to melt. This will cause sea levels to rise leading to more flooding. / Global warming could influence ocean currents and wind speeds. This could lead to stormier and less predictable weather. / Global warming could cause a decrease in rainfall in some areas. This will lead to droughts and crop failures causing famines. / Global warming could cause an increase in rainfall in some areas. This could lead to flooding which would bring diseases like cholera.

Q5 E.g. collecting data to show whether or not global warming/ climate change is occurring / monitoring the success of measures put in place to reduce global warming / monitoring how the environment is changing now and creating models to show how it will change / investigating ways to reduce carbon dioxide emissions (e.g. carbon capture and storage) / monitoring progress against initiatives such as the Kyoto protocol.

## 3. The Ozone Layer
### Page 213 — Application Question
Q1 a) Bromotrifuoromethane absorbs UV radiation and undergoes homolytic fission to form bromine radicals.
b) $Br\bullet + O_3 \rightarrow BrO + O_2$
$BrO + O\bullet \rightarrow Br\bullet + O_2$
c) $O_3 + O\bullet \rightarrow 2O_2$

### Page 213 — Fact Recall Questions
Q1 $O_3$
Q2 In the stratosphere.
Q3 a) $O_2 + h\nu \rightarrow O\bullet + O\bullet$
$O_2 + O\bullet \rightarrow O_3$
b) UV radiation.
c) $O_3 + h\nu \rightarrow O_2 + O\bullet$
Q4 It protects the Earth from harmful UVC and UVB radiation.
Q5 a) chlorofluorocarbon
b) Any three from: e.g. in fridges / in aerosols / in dry cleaning / in air conditioning.
c) CFCs can break down under UV light to form chlorine radicals which have ozone depleting properties.
Q6 a) $R + O_3 \rightarrow RO + O_2$
$RO + O\bullet \rightarrow R + O_2$
b) E.g. $Cl\bullet$ and $NO\bullet$.

# 4. Air Pollution

## Page 216 — Application Questions

Q1 a) $C_2H_6 + 3\frac{1}{2}O_2 \rightarrow 2CO_2 + 3H_2O$

*If you don't like having fractions in your equations you can get rid of them by multiplying the whole equation by the number on the bottom of the fraction. In this case you'd multiply by two and get $2C_2H_6 + 7O_2 \rightarrow 4CO_2 + 6H_2O$. Both equations are right and you'll get the marks for either in the exam.*

b) $C_4H_{10} + 6\frac{1}{2}O_2 \rightarrow 4CO_2 + 5H_2O$

c) E.g. $C_3H_8 + 3\frac{1}{2}O_2 \rightarrow 3CO + 4H_2O$

d) E.g. $C_5H_{12} + 5\frac{1}{2}O_2 \rightarrow 5CO + 6H_2O$

*These are just examples of correct equations. You sometimes get small amounts of carbon dioxide or unburnt carbon being produced alongside CO, in which case your equation could be slightly different to these.*

Q2 a) $N_2 + 2O_2 \rightarrow 2NO_2$

b) E.g. In internal combustion engines.

c) E.g. $NO_2$ reacts with sunlight to form ground level ozone which is a major component of photochemical smog. This irritates peoples eyes/aggravates respiratory problems/damages the lungs. / $NO_2$ can form NO• radicals which contribute to the degradation of the ozone layer.

Q3 In catalytic converters, the reactants adsorb to the surface of the catalyst. The larger the surface area the more reactant molecules can adsorb, so increasing the surface area increases the efficiency of the catalyst.

## Page 216 — Fact Recall Questions

Q1 a) Carbon dioxide and water.

b) Carbon monoxide and water (and sometimes particulate carbon or small amounts of $CO_2$).

Q2 Carbon monoxide molecules bind to the same sites on haemoglobin molecules in red blood cells as oxygen molecules. So oxygen can't be carried around the body.

Q3 E.g. unburnt hydrocarbons / nitrogen oxides.

Q4 a) Carbon monoxide / nitrogen oxides / unburnt hydrocarbons.

*If you get this question in your exam, DON'T say carbon dioxide. Catalytic converters don't remove $CO_2$ — in fact they make it.*

b) The reactant molecules adsorb to the surface of the catalyst. This weakens the bonds between the atoms in the reactant molecules forming radicals. These radicals join up to form new molecules which then desorb from the catalyst.

*When describing how a catalyst works it's important to use the correct terminology — make sure you use the words adsorb and desorb otherwise you might lose marks.*

Q5 E.g. infrared spectroscopy.

## Exam-style Questions — pages 218-220

1 a) (i) C=O bonds in carbon dioxide absorb infrared radiation *(1 mark)*.

(ii) The absorption of infrared radiation makes the C=O bonds in the molecule vibrate more *(1 mark)*.

b) (i) Any two from: e.g. oceans expand / ice caps melt / flooding / stormier, less predictable weather / reduced rainfall in some areas / droughts / crop failures / increased rainfall in some areas *(1 mark for each, maximum 2 marks)*.

(ii) E.g. injecting it as liquid into deep oceans / storing it deep underground (in old oil or gas fields under the seabed) / reacting it with metal oxides to form stable, easily stored carbonate minerals *(1 mark for each)*.

c) (i) E.g. fossil fuels are non-renewable and will eventually run out *(1 mark)*.

(ii) Any three from: e.g. solar power / hydroelectric power / wind power / wave power / hydrothermal power / bioethanol / biodiesel *(1 mark for 3 correct answers)*.

(iii) Any three from: e.g. ensuring all the chemicals involved are as non-toxic as possible / developing renewable raw materials / developing biodegradable or recyclable products / developing higher atom economy process which produce less waste / ensuring any waste products are non-toxic / ensuring any waste products are biodegradable or recyclable *(1 mark for each, maximum 3 marks)*.

d) (i) E.g. water vapour ($H_2O$) / methane ($CH_4$) *(1 mark for each)*.

(ii) Any two from: e.g. the amount of IR radiation one molecule of the gas absorbs / the concentration of the gas in the atmosphere / the residence time of the gas *(1 mark for each, maximum 2 marks)*.

2 (a) (i) $O_2 + h\nu \rightarrow O\bullet + O\bullet$ *(1 mark)*.
$O_2 + O\bullet \rightarrow O_3$ *(1 mark)*.

(ii) UV light also destroys ozone *(1 mark)*. The rate of formation of ozone by UV light roughly equals the rate of degradation of ozone by UV light *(1 mark)*.

(iii) The ozone layer protects us from harmful UV radiation *(1 mark)*.

(b) (i) E.g. Chlorofluorocarbons (CFCs)/ hydrochlorofluorocarbons (HCFCs) *(1 mark for any correct answer)*.

(ii) $Cl\bullet + O_3 \rightarrow ClO + O_2$ *(1 mark)*.
$ClO + O\bullet \rightarrow Cl\bullet + O_2$ *(1 mark)*.

(c) (i) The atmosphere is constantly moving and mixing *(1 mark)* so if one country produces lots of harmful CFCs, everyone will be affected *(1 mark)*.

(ii) E.g. yes the initiative has been successful. Since 1996 the amount of chlorine in the atmosphere has decreased *(1 mark)* and the amount of ozone in the atmosphere has stopped decreasing *(1 mark)*.

3 (a) (i) When there is little oxygen *(1 mark)*.

(ii) Incomplete combustion produces carbon monoxide *(1 mark)* which is poisonous *(1 mark)*.

(b) (i) $N_2 + O_2 \rightarrow 2NO$ *(1 mark)*.

*Make sure you've balanced the equation. If you just put $N_2 + O_2 \rightarrow NO$ you won't get the mark.*

(ii) E.g. damage to the ozone layer: NO• free radicals are formed from nitrogen monoxide *(1 mark)*. NO• free radicals react with ozone, so damage the ozone layer *(1 mark)*.
E.g. photochemical smog: NO reacts with sunlight to form ground-level ozone *(1 mark)*, which is the main constituent of photochemical smog *(1 mark)*.

(c) (i) $2CO + 2NO \rightarrow 2CO_2 + N_2$ *(1 mark)*.

(ii) The reactant molecules adsorb to the surface of the catalyst *(1 mark)*. This weakens the bonds between the atoms in the molecules *(1 mark)* so they can break and new bonds form to make the products *(1 mark)*. The products then desorb from the catalyst *(1 mark)*.

*Make sure you've used technical terms like 'adsorb' and 'desorb' — you won't get marks for written communication in the exam unless you do.*

(iii) When lead binds to the catalyst, the surface area of the catalyst available to bind reactants is decreased *(1 mark)*.

(d) (i) E.g. carbon dioxide *(1 mark)*.

(ii) Releasing $CO_2$ into the atmosphere is less polluting than releasing CO and NO into the atmosphere *(1 mark)*.

# Glossary

## A

**Accurate result**
A result that's really close to the true answer.

**Acid**
A substance that releases $H^+$ ions in aqueous solution (a proton donor).

**Activation energy**
The minimum amount of kinetic energy that particles need to have in order to react when they collide.

**Addition polymer**
A long-chain molecule made by lots of small alkene molecules adding together.

**Addition reaction**
A reaction where multiple reactants combine to form a single product.

**Adsorption**
The bonding of particles to a surface.

**Alcohol**
A substance with the general formula $C_nH_{2n+1}OH$.

**Aldehyde**
A substance with the general formula $C_nH_{2n}O$ which has a hydrogen and one alkyl group attached to the carbonyl carbon atom.

**Alkali**
A base that is soluble in water and releases $OH^-$ ions in aqueous solution.

**Alkaline earth metal**
An element in Group 2 of the periodic table.

**Alkane**
A hydrocarbon with the general formula $C_nH_{2n+2}$.

**Alkene**
A hydrocarbon with the general formula $C_nH_{2n}$ and containing at least one carbon-carbon double bond.

**Anhydrous salt**
A salt that doesn't contain any water of crystallisation.

**Anomalous result**
A result that doesn't fit in with the pattern of the other results in a set of data.

**Antacid**
A substance which neutralises stomach acid.

**Atom**
A neutral particle made up of protons and neutrons in a central nucleus, and electrons orbiting the nucleus.

**Atom economy**
The proportion of reactant atoms that become part of the desired product in a balanced chemical reaction expressed as a percentage.

**Atomic number**
The number of protons in the nucleus of an atom.

**Average bond enthalpy**
The energy needed to break one mole of a bond in the gas phase, averaged over the different compounds that the bond is found in.

**Avogadro's constant**
$6 \times 10^{23}$ — the number of particles in 1 mole of a substance.

## B

**Balanced equation**
An equation that has the same number of each type of atom and the same overall charge on each side.

**Base**
A substance that removes $H^+$ ions from an aqueous solution (a proton acceptor).

**Biodiesel**
A plant-based alternative to fossil fuels which is made by refining renewable fats and oils such as vegetable oils.

**Bioethanol**
A plant-based alternative to fossil fuels which is made by fermenting sugars from crops such as maize.

**Biofuel**
A fuel that's made from biological material.

**Blowing agent**
The gas (or other chemical) used to create the bubbles in the liquid plastic during the production of an expanded polymer.

**Bohr model**
A model for the structure of an atom proposed by Niels Bohr. He suggested that electrons only exist in fixed orbitals (shells) and not anywhere else.

**Bond enthalpy**
The energy required to break a bond between two atoms. Usually given as an 'average bond enthalpy', an average value for the particular bond over the range of compounds it is found in.

## C

**Carbocation**
An organic ion containing a positively charged carbon atom.

**Carbon capture and storage (CCS)**
A way of removing waste $CO_2$ and storing it to prevent its release into the atmosphere.

**Carbonyl compound**
A compound that contains a carbon-oxygen double bond.

**Carboxylic acid**
A substance which has a COOH group attached to the end of a carbon chain.

**Catalyst**
A substance that increases the rate of a reaction by providing an alternative reaction pathway with a lower activation energy. The catalyst is chemically unchanged at the end of the reaction.

**Catalytic converter**
A device fitted to car exhausts to remove pollutant gases such as carbon monoxide, nitrogen monoxide and unburnt hydrocarbons.

**Categoric data**
Data that can be sorted into categories.

**Causal link**
The relationship between two variables where a change in one variable causes a change in the other.

**Chain isomer**
A molecule that contains the same atoms as another molecule but has a different arrangement of the carbon skeleton.

**Charge density**
The amount of charge in relation to the size of an ion.

**Chlorofluorocarbon (CFC)**
A halogenoalkane containing fluorine and chlorine. CFCs contribute to ozone depletion.

**Cis-trans isomerism**
A special type of E/Z isomerism where two of the groups attached to the carbon atoms around the C=C double bond are the same.

**Closed system**
A system where nothing can get in or out.

**Collision theory**
The theory that a reaction will not take place between two particles unless they collide in the right direction and with at least a certain minimum amount of kinetic energy.

**Complete combustion**
Burning a substance completely in oxygen. Complete combustion of a hydrocarbon will produce $CO_2$ and $H_2O$ only.

**Compound ion**
An ion made up of a group of atoms with an overall charge.

**Concentration**
A measure of how many moles of a substance are dissolved per $dm^3$ of solution.

**Condensation reaction**
A reaction where two compounds join to form one larger compound and a small molecule is released. When the small molecule is water the reaction is also a dehydration reaction.

**Continuous data**
Data that can have any value on a scale.

**Coordinate bonding**
A covalent bond formed when one atom provides both of the shared electrons. Also called dative covalent bonding.

**Correlation**
The relationship between two variables.

**Cracking**
Breaking long-chain alkanes into smaller hydrocarbons.

**Crude oil**
A mixture consisting mainly of alkane hydrocarbons that can be separated into different fractions.

**Cycloalkane**
A type of alkane which has one or more carbon rings.

**Dative covalent bonding**
A covalent bond formed when one atom provides both of the shared electrons. Also called coordinate bonding.

**Dehydration**
A reaction where water is eliminated from the reactants.

**Delocalised electron**
An electron that is not attached to a specific atom.

**Dependent variable**
The variable that you measure in an experiment.

**Desorption**
The release of particles from a surface.

**Dipole**
A difference in charge between two atoms caused by a shift in the electron density in a bond.

**Discrete data**
Data that can only take certain values.

**Displacement reaction**
A reaction where a more reactive element pushes out (displaces) a less reactive element from an ionic solution.

**Displayed formula**
A way of representing a molecule that shows how all the atoms are arranged, and all the bonds between them.

**Disproportionation**
When an element is both oxidised and reduced in a single chemical reaction.

**Dynamic equilibrium**
In a reversible reaction, dynamic equilibrium is reached when the concentrations of reactants and products are constant, and the forwards reaction and the backwards reaction are going at the same rate.

**E-/Z-isomerism**
A type of stereoisomerism that is caused by the restricted rotation about a carbon-carbon double bond. Each of the carbon atoms must have two different groups attached.

**Electron**
A subatomic particle with a relative charge of 1– and a relative mass of 1/2000, located in orbitals around the nucleus.

**Electron configuration**
The number of electrons that an atom or ion has and how they are arranged.

**Electron shell**
A region of an atom with a fixed energy that contains electrons orbiting the nucleus.

**Electron shielding**
When inner electrons effectively screen the outer electrons from the pull of the nucleus.

**Electronegativity**
The ability of an atom to attract the bonding electrons in a covalent bond.

**Electrophile**
An electron-pair acceptor.

**Electrophilic addition**
A reaction mechanism where a double bond in an alkene opens up and atoms are added to the carbon atoms.

**Electrostatic attraction**
The force that holds positive and negative ions together in ionic compounds.

**Empirical formula**
The simplest whole number ratio of atoms of each element in a compound.

**Endothermic reaction**
A reaction that absorbs energy ($\Delta H$ is positive).

**Energy level**
A region of an atom with a fixed energy that contains electrons orbiting the nucleus.

**Enthalpy change**
The heat energy transferred in a reaction at constant pressure ($\Delta H$).

**Ester**
A molecule that contains the functional group RCOOR.

**Esterification**
Forming an ester by heating a carboxylic acid and an alcohol in the presence of a strong acid catalyst.

**Exothermic reaction**
A reaction that gives out energy ($\Delta H$ is negative).

**Expanded polymer**
A polymer that has gas bubbles within its structure (like a solid foam).

**First ionisation energy**
The energy needed to remove 1 electron from each atom in 1 mole of gaseous atoms to form 1 mole of gaseous 1+ ions.

**Fossil fuel**
Oil, coal or natural gas.

**Fractional distillation**
A process for separating crude oil into different fractions based on their boiling points.

**Fragment ion**
A charged fragment produced when a molecular ion breaks up inside a mass spectrometer.

**Free radical**
A particle with an unpaired electron, written like this — Cl· or $CH_3$·.

**Functional group**
The group of atoms that is responsible for the characteristic reactions of a molecule (e.g. –OH for alcohols, –COOH for carboxylic acids, C=C for alkenes).

**Functional group isomer**
A molecule that has the same molecular formula as another molecule, but with the atoms arranged into different functional groups.

**General formula**
An algebraic formula that can describe any member of a homologous series of compounds.

**Giant covalent structure**
A structure consisting of a huge network of covalently bonded atoms. Also called a macromolecular structure.

**Giant ionic lattice structure**
A regular repeated structure made up of ions.

**Giant metallic lattice structure**
A regular structure consisting of closely packed positive metal ions in a sea of delocalised electrons.

**Global warming**
The warming of the planet due to increased concentrations of greenhouse gases in the troposphere, which enhance the greenhouse effect.

**Greenhouse effect**
The absorption and re-emission of infrared radiation by greenhouse gases in the troposphere.

**Greenhouse gas**
A gas that absorbs and emits infrared radiation and so contributes to the greenhouse effect.

**Group**
A column in the periodic table.

**Halide**
A negative ion of a halogen.

**Halogen**
An element in Group 7 of the periodic table.

**Halogenoalkane**
An alkane with at least one halogen atom in place of a hydrogen atom.

**Hess's Law**
The total enthalpy change of a reaction is always the same, no matter which route is taken.

**Heterolytic fission**
When a covalent bond breaks to form a positively charged cation and a negatively charged anion.

**Homogeneous reaction**
A reaction where the reactants and products are in the same state.

**Homologous series**
A family of organic compounds that have the same general formula and similar chemical properties.

**Homolytic fission**
When a covalent bond breaks to form two electrically uncharged radicals.

**Hydrated salt**
A salt that contains water of crystallisation.

**Hydration reaction**
A reaction where water is added to a compound.

**Hydrocarbon**
A molecule that only contains hydrogen and carbon atoms.

**Hydrogen bonding**
The strongest intermolecular force. It occurs when polarised covalent bonds cause hydrogen atoms to form weak bonds with lone pairs of electrons on the fluorine, nitrogen or oxygen atoms of other molecules.

**Hydrolysis reaction**
A reaction where molecules are split apart by water molecules. The water molecules are also split into hydrogen ions ($H^+$) and hydroxide ions ($OH^-$).

**Hypothesis**
A specific testable statement, based on a theory, about what will happen in a test situation.

**Incomplete combustion**
Burning a substance in a poor supply of oxygen. Incomplete combustion of a hydrocarbon produces carbon monoxide, water and sometimes carbon and carbon dioxide.

**Independent variable**
The variable that you change in an experiment.

**Infrared (IR) spectroscopy**
An analytical technique used to identify the functional groups present in a molecule by measuring the vibrational frequency of its bonds.

**Intermolecular forces**
Forces between molecules, e.g. van der Waals forces, permanent dipole-dipole forces and hydrogen bonding.

**Ion**
A charged particle formed when one or more electrons are lost or gained by an atom or molecule.

**Ionic bond**
An electrostatic attraction between oppositely charged ions.

**Ionic equation**
An equation which only shows the reacting particles of a reaction involving ions.

**Ionisation**
The removal of one or more electrons from an atom or molecule, resulting in an ion forming.

**Isomerisation**
The process of turning one isomer of a molecule into another isomer.

**Ketone**
A substance with the general formula $C_nH_{2n}O$ which has two alkyl groups attached to the carbonyl carbon atom.

**Lattice**
A regular structure made up of atoms or ions.

**Le Chatelier's principle**
If there's a change in concentration, pressure or temperature, the equilibrium will move to help counteract the change.

**Lone pair**
A pair of electrons in an atom that is not shared with other atoms.

**Macromolecular structure**
A structure consisting of a huge network of covalently bonded atoms. Also called a giant covalent structure.

**Mass number**
The total number of protons and neutrons in the nucleus of an atom.

**Mass spectrometry**
An analytical technique used to find the structure of a molecule by looking at the pattern of ions it produces when it is bombarded with electrons.

**Mass spectrum**
A chart produced by a mass spectrometer.

**Maxwell-Boltzmann distribution**
A theoretical model that describes the distribution of kinetic energies of molecules in a gas.

**Miscible**
Capable of being mixed.

**Model**
A simplified picture or representation of a real physical situation.

**Molar mass**
The mass of one mole of something.

**Molar ratio**
The ratio of the moles of each reactant and product in a balanced chemical equation.

**Mole**
The unit of amount of substance. One mole is roughly $6 \times 10^{23}$ particles (Avogadro's constant).

**Molecular formula**
A way of representing molecules that shows the actual number of atoms of each element in a molecule.

**Molecule**
The smallest part of a covalent compound that can take part in a chemical reaction.

**Monomer**
A small molecule which is used to make a polymer.

**Neutron**
A subatomic particle with a relative charge of 0 and a relative mass of 1, located in the nucleus of an atom.

**Noble gas**
An element in Group 0 of the periodic table. These elements are extremely stable because they have a full outer electron shell.

**Nomenclature**
A fancy word for naming organic compounds.

**Nuclear model of the atom**
A model for the structure of an atom proposed by Rutherford. Suggests that atoms consist of a small positively charged nucleus surrounded by a cloud of negatively charged electrons.

**Nucleophile**
An electron-pair donor.

**Nucleophilic substitution reaction**
A reaction where a nucleophile attacks a polar molecule and replaces a functional group in that molecule.

**Nucleus**
The central part of an atom or ion, made up of protons and neutrons.

**Octane rating**
A measure of how likely a petrol is to auto-ignite. Higher octane fuels can be burnt more efficiently.

**Orbital**
A region of a sub-shell that contains a maximum of 2 electrons with opposite spins.

**Ordered / ordinal data**
Categoric data where the categories can be put in order.

**Organic solvent**
An organic substance in which other substances can dissolve.

**Oxidation**
Loss of electrons.

**Oxidation state**
The total number of electrons an element has donated or accepted. Also called an oxidation number.

**Oxidising agent**
Something that accepts electrons and gets reduced.

**Ozone layer**
The region of the atmosphere (stratosphere) which has a high concentration of ozone and protects the Earth from ultraviolet radiation.

**Peer review**
The evaluation of a scientific report by other scientists who are experts in the same area (peers). They go through it bit by bit, examining the methods and data, and checking it's all clear and logical.

**Percentage yield**
The amount of product that is actually obtained during a reaction expressed as a percentage of the amount of product that should form.

**Period**
A row in the periodic table.

**Periodic table**
A table of the elements arranged in order of increasing atomic mass and organised into periods and groups.

**Periodicity**
The trends in physical and chemical properties of elements as you go across the periodic table.

**Permanent dipole-dipole forces**
Intermolecular forces that
exist because the difference in
electronegativities in a polar bond
causes weak electrostatic forces of
attraction between molecules.

**Petrochemical**
Any compound that is made from
crude oil (or any of its fractions).

**Petroleum**
A mixture consisting mainly of alkane
hydrocarbons that can be separated
into different fractions.

**Photochemical reaction**
A reaction started by light (often
ultraviolet light).

**Photochemical smog**
A type of air pollution that forms
when certain pollutant gases react
with sunlight.

**Photodissociation**
When a covalent bond is broken
using energy from light.

**Pi (π) bond**
A type of bond formed when two
p-orbitals overlap sideways.

**Plum pudding model**
A model for the structure of an atom
proposed by Thomson. Suggests that
atoms consist of a positively charged
sphere with negatively charged
electrons embedded in it.

**Polar bond**
A covalent bond where a difference in
electronegativity has caused a shift in
electron density in the bond.

**Polar chemical**
A chemical containing bonding
electrons with different
electronegativities, so the electrons
in the bond are pulled more towards
one atom than the other and a dipole
is created.

**Polymer**
A long molecule formed from lots of
smaller molecules (monomers) joined
together.

**Positional isomer**
A molecule with the same molecular
formula as another molecule but with
the functional group in a different
position.

**Precise result**
A result taken using sensitive
instruments that measure in small
increments.

**Protocol**
An accepted method to test a certain
thing that all scientists can use.

**Proton**
A subatomic particle with a relative
charge of 1+ and a relative mass of 1,
located in the nucleus of an atom.

**Proton number**
The number of protons in the nucleus
of an atom.

**Quantum model**
The currently accepted model for
the structure of an atom, where
particles' positions are predicted by
probabilities.

**Redox reaction**
A reaction where reduction and
oxidation happen simultaneously.

**Reducing agent**
Something that donates electrons and
gets oxidised.

**Reduction**
Gain of electrons.

**Refluxing**
Heating a reaction mixture in
such a way that you boil it without
losing volatile solvents, reactants or
products. Any vaporised compounds
cool, condense and drip back into the
reaction mixture.

**Reforming**
The process of converting
hydrocarbons into cyclic
hydrocarbons.

**Relative atomic mass**
The average mass of an atom of an
element on a scale where an atom of
carbon-12 is exactly 12.

**Relative formula mass**
The average mass of a formula unit on
a scale where an atom of carbon-12 is
exactly 12.

**Relative isotopic mass**
The mass of an atom of an isotope of
an element on a scale where an atom
of carbon-12 is exactly 12.

**Relative molecular mass**
The average mass of a molecule on a
scale where an atom of carbon-12 is
exactly 12.

**Reliable result**
A result that can be consistently
reproduced in independent
experiments.

**Residence time**
How long a molecule spends in the
atmosphere before being broken
down.

**Salt**
A compound formed when the
hydrogen in an acid molecule
is replaced by a metal ion or
ammonium ion.

**Saturated hydrocarbon**
A hydrocarbon with no carbon-carbon
double bonds.

**Second ionisation energy**
The energy needed to remove
1 electron from each ion in 1 mole
of gaseous 1+ ions to form 1 mole
of gaseous 2+ ions.

**Sigma (σ) bond**
A type of bond formed when two
s-orbitals overlap.

**Silver nitrate test**
A test that uses silver nitrate to
identify halide ions in a solution.

**Simple covalent compound**
A compound with strong covalent
bonds within its molecules but weak
forces between its molecules.

**Skeletal formula**
A simplified organic formula which
only shows the carbon skeleton and
associated functional groups.

**Solvent layer**
A distinct layer of solvent, which
separates out from an aqueous
solution.

**Specific heat capacity**
The amount of heat energy it takes
to raise the temperature of 1 g of that
substance by 1 K.

**Standard conditions**
100 kPa (about 1 atm) pressure and a
stated temperature, usually 298 K.

**Standard enthalpy change of combustion**
The enthalpy change when 1 mole of a substance is completely burned in oxygen under standard conditions with all reactants and products in their standard states ($\Delta H_c^{\ominus}$).

**Standard enthalpy change of formation**
The enthalpy change when 1 mole of a compound is formed from its elements in their standard states under standard conditions ($\Delta H_f^{\ominus}$).

**Standard enthalpy change of reaction**
The enthalpy change when a reaction occurs in the molar quantities shown in the chemical equation, under standard conditions with all reactants and products in their standard states ($\Delta H_r^{\ominus}$).

**State symbol**
A symbol placed after a chemical in an equation that tells you what state of matter it is in.

**Stereoisomer**
A molecule that has the same structural formula as another molecule but its atoms are arranged differently in space.

**Structural formula**
A way of representing molecules that shows the atoms carbon by carbon, with the attached hydrogens and functional groups.

**Structural isomer**
A molecule with the same molecular formula as another molecule, but with the atoms connected in a different way.

**Sub-shell**
A sub-division of an energy level (shell). Sub-shells may be s, p, d or f sub-shells.

**Substitution reaction**
A reaction where some atoms from one reactant are swapped with atoms from another reactant.

**Successive ionisation energy**
The energy needed to remove each subsequent electron from each ion in 1 mole of positively charged gaseous ions.

**Theoretical yield**
The mass of product that should be formed in a chemical reaction, if no reactant or product is 'lost'.

**Theory**
A possible explanation for something. (Usually something that has been observed.)

**Thermal decomposition**
When a substance breaks down (decomposes) when heated.

**Thermal stability**
A measure of the tendency of a compound to decompose when heated.

**Titration**
A type of experiment used to find the concentration of a solution. It involves gradually adding one solution to a known volume of another until the reaction between the two is complete.

**Unsaturated hydrocarbon**
A hydrocarbon with one or more carbon-carbon double bonds.

**Valence-Shell Electron-Pair Repulsion Theory**
The theory that in a molecule lone pair/lone pair bond angles are the biggest, lone pair/bonding pair bond angles are the second biggest and bonding pair/bonding pair bond angles are the smallest.

**Valid result**
A result which answers the question it was intended to answer.

**Validation**
The process of repeating an experiment done by someone else, using their theory to make new predictions, and testing them with new experiments, in order to prove or refute the theory.

**Van der Waals forces**
The weakest intermolecular force, caused by temporary dipoles, which causes all atoms and molecules to be attracted to each other.

**Variable**
A quantity that has the potential to change.

**Volatile**
Has a low boiling point and so easily turns into a gas.

**Volatility**
A substance's tendency to evaporate (turn into a gas).

**Water of crystallisation**
The water contained in an ionic lattice.

**Yield**
The amount of product you get from a reaction.

**Z-/E- isomerism**
A type of stereoisomerism that is caused by the restricted rotation about a carbon-carbon double bond. Each of the carbon atoms must have two different groups attached.

**Zeolite**
A mineral that can be used as a molecular sieve because it has tiny pores in its structure.

# Acknowledgements

**Photograph acknowledgements**

Cover Photo **Martyn F. Chillmaid**/Science Photo Library, p 1 **Charles D. Winters**/Science Photo Library, p 2 Science Photo Library, p 3 **Robert Brook**/Science Photo Library, p 4 (top) **David R. Frazier**/Science Photo Library, p 4 (bottom) **Martin Bond**/Science Photo Library, p 8 Science Photo Library, p 9 **Prof. Peter Fowler**/Science Photo Library, p 10 **Charles D. Winters**/Science Photo Library, p 11 **Carol & Mike Werner/Visuals Unlimited, Inc.**/Science Photo Library, p 12 **James Holmes/Oxford Centre for Molecular Sciences**/Science Photo Library, p 15 **Andrew Lambert Photography**/Science Photo Library, p 18 **Andrew Lambert Photography**/Science Photo Library, p 20 Science Photo Library, p 21 Science Photo Library, p 23 **Andrew Lambert Photography**/Science Photo Library, p 25 **Charles D. Winters**/Science Photo Library, p 27 **Charles D. Winters**/Science Photo Library, p 29 **Charles D. Winters**/Science Photo Library, p 32 **Martyn F. Chillmaid**/Science Photo Library, p 33 (top) **Martyn F. Chillmaid**/Science Photo Library, p 33 (bottom) **Andrew Lambert Photography**/Science Photo Library, p 34 (top) **Andrew Lambert Photography**/Science Photo Library, p 34 (bottom) **Andrew Lambert Photography**/Science Photo Library, p 35 **TH Foto-Werbung**/Science Photo Library, p 36 (top) **Andrew Lambert Photography**/Science Photo Library, p 36 (bottom) **Andrew Lambert Photography**/Science Photo Library, p 39 **Martyn F. Chillmaid**/Science Photo Library, p 40 **Charles D. Winters**/Science Photo Library, p 41 **Martyn F. Chillmaid**/Science Photo Library, p 45 **Charles D. Winters**/Science Photo Library, p 58 **Charles D. Winters**/Science Photo Library, p 59 (top) **Charles D. Winters**/Science Photo Library, p 59 (middle) **Andrew Lambert Photography**/Science Photo Library, p 59 (bottom) **Bill Beatty, Visuals Unlimited**/Science Photo Library, p 60 (top) **GIPhotoStock**/Science Photo Library, p 60 (bottom) **GIPhotoStock**/Science Photo Library, p 62 **Carol & Mike Werner/Visuals Unlimited, Inc.**/Science Photo Library, p 63 **Sheila Terry**/Science Photo Library, p 64 **Lawrence Lawry**/Science Photo Library, p 67 (top) **Dr Tim Evans**/Science Photo Library, p 67 (bottom) **Dr Tim Evans**/Science Photo Library, p 71 (top) **Paul D Stewart**/Science Photo Library, p 71 (bottom) **Emilio Segre Visual Archives/American Institute of Physics**/Science Photo Library, p 72 **Martyn F. Chillmaid**/Science Photo Library, p 74 **Richard Treptow**/Science Photo Library, p 80 **Ria Novosti**/Science Photo Library, p 81 (top left) **Charles D. Winters**/Science Photo Library, p 81 (top right) **Charles D. Winters**/Science Photo Library, p 81 (bottom) **E. R. Degginger**/Science Photo Library, p 84 **Charles D. Winters**/Science Photo Library, p 85 Science Photo Library, p 89 (top left) **Martyn F. Chillmaid**/Science Photo Library, p 89 (top right) **Andrew Lambert Photography**/Science Photo Library, p 89 (bottom) **Andrew Lambert Photography**/Science Photo Library, p 90 (top) Science Photo Library, p 90 (bottom) **David Nunuk**/Science Photo Library, p 92 **Andrew Lambert Photography**/Science Photo Library, p 93 **Andrew Lambert Photography**/Science Photo Library, p 94 **Martyn F. Chillmaid**/Science Photo Library, p 95 (top) **Andrew Lambert Photography**/Science Photo Library, p 95 (bottom) **Andrew Lambert Photography**/Science Photo Library, p 97 (top) **CC Studio**/Science Photo Library, p 97 (middle) **P. Hattenberger, Publiphoto Diffusion**/Science Photo Library, p 97 (bottom) **Daniel Sambraus**/Science Photo Library, p 103 **Laguna Design**/Science Photo Library, p 105 **Martyn F. Chillmaid**/Science Photo Library, p 108 **Andrew Lambert Photography**/Science Photo Library, p 113 **Martyn F. Chillmaid**/Science Photo Library, p 117 **Robert Brook**/Science Photo Library, p 118 **Andrew Lambert Photography**/Science Photo Library, p 122 **Martyn F. Chillmaid**/Science Photo Library, p 123 **Martyn F. Chillmaid**/Science Photo Library, p 124 **Martyn F. Chillmaid**/Science Photo Library, p 125 **Paul Rapson**/Science Photo Library, p 126 (top) **Victor De Schwanberg**/Science Photo Library, p 126 (bottom) **Chemical Design Ltd**/Science Photo Library, p 127 **Gustoimages**/Science Photo Library, p 128 (top) **British Antarctic Survey**/Science Photo Library, p 128 (bottom) **Sinclair Stammers**/Science Photo Library, p 129 **Courtesy of Crown Copyright FERA**/Science Photo Library, p 133 **Martyn F. Chillmaid**/Science Photo Library, p 135 **Martyn F. Chillmaid**/Science Photo Library, p 137 **Martyn F. Chillmaid**/Science Photo Library, p 138 (top) **Charles D. Winters**/Science Photo Library, p 138 (bottom) **Leonard Lessin**/Science Photo Library, p 140 **Andrew Lambert Photography**/Science Photo Library, p 141 **Sheila Terry**/Science Photo Library, p 143 **Andrew Lambert Photography**/Science Photo Library, p 145 **CC Studio**/Science Photo Library, p 152 Science Photo Library, p 153 **Victor De Schwanberg**/Science Photo Library, p 154 **Ed Young**/Science Photo Library, p 155 **Andrew Lambert Photography**/Science Photo Library, p 156 **Andrew Lambert Photography**/Science Photo Library, p 157 **Harvey Pincis**/Science Photo Library, p 158 (top) **Andrew Lambert Photography**/Science Photo Library, p 158 (bottom) **Martyn F. Chillmaid**/Science Photo Library, p 160 **Cristina Pedrazzini**/Science Photo Library, p 162 **NASA**/Science Photo Library, p 165 **Andrew Lambert Photography**/Science Photo Library, p 168 **Ria Novosti**/Science Photo Library, p 172, **Gustoimages**/Science Photo Library, p 173 **NASA**/Science Photo Library, p 183 **Charles D. Winters**/Science Photo Library, p 184 **Martyn F. Chillmaid**/Science Photo Library, p 192 (top) **Sheila Terry**/Science Photo Library, p 192 (bottom) Science Photo Library, p 195 **Power and Syred**/Science Photo Library, p 196 **Emmeline Watkins**/Science Photo Library, p 198 Science Photo Library, p 206 (top) **Detlev van Ravenswaay**/Science Photo Library, p 206 (middle) **Alain Pitton/Look at Sciences**/Science Photo Library, p 206 (bottom) **Patrick Landmann/Visuals Unlimited, Inc.**/Science Photo Library, p 207 **Alex Bartel**/Science Photo Library, p 210 **Pascal Goetgheluck**/Science Photo Library, p 212 (top) **NASA**/Science Photo Library, p 212 (bottom) **NASA**/Science Photo Library, p 213 **Patrick Dumas/Eurelios**/Science Photo Library, p 214 **Tony Craddock**/Science Photo Library, p 215 (top) **Astrid & Hans-Frieder Michler**/Science Photo Library, p 215 (bottom) **Photostock-Israel**/Science Photo Library, p 216 **Astrid & Hans-Frieder Michler**/Science Photo Library, p 221 **Martyn F. Chillmaid**/Science Photo Library, p 222 **Garry Watson**/Science Photo Library, p 225 **Monty Rakusen**/Science Photo Library, p 226 Science Photo Library, p 232 **Jon Stokes**/Science Photo Library.

# Index

## A

accurate results  225
acids  31–33
activation energy  179, 191
addition polymers  137, 138
addition reactions  116, 142–145
adsorption  194, 215
air pollution  214–216
alcohols  151–159
aldehydes  156–158
alkaline earth metals  88–91
alkalis  32
alkanes  118–123
   boiling points  121, 122
   combustion  122, 123
   nomenclature  118–120
   production from alkenes  145
   properties  121–123
alkenes  133–136, 142–145
   nomenclature  133, 134
   production from alcohols  155
   reactivity  134, 135
ammonia  32, 72, 73, 194
anhydrous salts  34, 35
anomalous results  222, 223
antacids  90
$A_r$ (relative atomic mass)  11–13
atom economy  115–117,
   196, 206
atomic models  2, 8–10
atomic (proton) number  5, 6
atomic radius  84, 85
atoms  5–10
average bond enthalpies  180
Avogadro constant  15

## B

balancing equations  26, 27
bar charts  223
bases  31, 32
biodegradable polymers  139–141
biofuels  129, 153, 206
bleach  96
Bohr model  9, 10
bond enthalpies  164, 165,
   180–182
branched alkanes  119, 120, 126
breathalyser  168
bromine water  143

## C

calcium hydroxide  90
calorimeters  183
carbocations  142
carbon-12  11, 13
carbon capture and storage  210
carbon monoxide
   poisoning  123
   pollution  214, 215
carbonyl compounds  156
carboxylic acids  156–158, 160
catalysts  194–196
catalytic converters
   196, 214–215
categoric data  222, 223
causal links  224
chain isomers  108
chain reaction  131
charge density  83
chlorides  31
chlorofluorocarbons (CFCs)
   3, 161, 162, 212
cis-trans isomerism  112
closed systems  197
collision theory  191
combustion  122, 123, 156, 183
complete combustion  122
compostable polymers  140, 141
compound ions  58
concentration  17, 37, 193, 198
conclusions  224
continuous data  222, 223
coordinate bonding  62
correlation  224
covalent bonding  61–64, 69,
   134, 135
cracking  125
crude oil  124
curly arrows  130, 142, 164
cycloalkanes  118, 126, 127

## D

d-block elements  81, 82
Dalton, John  8
data  221, 222
dative covalent bonding  62
dehydration  155
delocalised electrons  74, 83
dependent variables  221

desorption  194, 215
diamond  64
dihalogenoalkanes  143
dipoles  69–73, 142
discrete data  221
displacement reactions  93
displayed formulas  104, 229
disposing of polymers  139–141
disproportionation  96, 97
distillation  124, 158
Döbereiner, Johann  79
double bonds  61, 134, 135
dynamic equilibrium  197

## E

E-isomers  111, 112
E/Z isomerism  111, 112, 135
electron configurations
   50–52, 81, 82
electron shells  9, 10, 50–55,
   80–82
electronegativity  69, 163
electrons  5–10, 50–52, 69
electrophiles  142
electrophilic addition  142–145
electrostatic attraction  58, 71
empirical formulas  20–24, 105
endothermic reactions  179, 180,
   198, 199
energy levels  50–52
enthalpy changes  178–190
   calculating  181, 182,
      184, 185
   measuring  183
   of combustion  178, 184,
      188, 189
   of formation  178, 186–188
   of reaction  178, 184, 185,
      189, 190
enthalpy notation  178
enthalpy profile diagrams
   179, 191
enzymes  195
equations  231
esterification  160
esters  160
ethanol  153–155, 199
ethanol production
   145, 154, 199

ethics  225
exam structure  226
exothermic reactions  178–180, 198, 199

**F**

fermentation  154
first ionisation energy  54
fluoridated water  97
formulas  20–25, 103–106
fossil fuels  128, 129
fractional distillation  124
fragmentation  170, 171
free radical substitution  131, 132
free radicals  130–132, 211–213
functional group isomers  109
functional groups  103

**G**

gas volumes  18, 29
general formulas  105
giant covalent structures  63, 64
giant ionic lattices  59
giant metallic lattices  74
global warming  208–210
graphite  63
green chemistry  205–207
greenhouse effect  128, 208
greenhouse gases  162, 208
ground-level ozone  214
Group 2 elements  88–90
Group 7 elements  92–95
groups  80

**H**

Haber-Bosch process  194
halide ions  92–95
halogenoalkanes  131, 132, 144, 161–165
halogens  92–95
hazards  225
Hess's Law  186
heterolytic fission  130, 142, 143
homologous series  105
homolytic fission  130, 131
hydrated salts  34, 35
hydration  145, 154
hydrocarbons  118–127, 214
hydrogen bonding  72, 152, 230
hydrolysis  164, 165
hydroxyl groups  151, 152
hypotheses  1

**I**

ice  72
incomplete combustion  123, 214
independent variables  221
indicators  36
induced dipoles  70, 71
infrared (IR) spectroscopy  167, 168, 215, 216
intermolecular forces  70–73, 152
internal combustion engines  214
ionic bonding  57–59
ionic compounds  58–60, 69
ionic crystals  59
ionic equations  26, 27
ionisation energies  54, 55, 85, 86
ions  6, 57, 58
isomerisation  126
isomers  108–112
    stereoisomers  111, 112
    structural isomers  108, 109
isotopes  6, 11, 12
isotopic abundances  11, 12

**K**

ketones  156–159
Kyoto protocol  210

**L**

lattices  59, 70, 74
Le Chatelier's principle  197–199
line graphs  223
linear molecules  66, 67
lone pairs (of electrons)  65–68

**M**

M peak  170
macromolecular structures  63, 64, 84
Mars probes  173
mass (nucleon) number  5, 6
mass spectrometry  170–173
mass spectrum  11, 12, 170–173
Maxwell-Boltzmann distribution  192–195
Mendeleev, Dmitri  79, 80
metallic bonding  74
metals  33, 45, 83
methanol  153
methyl orange  36

methylated spirits  153
miscibility  152
models  1, 2, 8–10
molar mass  15
molar ratios  28
molecular formulas  20, 21, 24, 25, 104
molecular lattices  70
molecular structures  84
molecules  61
moles  15–17
monomers  137
Montreal Protocol  162, 207, 212
Moseley, Henry  9, 80
$M_r$ (relative molecular mass)  13, 15, 16, 170

**N**

neutrons  5, 6, 9
Newlands, John  79
nitrates  31, 58
nitrogen oxides  212, 214
noble gases  71, 84, 88
nomenclature  103
    of alcohols  151, 152
    of aldehydes and ketones  156, 157
    of alkanes  118–120
    of alkenes  133, 134
    of carboxylic acids  157
    of esters  160
non-linear molecules  68
non-polar bonds  69
nuclear charge  54
nuclear model of the atom  8, 9
nuclear symbols  5, 6
nucleophiles  142, 163
nucleophilic substitution  163, 164
nucleus  5, 8, 9

**O**

octahedral molecules  68
octane ratings  125, 126
orbitals  50, 51
ordered (ordinal) data  222, 223
organic solvents  93
oxidation  44, 45, 156–159
oxidation states  40–45
oxidising agents  44, 156, 157
ozone layer  3, 161, 162, 211–213

## P

p-block elements  81, 82
Pauling Scale  69
peer review  2, 9
percentage error  225
percentage yield  113, 114, 116
periodic table  79–87, 234
periodic trends  83–87
periods  80–82
permanent dipole-dipole forces
    70–72
persistent organic pollutants
    (POPs)  207
petrol engines  125
petroleum  124–127
phenolphthalein  36
photochemical reactions  131
photochemical smog  214
photodissociation  131
pi (π) bond  134, 135
plum pudding model  8
polar bonds  69–73, 152, 163
poly(chloroethene)  138
poly(ethene)  137, 141, 195
polymers  137–141, 162
poly(tetrafluoroethene) (PTFE)
    138, 162
positional isomers  108, 109
precise results  225
predictions  1
pressure  198
primary alcohols  152, 157, 158
proton number  5, 6
protons  5, 6, 9

## Q

quality of written communication
    (QWC)  226, 227
quantum model  10

## R

radicals  130–132, 211–213
reaction mechanisms  130, 229
reaction rates  191–193
reactions
    of acids  31–33
    of alcohols  154–159
    of alkenes  142–145
redox reactions  44, 45
reducing agents  44
reduction  44, 45

refluxing  158
reforming  126
relative atomic mass  11–13, 79
relative formula mass  13
relative isotopic mass  11, 12
relative molecular mass  13, 15,
    16, 170
reliable results  225
renewable resources
    129, 205–206
residence time  162
reversible reactions  197–200
Rio Declaration  207
Rutherford, Ernest  8

## S

s-block elements  81
salts  31–35
saturated hydrocarbons  118
scatter graphs  223
scientific journals  2
second ionisation energy  55
secondary alcohols  152, 159
shapes of molecules  65–68, 121
shielding  54, 84–86
sigma (σ) bonds  134
silver nitrate test  94, 95, 165
simple covalent compounds  63
single bonds  61, 134
skeletal formulas  106, 230
solvent layer  93
specific heat capacity  183
spreadsheets  12
standard conditions  178
standard enthalpy change
    of combustion
        178, 184, 188, 189
    of formation  178, 186–188
    of reaction
        178, 184, 189, 190
standard form  228, 229
state symbols  30
steam hydration of ethene
    145, 154
Stockholm Treaty  207
straight chain alkanes  118, 125
structural formulas  104
sub-shells  50, 51
substitution reactions  116, 131,
    132, 163, 164
successive ionisation energies  55
sulfates  31, 58
sustainability  205–207

## T

temperature  192, 198, 199
tertiary alcohols  152, 159
testing
    for halides  94, 95
    for unsaturation  143
testing theories  1
tetrahedral molecules
    64, 67, 121
theoretical yield  113
theories  1–3
thermal decomposition  89
Thomson, J. J.  8
titrations  36–39
trends
    atomic radius  84, 85
    ionisation energy  85, 86
    melting and boiling point
        83, 84, 92
    reactivity  88, 92
trigonal bipyramidal molecules  68
trigonal planar molecules  67, 135
trigonal pyramidal molecules  67
triple bonds  61

## U

units  228, 232, 233
unsaturated hydrocarbons  133
UV radiation  131, 211

## V

Valence-Shell Electron-Pair
    Repulsion Theory  65
valid results  225
validating theories  2
van der Waals forces  70, 71, 84,
    121, 122
variables  3, 4, 221, 224

## W

water of crystallisation  34
wavenumber  167

## Y

yeast  154

## Z

Z-isomers  111, 112
Ziegler-Natta catalyst  195

# The Periodic Table

|  | Key |
|---|---|
| 1.0 | Relative Atomic Mass ($A_r$) |
| **H** | |
| Hydrogen | Atomic (proton) number |
| 1 | |

| Periods | Group 1 | Group 2 | | | | | | | | | | | | | Group 3 | Group 4 | Group 5 | Group 6 | Group 7 | Group 0 |
|---|---|---|---|---|---|---|---|---|---|---|---|---|---|---|---|---|---|---|---|---|
| 1 | | | | | | | | | | | | | | | | | | | | 4.0 **He** Helium 2 |
| 2 | 6.9 **Li** Lithium 3 | 9.0 **Be** Beryllium 4 | | | | | | | | | | | | | 10.8 **B** Boron 5 | 12.0 **C** Carbon 6 | 14.0 **N** Nitrogen 7 | 16.0 **O** Oxygen 8 | 19.0 **F** Fluorine 9 | 20.2 **Ne** Neon 10 |
| 3 | 23.0 **Na** Sodium 11 | 24.3 **Mg** Magnesium 12 | | | | | | | | | | | | | 27.0 **Al** Aluminium 13 | 28.1 **Si** Silicon 14 | 31.0 **P** Phosphorus 15 | 32.1 **S** Sulfur 16 | 35.5 **Cl** Chlorine 17 | 39.9 **Ar** Argon 18 |
| 4 | 39.1 **K** Potassium 19 | 40.1 **Ca** Calcium 20 | 45.0 **Sc** Scandium 21 | 47.9 **Ti** Titanium 22 | 50.9 **V** Vanadium 23 | 52.0 **Cr** Chromium 24 | 54.9 **Mn** Manganese 25 | 55.8 **Fe** Iron 26 | 58.9 **Co** Cobalt 27 | 58.7 **Ni** Nickel 28 | 63.5 **Cu** Copper 29 | 65.4 **Zn** Zinc 30 | 69.7 **Ga** Gallium 31 | 72.6 **Ge** Germanium 32 | 74.9 **As** Arsenic 33 | 79.0 **Se** Selenium 34 | 79.9 **Br** Bromine 35 | 83.8 **Kr** Krypton 36 |
| 5 | 85.5 **Rb** Rubidium 37 | 87.6 **Sr** Strontium 38 | 88.9 **Y** Yttrium 39 | 91.2 **Zr** Zirconium 40 | 92.9 **Nb** Niobium 41 | 95.9 **Mo** Molybdenum 42 | 98 **Tc** Technetium 43 | 101.1 **Ru** Ruthenium 44 | 102.9 **Rh** Rhodium 45 | 106.4 **Pd** Palladium 46 | 107.9 **Ag** Silver 47 | 112.4 **Cd** Cadmium 48 | 114.8 **In** Indium 49 | 118.7 **Sn** Tin 50 | 121.8 **Sb** Antimony 51 | 127.6 **Te** Tellurium 52 | 126.9 **I** Iodine 53 | 131.3 **Xe** Xenon 54 |
| 6 | 132.9 **Cs** Caesium 55 | 137.3 **Ba** Barium 56 | 138.9 **La** Lanthanum 57 | 178.5 **Hf** Hafnium 72 | 180.9 **Ta** Tantalum 73 | 183.8 **W** Tungsten 74 | 186.2 **Re** Rhenium 75 | 190.2 **Os** Osmium 76 | 192.2 **Ir** Iridium 77 | 195.1 **Pt** Platinum 78 | 197.0 **Au** Gold 79 | 200.6 **Hg** Mercury 80 | 204.4 **Tl** Thallium 81 | 207.2 **Pb** Lead 82 | 209.0 **Bi** Bismuth 83 | 209 **Po** Polonium 84 | 210 **At** Astatine 85 | 222 **Rn** Radon 86 |
| 7 | 223 **Fr** Francium 87 | 226.0 **Ra** Radium 88 | 227.0 **Ac** Actinium 89 | 261 **Rf** Rutherfordium 104 | 262 **Db** Dubnium 105 | 266 **Sg** Seaborgium 106 | 264 **Bh** Bohrium 107 | 277 **Hs** Hassium 108 | 268 **Mt** Meitnerium 109 | 271 **Ds** Darmstadtium 110 | 272 **Rg** Roentgenium 111 | | | | | | | |

The Lanthanides

| 140.1 **Ce** Cerium 58 | 140.9 **Pr** Praseodymium 59 | 144.2 **Nd** Neodymium 60 | 145 **Pm** Promethium 61 | 150.4 **Sm** Samarium 62 | 152.0 **Eu** Europium 63 | 157.2 **Gd** Gadolinium 64 | 158.9 **Tb** Terbium 65 | 162.5 **Dy** Dysprosium 66 | 164.9 **Ho** Holmium 67 | 167.3 **Er** Erbium 68 | 168.9 **Tm** Thulium 69 | 173.0 **Yb** Ytterbium 70 | 175.0 **Lu** Lutetium 71 |
|---|---|---|---|---|---|---|---|---|---|---|---|---|---|

The Actinides

| 232.0 **Th** Thorium 90 | 231.0 **Pa** Protactinium 91 | 238.1 **U** Uranium 92 | 237.0 **Np** Neptunium 93 | 242 **Pu** Plutonium 94 | 243 **Am** Americium 95 | 247 **Cm** Curium 96 | 245 **Bk** Berkelium 97 | 251 **Cf** Californium 98 | 254 **Es** Einsteinium 99 | 253 **Fm** Fermium 100 | 256 **Md** Mendelevium 101 | 254 **No** Nobelium 102 | 257 **Lr** Lawrencium 103 |
|---|---|---|---|---|---|---|---|---|---|---|---|---|---|